STP 990

Semiconductor Fabrication: Technology and Metrology

Dinesh C. Gupta, editor

ASTM
1916 Race Street
Philadelphia, PA 19103

ASTM Publication Code Number (PCN): 04-990000-46
ISBN: 0-8031-1273-4

Peer Review Policy

Each paper published in this volume was evaluated by three peer reviewers. The authors addressed all of the reviewers' comments to the satisfaction of both the technical editor(s) and the ASTM Committee on Publications.

The quality of the papers in this publication reflects not only the obvious efforts of the authors and the technical editor(s), but also the work of these peer reviewers. The ASTM Committee on Publications acknowledges with appreciation their dedication and contribution of time and effort on behalf of ASTM.

Printed in Ann Arbor, MI
July 1989

Foreword

The Fifth International Symposium on Semiconductor Processing was held at Santa Clara, California on 1-5 February, 1988 under the chairmanship of Dinesh C. Gupta, Siliconix Incorporated. The Symposium was sponsored by ASTM Commitee F-1 on Electronics and Semiconductor Equipment & Materials International [SEMI] in cooperation with National Institute for Standards and Technology [NIST], Stanford University Center for Integrated Circuits and IEEE Components, Hybrids & Manufacturing Technology Society.

The Symposium was made successful by the efforts of many persons who participated in the Advisory Board and various Committees. The guidence was provided by the Chairman and the Officers of ASTM Committee F-1 on Electronics and its various subcommittees including the Executive subcommittee. The following persons presided on the technical and workshop sessions: K.E.Benson, AT&T Bell Laboratories; M.I.Bell, J.R.Ehrstein, and R.D.Larrabee, National Institute for Standards and Technology; W.M.Bullis, Siltec Corporation; I-Wen Connick, Philips Research Laboratories; S.M.Cox, AT&T Technologies; T.E.Cynkar, Signetics Corporation; S.J.Fonash, The Pennsylvania State University; D.C.Gupta, Siliconix Inc.; W.A.Keenan, Prometrix Inc.; A.Lieberman, Particle Measuring Systems Inc.; J.W.Medernach, Sandia National Laboratories; D.Rogers, Cominco Ltd.; W.R.Schevey, Mancel Associates Inc.; P.S.Speicher, RADC/RBRE; R.B.Swaroop, Electric Power Research Institute; C.H.Ting, Intel Corporation; and R.H.Unger, Motorola Incorporated.

We are indebted to Kenneth Levy, KLA Instruments Corporation for the dinner speech, and are grateful to the members and guests of ASTM Committee F-1 and Standards Committees of SEMI who were called upon for special assignments during the two-year planning of the Symposium. Our special thanks to W.A.Baylies, Chairman, Committee F-1; P.L.Davis, SEMI; S.L.Kauffman, ASTM; R.I.Scace, National Institute for Standards and Technology and P.Wesling, Tandem Computers Incorporated.

Over one hundred and fifty scientists participated all over the world in the review process for the papers published in this publication. Without their participation, this publication would not have been possible.

And finally, we acknowledge the hard work and efforts of the staff of publication, review, editorial and marketing departments of ASTM in bringing out this book.

Contents

Introduction

This special technical publication is organized into six sections: (1) Crystal Growth and Epitaxial Deposition Techniques; (2) Fabrication Technology; (3) Microcontamination; (4) Metallization and Interconnects; (5) Material Defects and Gettering; and (6) Control Charts, Standards and specifications. The papers describe technology and metrology of these areas. The brief synopses on two workshops; (1) Gettering Techniques and Characterization; (2) Gallium Arsenide are presented in the Appendix.

CRYSTAL GROWTH AND EPITAXIAL DEPOSITION TECHNIQUES

Most of the monocrystalline silicon is manufactured by Czochralski method, the paper by Yamashita et al describes the effect of magnetic field on the segregation coefficient of dopant and on oxygen content during crystal growth. Robinson and Lawrence in their paper present the characteristics of a high rate single wafer novel epitaxial reactor. The properties and preparation of silicon are discussed in few papers and the metrology and surface quality in others in this section.

FABRICATION TECHNOLOGY

Ion implantation, CVD, polysilicon and plasma processing are discussed in depth in this section. One of the papers on dry etching presents reaction mechanisms and process to etch silicon dioxide. While process needs to be precise, controlled and accurate, every paper in this section describes the importance of metrology associated with the process. The paper by Ygartua and Swaroop provides information on the formation of defect-free buried layers using ion implantation. Subrahmanyan et al discuss ways to improve the accuracy of the junction-depth measurements. The paper by Starov and Lane gives a technique to improve poly-Si uniformity. Other papers in this section are on the processing and metrology issues related to dry etching.

MICROCONTAMINATION

Particle contamination is an important issue in semiconductor processing. It covers a wide area from the gases, chemicals and materials used in processing to the environment where fabrication takes place. The three papers in this section discuss particle standards, particle counters, and ways to reduce particles in process fluids.

METALLIZATION AND INTERCONNECTS

The strategies for the yield enhancement due to improvement in metallization and interconnects are described in this section. Discussed are various items such as, the film specularity of the sputtered aluminum, and double level metallization processes. The paper by Kuo describes major issues in an isolation process. He discusses oxide isolation, selective epitaxy for trench isolation, and silicon-on-insulator technologies.

MATERIAL DEFECTS AND GETTERING

This section covers a wide area relating to oxygen precipitates, metallic impurities and process-related defects. The gettering of defects and impurities during device fabrication provides better devices. This is exactly what is stressed in many papers in this section. The first four papers are on the detection and reduction of metallic impurities, and the measurement of minority carrier lifetime in semiconductor material.

Intrinsic and extrinsic gettering are widely employed in semiconductor processing for the reduction of material and in-process defects and contaminants. Various techniques, such as, the use of oxygen precipitates, poly on the backside of wafers, epitaxial encapsulation and the use of epitaxial misfit dislocations are described to provide intrinsic and extrinsic gettering. The paper by Goldstein and Makovsky describes the SIMS technique to measure oxygen content in semiconductor material.

CONTROL CHARTS, STANDARDS AND SPECIFICATIONS

And finally, the most important section in this publication is on Control Charts, Standards and Specifications. Four papers are presented. The paper by Friedman is on the use of on-line statistical process control for IC fabrication. Different ways to analyze production data are discussed. The paper by Keller et al describes the use of statistical techniques to test equipment and tool capability. The paper by Lowry discusses the impact on production and material quality programs brought about by the introduction of statistical process control in microelectronics manufacturing. It emphasizes the need to understand process capability and to employ statistical quality control limits rather than engineering spec limits. And the fourth paper in this section is on the Economic Impact of Standards on Productivity, once again stressing the need of Standards in semiconductor industry.

Dinesh C. Gupta
Editor.

Silicon Crystal Growth and Epitaxial Deposition Techniques

Kenichi Yamashita, Sumio Kobayashi, Toshihiko Aoki, Yasushi Kawata, and Toshio Shiraiwa

THE EFFECT OF A ROTATIONAL MAGNETIC FIELD ON MCZ CRYSTAL GROWING

REFERENCES: Yamashita,K., Kobayashi,S., Aoki,T., Kawata,Y.,and Shiraiwa,T., "The Effect of a Rotational Magnetic Field on MCZ Crystal Growing," Semiconductor Fabrication: Technology and Metrology, ASTM STP 990, Dinesh C. Gupta, editor , American Society for Testing and Materials, Philadelphia, 1989.

ABSTRACT: Czochralski(CZ) crystal growth under the vertical D.C. magnetic field with and without the horizontal rotating field is investigated by the numerical analysis and experiment.
The numerical analysis shows that the vertical magnetic field increases the effective segregation coefficient of phosphorus and the oxygen content of the grown crystal, and the horizontal rotating magnetic field is useful to decreases the oxygen content. This is due to the activation of convection flow in the meridional plane in the crucible by the rotating magnetic field. The experimental results of the effective segregation coefficient of phosphorus and oxygen content under the vertical magnetic field with and without horizontal rotating magnetic field verify the calculated results.

KEYWORDS: VMCZ, rotating magnetic field, segregation coefficient, oxygen concentration, melt convection

INTRODUCTION

Most of monocrystalline silicon for VLSI is manufactured by the CZ method. One of the most important problems is that the effective segregation coefficient of n-type dopants is low. In order to solve this problem, S.Kobayashi, one of the present authors, has calculated the effect of magnetic field on the effective segregation coefficient of phosphorus in CZ crystal growth, and reported(1) that the horizontal magnetic field has no good effect on it, but vertical magnetic

Yamashita, Aoki and Dr.Kawata are research scientists at Kyushu Electronic Metal Co.,Ltd; Kohokucho,Saga,Japan; Dr.Kobayashi is research scientist at Sumitomo Metal Industry Co.,Ltd; Amagasaki,Hyogo,Japan; and Dr.Shiraiwa is executive technical consultant at Osaka Titanium Co.,Ltd; Amagasaki, Hyogo, Japan.

7

field can increase it. The numerical analysis has been also expanded
to the oxygen distribution in a melt of a CZ crucible(2). It has been
reported that the vertical magnetic field suppresses the melt flow
from the melt surface region, where the oxygen content is low, to the
boundary region between crystal and melt, and consequently, oxygen
content in the grown crystal increases too high to be of commercial
use.
  In the present report, a horizontal rotating magnetic field is added
to the vertical magnetic field in order to increase the convection in
the meridional plane which decreases the oxygen content.
  The study is done by numerical analysis and experiment .The results
of melt flow and oxygen distribution in the melt are calculated and
experimental results of the effective segregation coefficient of phosphorus and oxygen content in the grown crystal under the vertical magnetic field with and without the horizontal rotating magnetic field
are reported.

NUMERICAL ANALYSIS

    The effects of a horizontal rotating magnetic field on oxygen
transport in the vertical MCZ method were numerically analyzed using
the mathematical model previously reported(2).
  The geometry of the analytical model is shown in Fig.1. A crystal
with the radius a(=0.05m) and the rotation speed Ns(=25rpm) is grown
from the melt with the depth C(=0.1m) in a crucible with the radius
b(=0.15m) and the rotation speed Nc(=0.5rpm). On the assumption of
axial symmetry, the differential equations governing the stream function, the vorticity, the azimuthal velocity, the temperature , the
oxygen concentration C and the electric potential were solved simultaneously by a finite deference method. The horizontal magnetic field
is assumed to be uniform, and given by the following equation.

$$B = b\cos\omega t x_0 + b\sin\omega t y_0 + B_0 z_0$$

where B_0 is the intensity of an vertical magnetic field, b the
amplitude of a rotating magnetic field,   the angular velocity of the
rotating magnetic field, t time, and x_0 ,y_0 and z_0, are unit vectors
in the Cartesian coordinates. The magnetic field due to the induced
current in the melt were neglected in the present analysis. Further,
time averaged electromagnetic force was used in the calculation of the
flow field.
  The boundary conditions adopted were as follows. The crucible and the
crystal are no slip surfaces, and the Marangoni effect is taken into
account on the melt free surface. The temperature of the crucible and
the crystal are specified, and the heat transfer across the melt free
surface is due to the thermal radiation into the surroundings with the
temperature of the crystal at melting point. The crucible and the melt
free surface are taken to be a source (C=1) and a sink (C=0) of
oxygen,and the equilibrium distribution coefficient of oxygen at the
crystal-melt interface is assumed to be unity. The entire periphery of
the melt is taken to be electrically insulating.

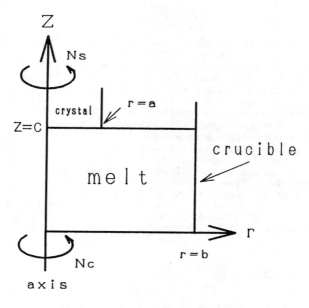

Fig.1 Geometry of the analytical model

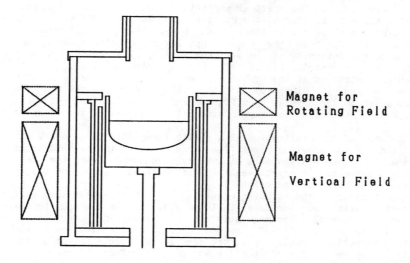

Fig.2 The schematic diagram of the CZ furnace

EXPERIMENT

Figure.2 shows the schematic diagram of the CZ furnace which was used for the present study. A direct current magnet which gives the vertical magnetic field encircles the chamber of the CZ furnace. The maximum magnetic flux density at the center of the crucible is 0.6T esla(T). A rotating magnetic field was given by a 60 Hz AC magnet which is set on the magnet for the vertical magnetic field. The rotating magnetic flux density at the center is about 10mT.
Crystal growth was performed with automatic diameter control.
Phosphorus doped silicon single crystal with 5"ϕ(or 4"ϕ)diameter was grown from a 35Kg melt, using a quartz crucible of 400 mm diameter.
As growing condition, crucible rotation is 0.5rpm, crystal rotation is 10 rpm, 15rpm and 20 rpm. Dopant concentration of phosphorus is from 10^{14}/cm^3 to 10^{15}/cm^3.
Oxygen content was measured by a FTIR spectrometer using ASTM conversion factor 4.81×10^{17} atoms/cm^3 for 2mm thick samples.(old ASTM)
Concentration of phosphorus was determined by the four point probe measurement after donor killer annealing for 30 min at 650°C.

RESULTS AND DISCUSSION

Flow and Oxygen Distribution in Melt (Calculated Results)

The meridional stream lines and oxygen distribution in the melt, calculation for two cases, without and with the rotating magnetic field, are shown in Fig.3 and 4 respectively. The magnetic fields adopted are 0.2T for the vertical magnetic field, and 5.8mT for the rotating magnetic field, and the rotating frequency (w/2π) adopted is 60Hz. The number of stream lines drawn in each figure is set to be a constant of 20, thus the contour spacing of the stream lines correspond to the intensity of the melt convection. The contour spacing of the oxygen distribution is set to be a constant of 0.05, and the oxygen concentration at the center of the crystal is indicated in each figure. Oxygen is dissolved into the silicon melt from the crucible and it moves to the crystal by diffusion and transportation of melt flow. Most of the dissolved oxygen evaporates from the melt surface as SiO.
In the case of the application of a vertical magnetic field only, as indicated in the previous paper(1), the convection in the meridional plane which transports the melt of low oxygen content from the melt surface region to the crystal-melt interface is suppressed and oxygen content in the crystal increases.
The application of the rotating magnetic field activates the melt convection with two vortexes in the meridional plane, and the activated melt convection consequently reduces the oxygen content in the crystal. The activation of the meridional melt convection by the rotating magnetic field is due to the centrifugal force unevenly induced in the melt. The azimuthal electromagnetic force, produced by the rotating field, is given by a cross product of an axially induced current and a horizontally applied magnetic field. Since the melt periphery is electrically insulating, the azimuthal electromagnetic

VMCZ 0.2T   RMF 0mT

Stream Lines

$\triangle\psi = 0.94 \times 10^{-8} m^3 s^{-1}$

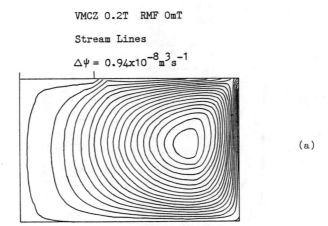

(a)

Oxygen   C = 0.55

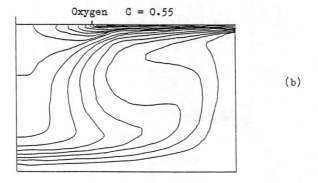

(b)

Fig.3 Calculated results for the vertical MCZ growth of 0.2T
without the rotating field. (a) Streamlines; the contour
spacing is $0.94 \times 10^{-8} m^3 s^{-1}$. (b) Oxygen distribution;
the concentration at the crystal center is 0.55.

VMCZ 0.2T   RMF 5.8mT

Stream Lines

$\triangle \psi = 2.26 \times 10^{-7} m^3 s^{-1}$

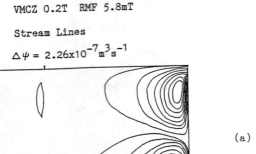

(a)

Oxygen   C = 0.14

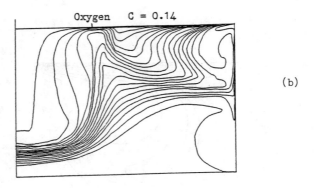

(b)

Fig.4 Calculated results for the vertical MCZ growth
of 0.2T with the rotating field. (a) Streamlines;
the contour spacing is $2.26 \times 10^{-7} m^3 s^{-1}$. (b) Oxygen
distribution; the concentration at the crystal center is 0.14.

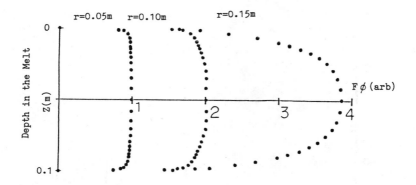

Fig.5 Azimuthal electromagnetic force produced by the rotating field.

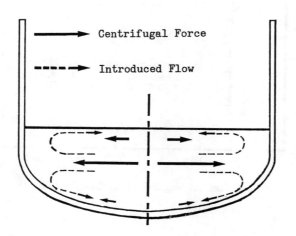

Fig.6 Meridional convection with two vortexes.

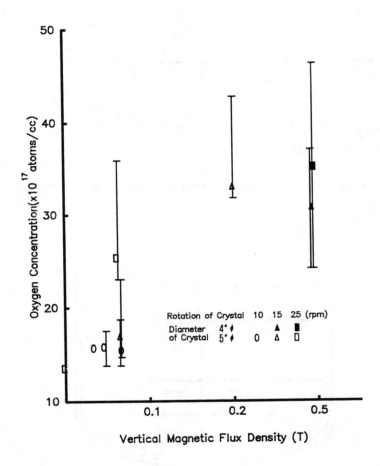

Fig.7 Oxygen content at the center points of wafers which were sliced out from the top to the bottom of the crystal rod grown under the only vertical magnetic field.

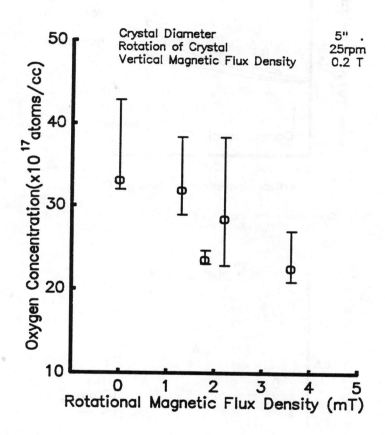

Fig.8 Oxygen content at the center points of wafers which were sliced out from the top to the bottom of the crystal rod grown under the various rotating magnetic field.

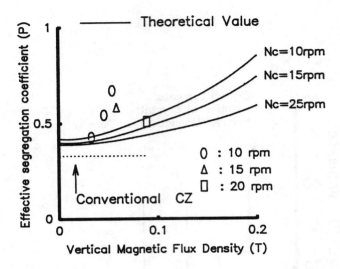

Fig.9 Calculated and experimental results of the effective segregation coefficient without the rotating field.

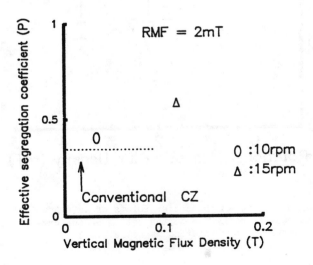

Fig.10 Experimental result of the effective segregation coefficient with the rotating magnetic field.

forces become maximum in the mid-depth plane of the melt as   shown   in Fig.5,   and yield uneven distribution of the rotating flow velocity in the melt. Consequently the centrifugal force induced in the melt has a maximum   in the mid-depth plane,   and activates the meridional convection with two vortexes as shown schematically in Fig.6.

Experimental Result of Oxygen Content.

Figure7 shows oxygen content in the grown crystal under the vertical   magnetic field only.   As shown in the figure,   oxygen content increases with the vertical magnetic field.   Figure8 show oxygen content in   the   grown crystal under the various rotating magnetic field added to the vertical magnetic field of 0.2T.   It shows   that   the   rotating magnetic field decreases the oxygen content.

Effective Segregation Coefficient of Phosphorus.

Figure9 shows calculated and experimental results of the effective segregation coefficient of phosphorus of CZ under   the   vertical   magnetic field without the rotating magnetic field.   Experimental results of the effective   segregation   coefficient   of   phosphorus where   the rotating magnetic field of 2mT is added on the vertical magnetic field is shown in Fig.10,   which shows the effective segregation coefficient is modified.

CONCLUSION

Numerical   analysis and experiment of CZ growth under the vertical magnetic field with and without the horizontal rotating magnetic field have been carried out. The results are follows. The effective segregation coefficient of phosphorus increases. The oxygen content increases under the vertical magnetic field only, but it can be decreases by the rotating magnetic field.   The present study shows   that   the   rotating magnetic   field   can   be   applied   to   control the flow of melt in all process of CZ method   including   horizontal   MCZ   and   vertical   MCZ, replacing the crucible rotation.

ACKNOWLEDGMENTS

We express our gratitude to research scientists of crystal growing laboratory of Semiconductor Research Laboratories of Kyushu Electronic Metal Co.,Ltd.

REFERENCES

(1) S.Kobayashi, J.Crystal Growth, 75,301 (1986)

(2) S.Kobayashi, J.Crystal Growth, 85,69 (1987)

Lawrence D. Dyer

SILICON SLICE FRACTURE ANALYSIS

REFERENCE: Dyer, L. D., "Silicon Slice Fracture Analysis,"
Semiconductor Fabrication: Technology and Metrology, ASTM STP
990, Dinesh C. Gupta, editor, American Society for Testing
and Materials, 1989.

ABSTRACT: Slice fracture problems can occur in a host of
bare slice and patterned wafer fabrication processes. Some
knowledge of how to diagnose the source of the fracture can
aid in timely response to such problems. The purpose of this
paper is to describe some of the tools and the techniques for
analyzing silicon slice fractures. Included are: 1) a review
of fracture markings in silicon similar to those in glasses
and ceramics, plus a new marking that appears on crystalline
fracture surfaces, 2) a description of inspection techniques
and equipment and, 3) mention of some simple testing
techniques. Examples are given of the use of markings and
techniques in deducing probable causes of fracture and in
enhancing process development in wafer fabrication.

KEYWORDS: slice fracture, silicon fracture analysis, use of
fracture markings, wafer cracking.

INTRODUCTION

Fracture occurs at many steps in wafer fabrication processes as
well as in wafer manufacture [1]. The specialists sustaining the processes may not have training or experience in fracture, and the
problems may recur at irregular intervals. Slice fracture causes direct
losses of broken slices, indirect losses of other slices or devices
from particles generated, and downtime for cleanup. Automation
increases the danger of massive loss, and production schedules require
a timely response. The purpose of this paper is to describe some of the
tools and the techniques for analyzing silicon slice fractures to
determine a probable cause. First will be given a brief update on
fracture markings, second, a description of equipment and methods, and

Dr. Dyer is a Sr. Member of Technical Staff in the Silicon Products
Dept. at Texas Instruments, P.O. Box 84, Sherman, Texas, 75090.

third some examples of analysis of slice fracture problems.

FRACTURE MARKINGS

Fracture markings can be grouped into three classes: 1) those nearly parallel to the direction of crack travel, 2) those nearly perpendicular to the direction of crack travel, and 3) the origin and its surrounding mirror region and associated boundaries. With the exception of one distinctive marking named faceted-Wallner areas [2], these features were all described in detail in a previous Symposium [3], and have analogous counterparts in glass and ceramic fracture. Faceted-Wallner areas consist of interlaced ridges and valleys parallel to Wallner lines [4] and are formed in the same way except that crystallinity modifies the extent of the crack deviation off the nominal fracture plane. They occur mainly near the origin of a fracture, and often have a distinctive "mustache" appearance. Table 1 illustrates schematically the various fracture markings and their uses.

INSPECTION EQUIPMENT AND METHODS

Minimum equipment for slice fracture analysis is a low power stereo microscope equipped with a fluorescent or other broad-source microscope light. The microscope should be adjustable so as to accommodate large slices. For documenting special features and for very thin slices, it may be necessary to use a compound microscope.

The method of inspection is to trace the fracture markings on the various fracture surfaces back to an origin, then to examine the surface around the origin for clues to the cause. Often the fractured slice will have to be assembled in jig-saw puzzle fashion to make sense of the breaking pattern. In this case, as many fracture surfaces are inspected as are needed to establish directions of crack travel and to find all origins (usually just one). Next, the stress situation imposed by the apparatus and process are considered, including any thermal stress. Previous equipment and processes through which the slice has passed must be kept in mind as possible causes or contributors.

A number of slice fracture problems have been solved or at least characterized by the foregoing approach; namely, exit chipping [5,6], saw edge fractures [1], crow's-foot fractures from chuck burrs [7], edge cracks from a resistivity-stabilization furnace process [1], edge cracks from polishing [1], and slice breakage in furnace processes from backside scratches [1]. The present paper expands upon the latter problem and gives several other examples of the application of the method to slice fracture problems in wafer fabrication facilities.

Sometimes it is necessary to test a representative sample of slices to see if there is some inherent weakness. Testing may be done with standard slice fracture testing methods such as biaxial flexure [8] and four-point twisting [9]. Sometimes biaxial flexure testing is chosen because it is not sensitive to edge condition. At other times

TABLE 1.--Appearance and use of fracture markings on silicon slices.[a]

Fracture marking name	Appearance and direction of crack travel	Parallel (=) or perp. ($\perp$) to crack travel	uses
Rib (Conchoidal lines)		$\perp$	Finding origin, dir. of travel
Hackle (Tear marks)		=	"
River lines		=	"
Lance marks		=	Finding origin, dir. of torque
Wallner lines		$\perp$	finding origin, crack velocity
Faceted-Wallner area		...	finding origin
Original crack	$\|c\|$	...	Measuring fract. stress: $\sigma_f = k_1 c^{-1/2}$
Mirror region	r	...	Measuring fract. stress: $\sigma_f = k_2 r^{-1/2}$

a.(Note: Photomicrographs of the markings appear in References 2 & 3)

four-point twisting is selected because it puts stronger emphasis on the edge of the slice. The testing can be done with very simple equipment, such as a lever [10] or drill press [11] for loading, a ball or piston for application of load with a standard geometry, a jar lid for slice support, and step-on scales for force measurement. (See, for example, Fig. 1). Equations to convert the measured fracture loads to stress are available for several variations [8-19]. A good example of apparatus and use of both biaxial flexure testing and four-point twisting is shown in reference [19]. There is considerable variance in

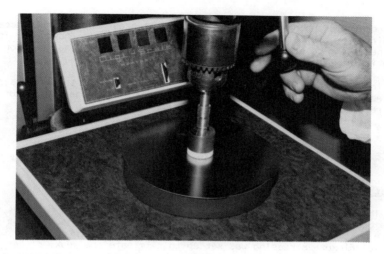

FIG. 1. SIMPLE APPARATUS FOR BIAXIAL FLEXURE
STRESS TESTING OF SILICON WAFERS.

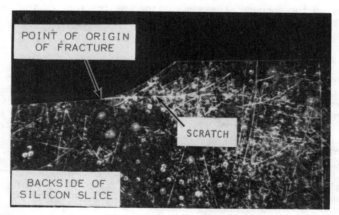

FIG. 2. ORIGIN OF FRACTURE AT BACKSIDE SCRATCH.
DARKFIELD 30 X MAGNIFICATION.

the results of using the various theoretical treatments, partly because of differing boundary conditions. For many situations, however, it is not necessary to determine the stress itself, but only the loads or the relative stresses compared to those of standard samples.

In the case of silicon in air, Chen [19] has shown that stress <u>rate</u> has no effect on fracture strength, therefore it is unnecessary to have accurate knowledge of the rate of load application.

SLICE FRACTURE EXAMPLES

First Example

The first example appeared as thousands of wafer fractures that were occurring some time ago in wafer fabrication furnace operations. Since most slices were unaffected, a screening test (proof test) using biaxial flexure stressing was set up to eliminate the weak slices (similar in principal to method of Fig 1.). Accumulated losses in broken slices alone were in the millions of dollars. When at last the broken weak slices were examined as described above, each origin on a fracture surface coincided with a place on the backside of the wafer at which a scratch was tangent to the fracture surface (Fig. 2), usually near the center of the slice. The stress situation in furnace operations with slices is well known: wafers undergo transient tensile hoop stresses as they cool down in furnace tubes. This causes them to bow one way or the other. If a scratch is located on the convex side of the wafer, it is subject to a bending tensile stress that can exceed the crack progagation stress for the scratch. After it was clear that scratches combined with the furnace stress situation was the root of the problem, all that remained was eliminating the source of the scratches.

Second Example

The second example also occurred in wafer fabrication furnace operations, but all origins were located at slice edges. Fig. 3 shows the typical appearance of a slice fractured in a furnace operation and having an origin of the type found. Fig. 4 shows a typical origin at the edge of the slice. Three types of observations on the slices were made: First, the distance from the crack origin to the flat was determined. Second, the slice edge was examined for evidence of impact in the vicinity of the fracture origin, and third, the slice surfaces and edge were examined for additional cracks initiated near the fracture origin. Fifty-eight percent of the slices showed visible evidence of edge surface disturbance from edge impact. Seventy percent of the slices showed additional primary cracks starting at the edge very near the fracture origin. Eighty-eight percent initiated within 1/2 inch of the flat. Investigation into the process revealed that the slices were dropped onto two rails in a fused silica carrier, flat down. The cause of the fractures was concluded to be the combination of impact from dropping the slices into the carrier, plus the stress of putting the slices through the furnace process. All that remained to solve the problem was to prevent the slices from being dropped so vigorously.

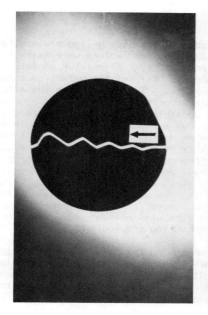

FIG. 3. APPEARANCE OF
FURNACE-FRACTURED SLICE.

FIG. 4. APPEARANCE OF
FRACTURE SURFACE RE-
SULTING FROM EDGE IM-
PACT OF SILICON WAFER.

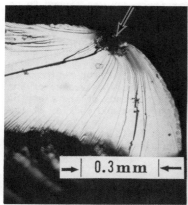

FIG. 5. WAFER FRACTURED
AT N+ DIFFUSION STEP.
ORIGIN AT ARROW.

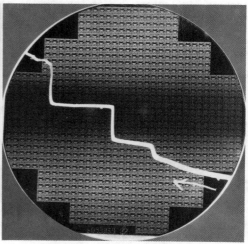

FIG. 6. WAFER FRACTURED AT
EMITTER ANNEAL. CRACK DI-
RECTION SHOWN BY ARROW.

Third Example

The third problem was the sudden appearance of vaguely similar broken slices at several work stations. Broken wafers were assembled from furnace processes called 1) third oxidation, 2) emitter anneal, 3) n+ diffusion, and 4) channel stop anneal. All of the wafer fractures originated at or near the slice edge. Two started on the slice surfaces near the edge and the remainder originated within the rounded part of the periphery, where it is possible to impact during transfer or positioning operations. Figure 5 shows a fracture surface containing the fracture origin on a wafer at the N+ diffusion step. Figure 6 shows a whole-slice view of a typical fracture at emitter anneal. All of the edge-originated fractures showed one or more features that are characteristic of impact or high stress contact: 1) multiple, parallel cracks initiated near the impact, 2) very small mirror size, 3) flake chips near the origin. Some slices showed colored layers on the fracture surfaces near the origin, i.e. oxide or other layers deposited. In these cases the fracture was present when the colors formed and the fracture was propagated during the cooldown cycle.

After these slices had been examined and the results reported, the problem was found to be in a temporary slice loader using flip transfer from plastic to quartz cassettes. It was surmised that a fraction of all the wafers received edge cracks that later propagated during the thermal stressing of the various operations.

Fourth Example

Observations: The fourth example occurred in large diameter ion implantation machines. Fig. 7 shows the locations of the fracture origins relative to the wafer flat and to the tabs on the clamping ring of the ion implanter. One of the twelve wafer fractures was found to be caused by impact. All of the other origins were located on the back surface near the slice edge. Nine out of eleven started at locations associated with the clamping surface; Fig. 8 shows a typical origin occurring at the top or the bottom ends of the tabs, while Fig. 9 shows the one that occurred along the side of the tab. Each origin had a faceted-Wallner area associated with it, and a mirror region surrounding it. The size of the mirror regions varied widely. Two of the nine origins occurred on one slice at opposite ends of the clamping tab. Two other origins lay at the edge of the flat and one lay at the opposite end of a diameter through this point. The latter showed evidence of impact to the wafer edge, which could have happened in earlier processing. Fig. 10 shows the two origins near the flat.

No features were found on any of the slice surfaces near the origins that would indicate scratches, impacts, or other flaws that would have overweakened the silicon.

Interpretation of Observations: In glasses and some ceramics it has been established that fracture stress is inversely proportional to the square root of the radius of the mirror region that occurs between the initial flaw and the beginnings of a hackle region [20]. The wide variation in mirror size above the faceted-Wallner areas likewise indicates a large variation in breakage stress [2]. This observation

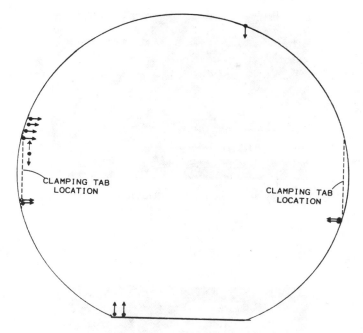

FIG. 7.   LOCATIONS OF FRACTURE ORIGINS
RELATIVE TO TAB LOCATIONS.

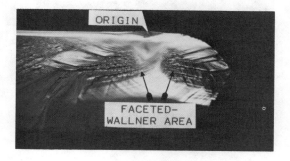

FIG. 8.   TYPICAL ORIGIN ASSOCIATED
WITH ENDS OF CLAMPING TAB.

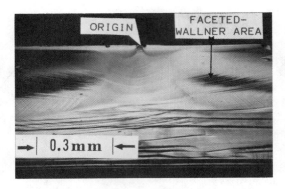

FIG. 9.   ORIGIN ASSOCIATED WITH
          SIDE OF CLAMPING TAB.

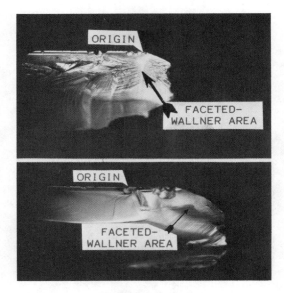

FIG. 10.   ORIGINS ASSOCIATED
           WITH EDGE OF FLAT.

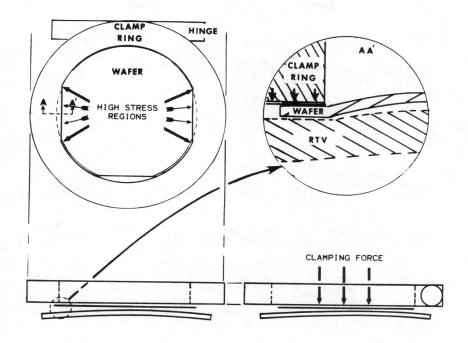

FIG. 11.   SCHEMATIC DIAGRAM OF WAFER CLAMPING
            BY ION IMPLANTATION STATION.

tends to rule out causes that are based on constant depth of damage
from some source, such as backside damage.   The non-existence of
evidence for some backside impact and the location of so many of the
origins near the clamping tabs eliminates the possibility of previous
impact or handling damage.   The absence of any fractures starting from
the polished (exposed) side of the wafer shows that neither the initial
wafer bow imposed by the rubber mat in the implantation equipment nor
the   additional bow imposed by the thermal gradient during the
implantation cause the fractures by simple biaxial bending.   Instead,
the locations of the origins on the backsides of the wafers near the
clamping tabs suggests that the breaks were caused by the reverse type
of bending where the tabs force the slice down into the rubber. Figure
11 shows a schematic diagram of the clamping fixture used for ion
implantation and the location of the highest stresses this type of

fixture imposes on a wafer. After the problem had been identified, a redesign of the fixture alleviated this particular breakage problem.

ACKNOWLEDGMENTS

The author would like to express appreciation to Charlie Driscoll, Rod Roques, Harry Fisher, Andy O'Hara, Julius Horvath and Sam Rea for helpful input and discussions.

REFERENCES

[1] Dyer, L.D., "Damage Aspects of Ingot-to-Wafer Processing," Emerging Semiconductor Technology," ASTM STP 960, D. C. Gupta and P.H. Langer, Eds., American Society for Testing and Materials, 1986, pp. 297-312.

[2] Dyer, L.D., "Faceted-Wallner Areas in Silicon Fracture," Electrochemical Society Extended Abstracts, Vol. 87-2, 1987, pp. 995-996.

[3] Dyer, L.D., "Fracture Tracing in Semiconductor Wafers," Semiconductor Processing ASTM STP 850, Dinesh C. Gupta, Ed., American Society for Testing and Materials, 1984, pp. 297-308.

[4] Wallner, H., "Linienstrukturen an Bruchflachen," Zeitschrift fuer Physik, Vol. 114, 1939, pp. 368-378.

[5] Dyer, L.D., "Exit Chipping in I.D. Diamond Sawing of Silicon Crystals," Electrochemical Society Extended Abstracts, Vol. 81-1, 1981, pp. 785-786.

[6] Dyer, L.D., "Exit Chipping in I.D. Sawing of Silicon Crystals," JPL LCSA Wafering Workshop, Phoenix, Ariz., 8-10 June 1981. JPL PUBL. 82-9, pp. 269-277. Also in "Silicon Material Preparation and Economical Wafering Methods," ed. by R. Lutwack and A. Morrison(Noyes Publications, Park Ridge, N.J. (1984)), pp. 542-550.

[7] Dyer, L.D., and Medders, J.B., "Defects Caused by Vacuum Chuck Burrs in Silicon Wafer Processing." VLSI Science and Technology/ 1984 Vol. 84-1, 1984, pp. 48-58.

[8] Wachtman, J.B., Jr., Capps, W., and Mandel, J., "Biaxial Flexure Tests of Ceramic Substrates," Journal of Materials, Vol. 7, jmlsa, No.2, 1972, pp. 188-194.

[9] Peery, D.J., "Aircraft Structures," Chapter 13, (McGraw-Hill, New York, 1960).

[10] Hu, S.M., "Critical Stress in Silicon Brittle Fracture, and Effect of Ion Implantation and Other Surface Treatments," Journal of Applied Physics, Vol. 53, No. 5, 1982, 3576-3580.

[11] Dyer, L.D., "The Effect of Common Etchants on the Fracture Strength of Sawed Silicon Slices," The Electrochemical Society Extended Abstracts, Vol. 86-1, 1986, pp. 228-229.

[12] Kirstein, A.F., and Woolley, R.M., "Symmetrical Bending of Thin Circular Elastic Plates on Equally Spaced Point Supports," Journal of Research of the National Bureau of Standards, Vol. 71C, No. 1, 1967, pp. 1-10.

[13] Wilshaw, T.R., "Measurement of Tensile Strength of Ceramics," Journal of the American Ceramic Society, Vol. 51, No. 2, 1968, p. 111.

[14] Shetty, D.K., Rosenfeld, A.R., Duckworth, W.H., and Held, P.R., "A biaxial-Flexure Test for Evaluating Ceramics Strengths," Journal of the American Ceramic Society, Vol. 66, No. 1, 1983, pp. 36-42.

[15] Field, J.E., Gorham, D.A., Hagan, J.T., Swain, M.V. Swain, and Van Der Zwaag, S., "Liquid Jet Impact and Damage Assessment for Brittle Solids," Proceedings of the 5th International Conference on Rain Erosion and Allied Phenomena, Cambridge, England, Sept. 1979.

[16] Szilard, R., "Theory and Analysis of Plates, Classical and Numerical Methods," (Prentice-Hall, Englewood Cliffs, N.J. 1974), p. 168.

[17] Kao, R., Perrone, N., and Capps, W., "Large-Deflection Solution of the Coaxial-Ring--Circular-Glass-Plate Flexure Problem, "Journal of the American Ceramic Society, Vol. 54, 1971, pp. 566-571.

[18] Enstrom, R.E., and Doane, D.A., "A Finite Element Solution for Stress and Deflection in a Centrally Loaded Silicon Wafer," Semiconductor Characterization Techniques, ed. by P.A. Barnes and G.A Rozgonyi, Electrochemical Society PV 78-3, 1978, pp. 413-422.

[19] Chen, C.P., "Effect of Loading Rates on the Strength of Silicon Wafers," DOE/JPL Publ. No. 5101-190, 15 Dec. 1981.

[20] Levengood, W.C., "Effect of Origin Flaw Charactistics on Glass Strength," Journal of Applied Physics, Vol. 29, No. 5, 1958, pp. 820-826.

McDonald Robinson and Lamonte H. Lawrence

CHARACTERIZATION OF HIGH GROWTH RATE EPITAXIAL SILICON FROM A NEW SINGLE WAFER REACTOR

REFERENCE: Robinson, McD. and Lawrence, L. H., "Characterization of High Growth Rate Epitaxial Silicon from a New Single Wafer Reactor," Semiconductor Fabrication: Technology and Metrology, ASTM STP 990, Dinesh C. Gupta, Ed., American Society for Testing and Materials, Philadelphia, 1989.

ABSTRACT: A new single wafer epitaxial silicon reactor, the Epsilon One, is characterized by automated cassette-to-cassette wafer handling, rapid thermal cycle, and high deposition rate for wafers up to 150 mm diameter. This paper describes the reactor, and its results in terms of epi thickness and doping uniformity, epi/substrate transition width, and epi defect density.

KEYWORDS: silicon epitaxy, single wafer reactor, uniformity, autodoping, defects, edge crown.

In the approximately twenty years that epitaxial silicon reactors have been commercially sold, the trend has been toward larger batch sizes and larger equipment. However with increasing wafer diameter and tighter epi specifications, experienced epi users have recently suggested that a single wafer approach could be advantageous [1,2]. Responding to this perceived need, ASM Epitaxy, a subsidiary of ASM America, has developed and will introduce to the market this year an automated single wafer epi reactor called the Epsilon One.

This paper briefly describes the Epsilon One, and discusses in some detail properties of epi films grown in the reactor.

DESCRIPTION OF THE EQUIPMENT

The Epsilon One reactor processes a single silicon wafer at a time at atmospheric pressure in the radiantly heated, low profile horizontal deposition chamber shown in Fig. 1. Process gas enters from the left in the figure, and makes a single pass over the rotating wafer and susceptor. Although gas velocity is high (0.5 to 1.5 m/sec), the flow is laminar and free of recirculation. Throughput is achieved by rapid heating and cooling, and by growing epi silicon at the unusually high rate of 5 μm/minute. The wafer and susceptor assembly are heated from both sides by tungsten halogen lamps backed by gold plated, water cooled reflectors. The upper and lower lamp arrays are turned 90° to each other.

Dr. Robinson is Manager of R&D, ASM Epitaxy, Tempe, AZ 85282 and Mr. Lawrence is President, Lawrence Semiconductor Laboratories, San Jose, CA 95129.

Multiple lamp zones provide real time thermal profile control for uniform wafer heating. Temperature measurement is by thermocouple to avoid the need for correction. The master temperature is measured by a thermocouple that is inserted into the underside of the susceptor at its center of rotation. Because the wafer/susceptor combination is heated from both sides, the thermocouple and wafer temperatures are within a few degrees of each other.

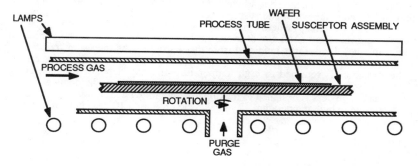

Fig. 1. Schematic cross section of process chamber

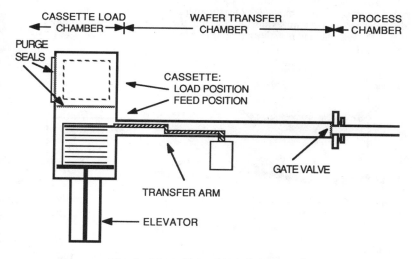

Fig. 2. Automated wafer handling

Wafer handling is automated as shown in Fig. 2. The wafer transfer arm moves wafers through a nitrogen purged transfer chamber, from either of two cassettes to the process chamber. The cassette entry port is load locked so that the wafer transfer and process chambers are not exposed to air during operation.

To process wafers the operator loads a cassette, closes the door and starts the reactor. The wafers, and those in a second cassette if present, are processed without operator intervention. The two cassette load chambers are separately load locked so that one cassette can be changed while the other is in process. After a cassette is loaded and the cassette load chamber purged, the wafers are not exposed to air until the operator removes the completed cassette.

To initiate the epi process, the wafer transfer arm loads the wafer onto a preheated susceptor. The gate valve to the wafer transfer chamber closes, and further heating to 1190°C takes about one minute. After a hydrogen bake to remove native oxide and a brief, optional HCl etch, the wafer and susceptor cool in about 30 sec to the deposition temperature of 1135°C. Except where otherwise noted, the epi described in this paper was grown at 5 µm/min from a mixture of trichlorosilane and hydrogen. After a partial cool (about 1 minute) the wafer is unloaded from the susceptor. As the wafer transfer assembly returns the processed wafer to the cassette and prepares the next wafer for loading, the susceptor is returned to high temperature and any deposited silicon is removed with an HCl etch. In this way the deposition conditions are made identical for each wafer. The epi process is designed to maximize throughput and minimize the time the wafer is exposed to high temperature. Typical cycle time for a 10 µm epi film is 9 - 10 minutes.

EPI CHARACTERIZATION

Thickness, Resistivity and Sheet Resistance

Within Wafer Thickness and Resistivity Profile

Fig. 3 shows representative within wafer thickness (FTIR) and resistivity (four point probe) profiles on a 150 mm wafer. Measurements were made at 5 mm intervals across a diameter, with a 5 mm exclusion zone at the wafer edge. Within wafer uniformity of both thickness and resistivity is approximately ± 1.5%, calculated as [(max - min)/(max + min)] x 100%.

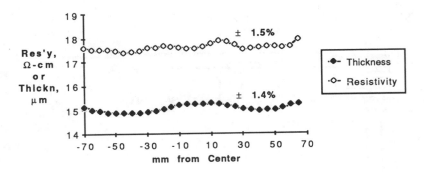

Fig. 3. Radial thickness (FTIR) and resistivity (four point probe). Boron doped epi on antimony doped N+(100), 150 mm substrate.

The thickness profile is symmetrical about the wafer center. In the absence of rotation there would be as much as 20% thickness difference between the upstream and downstream edges of the wafer. Rotation achieves the uniformity that was formerly achieved in horizontal and radiantly heated barrel reactors by tilting the susceptor. The resistivity profile has the same uniformity with or without rotation, and as seen in Fig. 3 lacks the symmetry of the thickness profile. The differing profiles are explained by silicon vs. dopant deposition dynamics. To a first approximation, silicon deposition rate at this temperature (1135°C) is determined by depletion and gas dynamics [3,4], whereas dopant incorporation is more sensitive to temperature uniformity [5,6]. The resistivity profile on each susceptor, while quite uniform, tends to have a characteristic "signature" that may reflect slight irregularities in the susceptor, and therefore slight differences in wafer temperature profile.

Wafer to Wafer (Run to Run) Thickness and Resistivity

Fig. 4 shows wafer to wafer (run to run) center thickness and resistivity, measured on a continuously processed cassette of 24 wafers. Nominal epi thickness is 10 um, and nominal epi resistivity is 27 Ω-cm, P type.

The center thickness is uniform to less than ± 1%, while the center resistivity is uniform to about ± 3%. The uniformity of wafer to wafer thickness suggests that the gas flow controllers and the trichlorosilane liquid/vapor controller have remarkable repeatability. The drift of center resistivity with time is believed to be a temperature effect, since dopant incorporation is much more temperature sensitive than is the deposition rate. The downward drift in resistivity over the first half of the cassette suggests a gradual and slight increase in wafer temperature from one run to the next (boron incorporation increases with temperature [5]), perhaps caused by the system as a whole warming to a steady state average temperature. This suggests that the best uniformity will be achieved in production with the reactor running continuously.

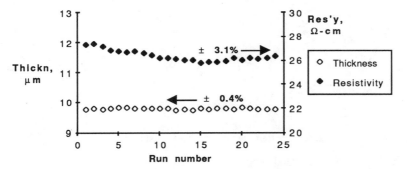

Fig. 4. Wafer to wafer (run-to-run) center thickness and resistivity. Boron doped epi on antimony doped N+ (100), 150 mm substrate.

Fig. 5 shows how within wafer uniformity varies from wafer to wafer (run to run), over 48 consecutive 150 mm wafers. Thickness and resistivity were measured at 9 points on each of two perpendicular axes (90° apart), to within 5 mm of the wafer edge. Each data point thus represents (max - min)/(max + min), expressed as ±%, of 17 measurement points on one wafer. Over the 48 wafers, within wafer thickness uniformity varies from about ± 1.0% to ± 1.5%, and the within wafer resistivity uniformity varies from about ± 2% to about ± 4%.

Epi sheet Resistance Profile

Fig. 6 shows contour maps of epi sheet resistance on two 100 mm wafers, measured on a Prometrix "Omnimap" four point probe [7]. The wafers received epi on the same susceptor using identical deposition conditions in back-to-back runs. The contour lines, drawn at 1% intervals, show that sheet resistance varies a little over ± 1% if all points are included. The standard deviation of all points is about 0.6% on both wafers. The two contour maps show a similar, slight asymmetry which may represent the effect on temperature (and therefore on resistivity) of slight susceptor irregularities.

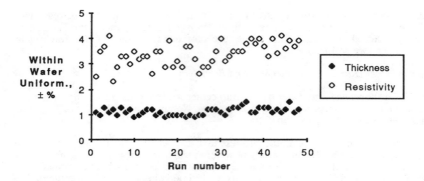

Fig. 5. Within wafer thickness and resistivity in successive epi runs. Boron
doped epi on antimony doped N+(100), 150 mm substrate.

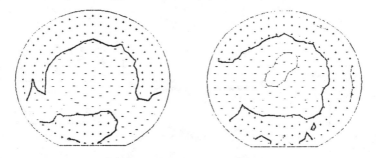

Fig. 6.   Contour map of epi sheet resistance

Epi/Substrate Interface and Autodoping

The width and shape of the doping profile between the substrate or buried layer and
the epi is determined by a combination of solid state outdiffusion and gas phase
autodoping [8,9]. We present here several measured epi-to-substrate doping profiles
from the Epsilon One reactor, along with some comparison results from other epi
reactors. The combined high gas velocity, absence of recirculation, rapid thermal cycle,
and high growth rate of the single wafer reactor appear to reduce autodoping to the level
obtained in other reactors by reducing pressure, temperature and growth rate.

N Epi on Arsenic Doped, N+ Substrate

Fig's. 7a and 7b compare in-depth spreading resistance profiles of N/N+ epi layers
grown in the single wafer reactor and in a vertical "pancake" reactor [10]. In both cases
the substrate is arsenic doped to .003 Ω-cm ($\approx 2 \times 10^{19}$ cm^{-3}), and the N type epi layer is
phosphorus doped to about 5 Ω-cm ($\approx 1 \times 10^{15}$ cm^{-3}). The substrates are 100 mm
diameter, and are not back sealed. The vertical reactor data have been adjusted
horizontally and vertically by small, constant factors to line up with the Epsilon One data
for comparison purposes.

Fig. 7a shows that in the vertical reactor, the epi carrier concentration decreases continuously with distance from the substrate to the top surface (right to left in the figure), suggesting that the back of the wafer acted as a source of dopant throughout epi deposition. The absence of back side autodoping in the Epsilon One profile can be attributed to the single wafer design, i.e. there is no wafer "upstream" of another, and to the absence of the gas recirculation that is characteristic of both vertical and barrel epi reactors.

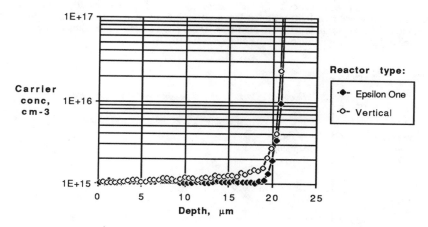

Fig. 7a. Spreading resistance profiles of N epi on As-doped, N+ substrate; comparison of Epsilon One and vertical pancake reactors.

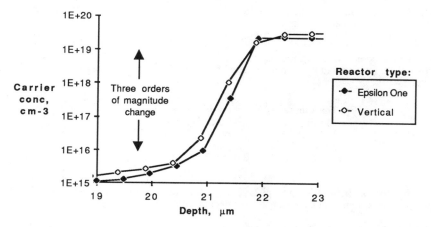

Fig. 7b. Spreading resistance profiles of N epi on As-doped, N+ substrate; comparison of Epsilon One and vertical pancake reactors.

In Fig. 7b the same data is re-scaled to show that the transition from the heavily doped substrate to the epi is more abrupt in the Epsilon One profile. This appears to result from both reduced back side autodoping and reduced time at deposition temperature in the single wafer reactor. The transition width for three orders of magnitude doping change (1 x 10^{19} cm^{-3} to 1 x 10^{16} cm^{-3}) is 0.85 μm for the single wafer reactor and 1.13 μm for the vertical reactor.

P Epi on Boron Doped, P+ Substrate

P epi on P+ substrates is of interest for much of today's CMOS technology, and may be of interest for advanced bipolar technology [11]. Fig. 8 shows the transition from a P+ substrate to a lightly doped P type, thin epi layer, measured by spreading resistance. The substrate is 125 mm diameter, oxide back sealed. The transition width for three orders of magnitude of doping change is 0.6 μm.

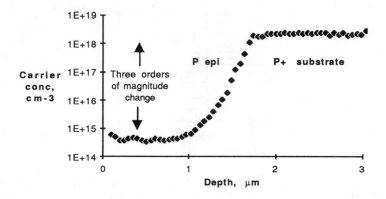

Fig. 8. Spreading resistance profile of 1.7 μm P type epi on B-doped, P+ oxide back sealed substrate.

Uncorrected spreading resistance measurements on thicker P/P+ epi layers have shown the transition widths for three orders of magnitude change in spreading resistance to be:

Epi Thickness	Transition Width
15 μm	1.35 μm
30 μm	1.4 mm
50 μm	1.5 μm
100 μm	2.0 μm

In the 15 μm to 100 μm epi layers the transition width increases roughly as (time)$^{1/2}$, consistent with solid state diffusion control.

Autodoping from Patterned Arsenic Buried Layer

In recent years there have been many publications showing that autodoping from patterned arsenic buried layers is lowered when epi is grown at reduced pressure [12, 13]. Since the Epsilon One reactor operates at atmospheric pressure, we explored other options to reduce arsenic autodoping.

Fig. 9 shows the test structure for these measurements. The substrate is lightly doped (100) P type, containing patterned arsenic and boron buried layers doped to about 5×10^{19} cm^{-3} and 1×10^{17} cm^{-3} peak concentrations, respectively. After epi growth the wafers were cross sectioned and the carrier concentration profiles measured along the dotted lines.

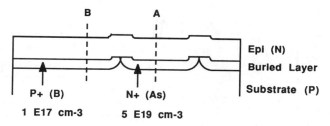

Fig. 9. Buried layers and epi, showing location of spreading resistance profiles.

Epi films were grown on the above structure in the single wafer reactor at atmospheric pressure (760 torr) using trichlorosilane, and in a vertical pancake reactor at 100 torr total pressure using dichlorosilane. Fig. 10 shows the resulting carrier concentration profiles from the vertical reactor [14]. The width of the transition from the arsenic buried layer to the epi (measurement "A") is similar to previously reported reduced pressure epi profiles in the vertical reactor [15].

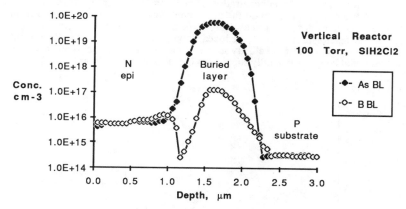

Fig. 10. Autodoping profiles in epi from vertical pancake reactor over patterned arsenic buried layer (As BL) and boron buried layer (B BL).

Fig. 11 shows a carrier concentration profile at position "A" in an epi film from the single wafer reactor, superimposed onto the corresponding vertical reactor profile. The transition from the buried layer to the epi is almost identical in the two profiles. The key process step in the single wafer reactor to achieve this profile is a momentary increase in the horizontal gas velocity from about 0.5 m/sec to 1.5 m/sec during the first 0.4 μm (6 seconds) of deposition, and, during the same interval, omitting dopant from the gas. A separate series of experiments (data not included here) established that the increased gas velocity has the largest effect. We postulate that the high gas flow creates a steep gas phase concentration gradient for the vaporizing arsenic, thereby enhancing its transport away from the surface. Reduced pressure accomplishes the same purpose in the vertical reactor by increasing the gas phase diffusion coefficient.

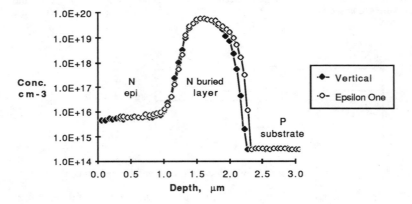

Fig. 11. Comparison of autodoping profiles from vertical pancake reactor (100 torr, SiH₂Cl₂) and Epsilon One reactor (760 torr, SiHCl₃), over patterned arsenic buried layer.

Fig. 12 shows the carrier concentration at position "B" of an epi film from the single wafer reactor, superimposed on the corresponding vertical reactor profile from Fig. 10. The vertical reactor profile shows an N type peak at a depth of 1.0 μm, whereas the single wafer reactor profile shows reduced doping at the same depth. The result suggests that high horizontal gas velocity in the single wafer reactor, combined with a thin undoped initial layer, successfully suppresses lateral arsenic autodoping.

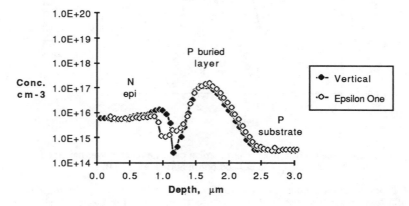

Fig. 12. Comparison of autodoping profiles from vertical pancake reactor (100 torr, SiH₂Cl₂) and Epsilon One reactor (760 torr, SiHCl₃), over patterned boron buried layer, showing differing amounts of lateral autodoping from nearby arsenic buried layers.

Defect Density

Defect density is an important measure of epi quality. Epi defect density measurement is typically by bright light and laser scanner for haze, stacking faults, projections and particles, and by microscope for the above defects and slip. Chemical defect etching and microscope examination are also done to check for metallic contamination and to locate slip or misfit dislocaions that might have been missed on the unetched wafer.

Defects revealed by Bright Light and Laser Scanner

Studies in the Epsilon One reactor have shown no evidence that the epi defect density depends on growth rate up to 5 μm per minute. Fig. 13 shows the number of reflective sites measured after epi on each of twelve P+, oxide back sealed, 125 mm wafers. The wafers were divided into three groups, and each group of four wafers received 10 μm of undoped epi at one of three growth rates. The sequence of growth rates was varied to minimize time or cassette position dependence in the results. Fig. 13 contains both laser scanner and bright light (10^5 lux) measurements, with a 4 mm edge exclusion zone. The laser scanner's "haze" channel count (particle size $<\approx 1$ μm) was omitted so that the bright light and laser counts would be comparable. Within the scatter of the data, the reflective site counts are independent of deposition rate.

The sites were identified by Nomarski interference microscopy. Of a total of 61 reflective sites on the 12 wafers, the following were identified:

Number	Identity
56	Particles (i.e. not epi defects)
3	Circles of contamination ≈ 10 μm diameter
1	Epi stacking fault
1	Scratch, extending 5 mm inside the exclusion zone

Fig. 14 shows total reflective site count by laser scanner and bright light inspection on a series of 17 epi wafers. The wafers received 30 μm of 40 Ω-cm boron doped epi, deposited at 5 μm/min. The substrates were 150 mm diameter, P+ with oxide back seal. With the exception of wafer number 15, there were fewer than 10 reflective sites per wafer after epi. Wafer number 15 had a rather high reflective site count (35) on the laser scanner before epi. These laser scanner counts include the "haze" channel, which is supposed to include particles and defects down to ≈ 0.2 μm diameter.

Slip and Dislocations

Slip and dislocations in silicon are caused by thermal stress, whch in turn is caused by nonuniform temperature. At the temperatures used in these studies (up to 1190°C), the yield stress of silicon is low enough that only a few degrees of temperature nonuniformity can be tolerated. In the single wafer design temperature is uniform to approximately ± 5°C during heating, cooling and deposition. As a result, P+ wafers are always slip free after epi. Most N+, N- and P- wafers are slip-free, and where slip does occur it is confined to the outer 3 mm of the wafer and can be seen only under the microscope.

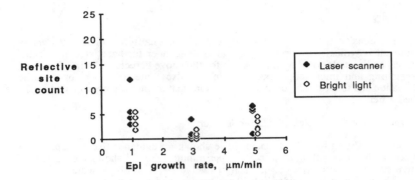

Fig. 13. Reflective site count as a function of epi growth rate by laser scanner and bright light inspection; four 125 mm wafers each at 1, 3, and 5 mm/min.

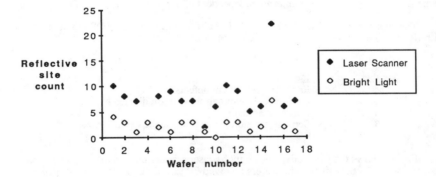

Fig. 14. Reflective site count after epi deposition, by laser scanner and bright light inspection; 150 mm wafers.

Haze and Metallic Contamination

Haze is not observed on wafers from the single wafer reactor, except for occasional wafers having contamination before epi. Haze that originates within an epi reactor usually has one of two causes: contaminated process gas or metal contamination. The most common process gas contaminants are air and water vapor. Studies have shown that in batch type epi reactors water vapor adsorbs onto the reactor wall each time the bell jar is opened, and then desorbs over several minutes during the next process cycle [16]. The study also showed that as little as 1 ppm of oxygen during reactor heatup can cause haze. The load locked cassette entry of the single wafer reactor excludes air, and therefore water vapor, from the process chamber during the entire process cycle. A side benefit of air exclusion is that unwanted deposits on the fused quartz deposition chamber are minimized, and those that do form are easily removed by a vapor HCl etch.

The two most frequent metal sources in epi are improper wafer handling during load and unload, and contamination from the susceptor [17]. Metal contaminants form precipitates in the silicon that cause saucer pits to form during defect etching, and serve as nucleation sites for oxidation-induced stacking faults during post-epi oxidation. Numerous etched wafers, and occasional oxidized and etched wafers, have shown that the single wafer reactor produces contamination free epi as long as the susceptor coating is free of cracks or pinholes. (Contamination free here is as defined by the usual epi inspection method, that is, free of saucer pits or oxidation-induced stacking faults.) The automated wafer handler is an important contributor to both contamination-free and low defect epi.

Edge Crown

Epi from the single wafer reactor has no edge crown, i.e. growth rate is not enhanced at the wafer edge. This may be a particular advantage in applications requiring thick epi, where in conventional epi reactors there may be 20 µm or more of edge crown in a 100 µm epi film. We have not systematically studied the reason for the lack of edge crown, but believe that it might be related to the unusually high growth rate.

SUMMARY

The Epsilon One single wafer silicon epitaxial reactor marks a significant departure from the trend of the last twenty years toward larger batch reactors. The approach in the single wafer reactor is to achieve throughput by rapid heating and cooling, high deposition rate and automated wafer handling, while depositing on a single wafer at a time. This permits epi to be grown on 150 mm substrates with thickness uniform to less than ± 1.5% and resistivity uniform to less than ± 4% within-wafer and wafer-to-wafer. The epi is free of edge crown and typically has fewer than 10 defects and particles per 150 mm wafer. Limited autodoping data shows autodoping to be comparable to a vertical epi reactor operated at reduced pressure.

ACKNOWLEDGEMENTS

It is impossible in this small space to give adequate credit to the many people who have contributed to the development of the Epsilon One epi reactor. Dr. D. M. Jackson initiated the project, and Dr. A. P. Ferro has guided it since its inception. Dr. W. L. Johnson, W. B. de Boer and A. E. Ozias contributed key innovations. R. Haro, M. R. Hawkins, A. Olsen, J. F. Wengert and the members of their development teams have made the reactor a reality.

REFERENCES

[1] C. W. Pearce, Ch. 2 in VLSI Technology, S. M. Sze, Ed., McGraw Hill Book Co. (1983), p. 51.

[2] M. Ogirima and R. Takahashi, Proceedings of the Tenth International Conference on Chemical Vapor Deposition, G. W. Cullen, Ed., The Electrochemical Society, Pennington, NJ (1987), p. 204.

[3] F.C,. Eversteijn, Philips Research Reports, 29, 45 (1974).

[4] J. Bloem, in Semiconductor Silicon 1977, H. R. Huff and E. Sirtl, Eds., The Electrochemical Society, Pennington, NJ (1977), p. 201.

[5] H.B. Pogge, Handbook on Semiconductors, Vol. 3, "Materials, Properties and Preparation", S. P. Keller, Ed., North-Holland Publishing Co. (1980), p. 335.

[6] M. W. M. Graef, B. J. H. Leunissen and H. H. C. de Moor, Journal of the Electrochemical Society, 132, 1942 (1985).

[7] Private communication, W. Johnson and A. Keenan, Prometrix Corporation, Sunnyvale, CA.

[8] G. R. Srinivasan, Journal of the Electrochemical Society, 127, 1334 (1980).

[9] McD. Robinson, Ch. 6 in Impurity Doping Processes in Silicon, F.F.Y. Wang, Ed., North Holland Publishing Co. (1981), p. 259.

[10] Private communication, C. Korman, General Electric Corporate Research and Development, Schenectady, NY.

[11] J. A. Kirchgessner and G. P. Woods, Proceedings of the Tenth International Conference on Chemical Vapor Deposition, G.W. Cullen, Ed., The Electrochemical Society, Pennington, NJ (1987), p 233.

[12] M. Ogirima, H. Saida, M. Suzuki, and M. Maki, Journal of the Electrochemical Society, 124, 903 (1977).

[13] R. B. Herring, Solid State Technol., 22, [11], 75 (1979); and R. B. Herring, Proceedings of the Seventh International Conference on Chemical Vapor Deposition, T. O. Sedgwick and H. Lydtin, Eds., The Electrochemical Society, Pennington, NJ (1979), p. 126.

[14] Private communication, C-C. D. Wong, Integrated Device Technology, Santa Clara, CA.

[15] S. M. Fisher, M. L. Hammond, and N. P. Sandler, Emerging Semiconductor Technology, ASTM STP 960, D. C. Gupta and P. H. Langer, Eds., American Society for Testing and Materials (1986) p. 33; and S. M. Fisher, M. L. Hammond, and N. P. Sandler, Solid State Technol., 29, [1], 107 (1986).

[17] C. J. Werkhoven, Aggregation Phenomena of Point Defects in Silicon, E. Sirtl and J. Goorissen, Eds., The Electrochemical Society, Pennington, NJ (1983), p 144.

Hisaaki Suga, Minoru Ichizawa, Kazuyoshi Endo and

Kenji Tomizawa

SOFTENING OF SI AND GAAS DURING THERMAL PROCESS

REFERENCE: Suga, H., Ichizawa, M.,Endo, K., and
Tomizawa, K., "Softening of Si and GaAs during thermal
process," Semiconductor Fabrication: Technology and
Metrology ASTM STP 990, Dinesh C. Gupta, editor,
American Society for Testing and Materials, 1989.

ABSTRACT: Semiconductor materials for highly integrated
circuit devices need the resistance for the slippage
during thermal process to prevent the defect induced
degradation. Temperature dependence of strength of
cz-Si and pcz-GaAs was investigated by micro-Vickers
hardness tester. Hardness of cz-Si wafers lowers
sharply with testing temperature and with precipitated
oxygen content. Hardness of pcz-GaAs wafers starts to
decrease at a temperature about 400°C lower than is
the case for Si wafers. Dopant content dependence of
hardness between 600 and 700°C was not observed in
Si doped or Zn doped pcz-GaAs wafers.

KEYWORDS: silicon wafer, gallium arsenide, high temperature hardness, thermal process, solid solution hardening, oxygen precipitation

Substrates for highly integrated semiconductor microdevices need for a certain reasonable strength against the
fabrication damages due to the stress-intensified structure
during thermal process. Czochralski grown silicon wafers
contain inherently supersaturated interstitial oxygen, which
contributes to the introduction of gettering sinks for
unwanted impurity and the resistance against dislocation
movement.

Dr. Suga, Ichizawa and Tomizawa are manager and sub-
manager at material testing research lab. of Central Research Institute, and manager at gallium arsenide division
of Compound Semiconductor Center, Mitsubishi Metal Co.,
1-297, Kitabukuro, Omiya, Japan 330. Endo is manager at
R & D center of Japan Silicon Co. 314 Kanauchi, Nishi-
sangao, Noda, Japan 278.

43

Dislocations in Si are known to be locked by dissolved oxygen atoms[1,2] but it was not affected by the precipitate itself. Main role of precipitates on the deformation is a nucleation center of dislocation by punching-out around them. Once a mobile dislocation is nucleated on a slip plane, the macroscopic deformation can start at low stress and it depends on the dislocation mobility[3].

Thus, as long as Si wafer contains no mobile dislocation, the strength may not depend on the dissolved oxygen content. But as the generation of dislocations becomes easy around the oxygen precipitates introduced after thermal process, the strength is thought to decrease. This change might depend on the content of precipitated oxygen.

The precipitation proceeds with thermal treatment below the oxygen solubility curve[4]. Wafer with higher content of oxygen has the faster precipitation rate. Therefore, we must consider the compromise of optimum initial oxygen content for suppression of slippage and enhancement of intrinsic gettering efficiency[4]. We report the hardness change of Si and GaAs at high temperature, and softening of annealed Si wafers in order to design the proper fabrication process.

EXPERIMENTAL PROCEDURE

Dislocation-free cz-Si wafers with oxygen content of 0.5 to 1.1×10^{18} atoms/cm^3 were prepared for hardness test. Wafers with lowest oxygen content were made by magnetically cz-method. On the test high temperature micro-Vickers tester (Nikon EOF-4) was employed. Indentation loading of 50g on (100) or (111) surface was kept for 15 sec. at each temperature ranging for 600°C to 900°C under argon ambient. After indentation, indentation size and length of generated slip line emerged on the wafer surface was examined.

The thermal process employed for examining the effect of oxygen precipitation in Si on the strength was the low and high consecutive annealing[4]. At first wafers were annealed for 8 hrs at 650°C for nucleation of oxygen precipitates, and then they were ramped at the rate of 2.5°C/min up to 1100°C for growth of the precipitates. At the temperature, wafers were kept for 2 hrs for sufficient growth of oxygen precipitates and then they were unloaded from the furnace.

GaAs wafers used were made with As pressure controlled Czochralski(pcz) growth method[5]. Dislocation densities of as-grown wafer were ranged between 3000 to 32000/cm^2. Dopant employed was Si or Zn.

RESULTS

Dependence of Interstitial Oxygen Content (Oi) on Hv of cz-Si

Fig. 1 shows the relationships between the micro-
Vickers hardness, Hv, of Si wafers at high temperature
between 600°C and 900°C and the initial oxygen content of
as-grown wafers. As-grown wafers used did not show any
indication of oxygen precipitation by FTIR(JEOL: JIR-40X)
method and by TEM(HITACHI: H800LB) analysis. Yonenaga et
al. showed that the oxygen content dependence of the upper
yield stress in dislocation-free cz-Si was negligibly
small[6]. Solid solution hardening in dilute alloy is known
to accord with $C^{1/2}$(C: content of impurity) law[7]. Although large dispersion of data at each temperature blurs
the fittness of $C^{1/2}$ dependence, we can not negate the $C^{1/2}$
dependence on Si wafer strength in the present experiment.

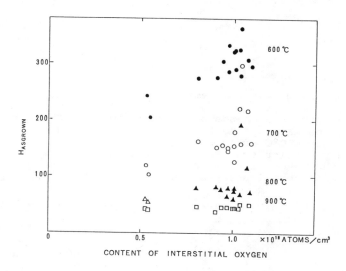

Fig. 1 Micro-Vickers hardness of as-grown cz-Si wafers
at high temeperature v.s. content of interstitial oxygen

Oxygen atoms can be effective as the strengthener. Practic-
ally in the fabrication processes of IC device related to
cz-Si wafer, we had better pay an attention rather to the
strong temeperature dependence than the oxygen content
dependence in treating the wafer without precipitates,
considering the large decrease of the strength.

Hv softening on the thermal process

Fig. 2 shows the relationship between the content of
precipitated oxygen in Si wafer after two consecutive
thermal treatment and the total content of oxygen in wafer.

After this thermal treatment, Si wafers with total content of oxygen of higher than 1.0×10^{18} atoms/cm^3 shows the significant volume of oxygen precipitation. This critical content of oxygen precipitation depends on the type of thermal process and condition of crystal growth[8]. We only selected this combination of the sample and process conditions to make the significant difference of oxygen precipitation among the samples used.

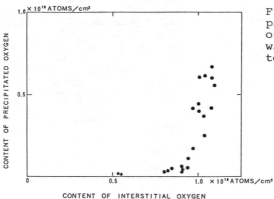

Fig. 2 Content of precipitated oxygen of annealed cz-Si wafers v.s. the total oxygencontent.

Fig. 3 shows the change of hardness of as-grown cz-Si wafers with thermal treatments. Although softening of as-grown wafers at 600°C after the two consecutive annealing is comparably smaller than that at higher temperatures, at most of the cases significant softening occurs more or less after the thermal process. Furthermore, highly precip-

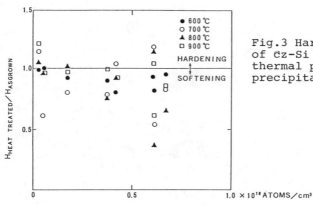

Fig.3 Hardness change of cz-Si wafer with thermal process v.s. precipitated oxygen.

itated wafers seem to be significant in the softening.
This fact suggests that the generation of dislocation around
the grown oxygen precipitates would cause the low stress
reaction on the slip planes and the hardening by precipitates can not be expected so much.

Fig. 4 shows the relationship between hardness of
precipitated cz-Si wafers and their interstitial oxygen
content, Oi, after the precipitation. As shown in Fig.4,
Oi dependence on the hardness seems to be almost nothing
at any temperature between 600°C and 900°C. Furthermore, it
is noteworthy that the hardness of two annealed MCZ-Si
wafers is extremely lower than that of other cz-Si wafers.

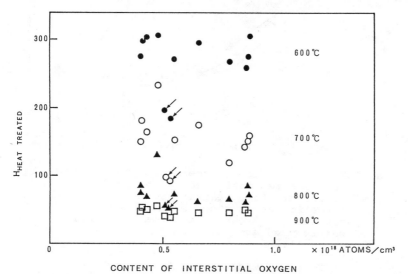

Fig. 4 Hardness vs. interstitial oxygen content after
the precipitation. Arrow shows MCZ-Si wafers.

Compared with data in Fig. 1, Oi content dependence on the
hardness of annealed wafer is found to be quite different.
If the hardness is determined generally only by Oi itself,
this difference should not exist. Several reasons for this
difference can be thought. In the following we will discuss.

Temperature dependence on Hv of GaAs

Fig. 5 shows the temperature dependence of the hardness
about As pressure controlled Czochralski grown GaAs single
crystals relative to that of cz-Si wafers. It is clear that
the strength of GaAs wafers corresponds to that of cz-Si
wafers, except that the temperature is lower by about 400°C.
Among the GaAs wafers, silicon doped wafer has the higher

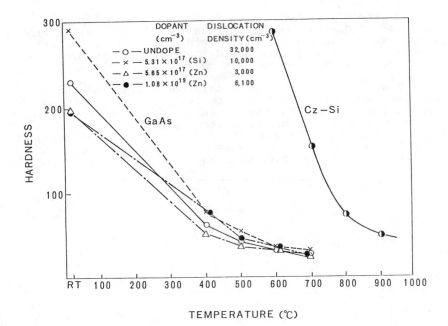

Fig. 5 Temperature dependence of the hardness about
As pressure controlled Czochralski grown GaAs
single crystals relative to that of cz-Si wafer
investigated in the present experiment. Dopant
content and grown-in dislocation density of GaAs
wafers used are shown in the figure.

strength than Zn doped wafer with the comparable content
of doping. In these dislocated GaAs wafers locking force
might determine the dislocation mobility[8]. Through this
mechanism doped silicon atoms could play an effective role
of the suppresser for dislocation multiplication.

Yonenaga et al showed the importance of dislocation
locking in the yielding behavior of dislocated GaAs single
crystal with silicon content of 2-20 x 10^{15} atoms/cm^3 at
400°C to 500°C[8]. As shown in Fig. 5, the dependence of
the hardness on the dopant content is not systematic even
at 400°C and 500°C. The hardness of Zn doped wafer with low
doping is lower than that of undoped wafer. This fact might
imply that solid solution softening occurs in Zn doped
wafer. This is consistent with the results by Nakada et al
[10]. Anyway, doping effect of Zn on the wafer strengthening
is complex. The difference of a factor of 4.4 times in
strength should exist between two Zn doped wafers, if $c^{1/2}$
dependence is supposed in our cases.

DISCUSSION

Cz-Si

On the thermal process, apparent softening of cz-Si wafers was found to proceed with inevitable precipitation of oxygen. But this precipitation induced softening is complex to understand, because the difference of hardness between wafers of same interstitial but different total oxygen content exists explicitly.

There are several possibilities why this difference appears.

1. Is the hardness of MCZ-Si wafers too low? But MCZ-Si wafers are not special to change the hardness in the impurity level or lattice defect density.

2. Is delta Oi measurement too rough to estimate the absorbance at $1107cm^{-1}$? Even so, as delta Oi can not be overestimated, we can expect rather the larger softening.

3. Does somewhat of the precipitation hardening still exist? This might occur and we will discuss later.

4. The hardness of cz-Si may be independent on delta Oi. Would the thermal process bring about the other hardening? But this kind of hardening belongs to the intrinsic hardening related to Peiels barrier or process induced contamination and we have no clue about them.

Now, we will think about the possibility of precipitation softening which was caused by generation of prismatic dislocation loops around the oxygen precipitates[2]. However, although overall softening is observed, as shown in Fig. 3, Fig. 4 clearly implies that the precipitation could contribute to the hardening but softening.(See the large difference of hardness between MCZ-Si and cz-Si at comparable content of interstitial oxygen.) This fact may mean that the precipitation occured in cz-Si can act as a strengthener and a weakner.

As a weakener, precipitates themselves would induce in some case the initiation of dislocation nucleation, and the precipitation itself would lower the content of interstitially dissolved oxygen, as a result, to lose the solid solution hardening. As a strengthener, precipitates can prevent the dislocation from moving forward.

In the following, we only treat this problem as a simplified additive contributions of two hardenings.

First of all, we have to notice that the difference of temperature dependence in the two hardening mechanisms

could exist, because the barrier height to overcome for
dislocation motion differs with the nature of obstacles.
Easiness of dislocation movement at high temperatures becomes different between annealed and as-grown wafers.
Oxygen precipitate growth during thermal process would bring
about some change of the hardness. We can find in Fig.3 that
lowering of the hardness at 600°C is smaller than that at
higher temperatures. Although the strength at arbitrary
temperature, after all, involves the problem about its
temperature dependence, we need the rough estimate of both
contributions of precipitation hardening and solid solution
hardening in order to understand the softening.

In a dilute alloy, dislocation length between two
obstacles is inversely proportional to the square root of
the content of obstacles. The resistance for dislocation
movement is inversely proportional to this mean free length
between obstacles. Then, we can formulate the content
dependent strength, σ_T, as the following equation,

$$\sigma_T = A \times (O_T - \Delta Oi)^{1/2} + B \times \Delta Oi^{1/2} \qquad (1)$$

where A and B are proportional constant for solid solution
hardening and for precipitation hardening, respectively.
O_T means the total oxygen content in wafer. As as-grown
wafer contains no precipitate($\Delta Oi = 0$), the ratio of
strength of precipitated wafer to that of as-grown wafer,
that is,

$$\frac{\sigma_T}{\sigma_{A.G.}} = (1 - \frac{\Delta Oi}{O_T})^{1/2} + \frac{B}{A} \times (\frac{\Delta Oi}{O_T})^{1/2} \qquad (2)$$

Fig. 6 shows the ratio of the strength of precipitated
material to that of material before precipitation as a
function of degree of precipitation. Ratio, B/A means the
ratio of precipitation hardening to solid solution hardening. Comparing Fig. 3 with Fig. 6, we can find that the
precipitation induced softening is mostly caused by the
loss of solid solution hardening. The contribution of
precipitation to the strength might be 10 to 30% of solid
solution hardening.

This conclusion should not extend simply to all cases,
because a role of nucleation center of dislocations depends
on the morphology of oxygen precipitates. With prolonged
thermal process in the range of precipitation temperature,
oxygen precipitates emit the dislocations around them for
releasing the accumulating elastic strain energy due to the
lattice misfit between the precipitate and silicon matrix.
In such a case large drop of the strength might be expected.

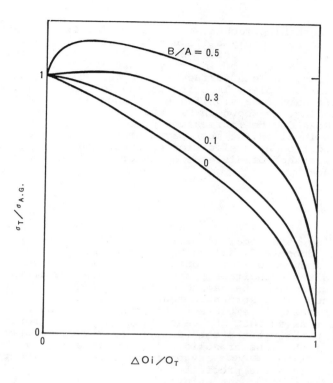

Fig. 6 Ratios of the strength of preciptated material
to that of the material before precipitation.

Thus, to know the detail about the oxygen precipitation
in cz-Si is important to understand the softening. The
oxygen precipitation is known to depend on the thermal
history during crystal growth, supersaturation of interstitial oxygen, and introduction of nucleus center for oxygen
precipitation, such as some complexes or clusters composed
of impurity atoms and/or native point defects[11].

Intrinsic gettering is effective to accomodate some
unwanted contamination[12]. Source of gettering sink is
such as dislocation, stacking fault and small oxygen precipitate. In order to introduce these defects in the core of
wafer a great deal of oxygen precipitation may be necessi-
tated, but this treatment might bring about the more probable slippage during processing by the above-mentioned
softening. Thus, it is important to design the device
fabrication process coordinated with silicon wafer subjected
to different thermal growth history and/or their precipi-

tation characteristics.

GaAs
    Strengthening mechanism of GaAs wafer is now not clear
[13]. It is reasonably difficult to analyze it, because so
many origin of degradation, such as grown-in high dislocation
density, high level of impurity, unstoichiometry, intrinsic
point defect, As lean surface region and so on, still exist
in available samples. Impurity doping to GaAs do not give
straightforward to a significant enhancement for the
strengthening, as shown in Fig. 5.
    In GaAs device fabrication process, no matter how much
doping is involved, we must pay a great attension to avoid
the degradation by dislocation movement and multiplication,
if the existance of dislocation is critical to device
performance.

CONCLUSION

    As far as a local deformation in dislocation-free
wafers is concerned, softening by the generation of precipitation induced dislocations does not always occurs at
similar stress condition, possibly because the dislocation
multiplication may be caused by the limited number of
imhomogeneously distributed sources. But when the long time
thermal process is employed we must always encounter the
enhanced risk against the generation of sources for a long
range slip through the active layer of device, possibly
because of the loss of solid solution hardening by the
interstitially dissolved oxygen atoms and the dislocation
emission around the precipitates.
    On dislocated GaAs wafers, intrinsically low strength
should be considered before designing the thermal process,
because doping effect on the strength would not be expected
sufficiently.

ACKNOWLEDGEMENT

    The authors wish to thank Y. Saito, director, R&D
division, JAPAN SILICON CO. for finantial support and I.
Suzuki, R&D division, JAPAN SILICON CO. for Oi measurement.

REFERENCES

[1] Hu, S.M.,"Dislocation Pinning Effect of Oxygen Atoms in
     Silicon," Applied Physics Letters, Vol. 32, No. 2, July
     1977, pp 53-55.
[2] Sumino,K.,"Interaction of Dislocations with Impurities

and its Influence on the Mechanical Properties of Silicon Crystals", <u>Materials Research Society Symposia Proceedings</u>, Vol. 14, 1983, Elsevier Science Publishing Co., pp 307-321.

[3]   Nishino, Y., and Imura, T., "Generation Process of Dislocations in Precipitate-Containing Silicon Crystals," <u>physica status solidi(a)</u>, Vol. 73, 1982, pp 173-182.

[4]   Suga, H,. and Murai, K.,"Effect of Bulk Defects in Silicon on SiO$_2$ Film Breakdown, <u>Emerging Semiconductor Technology</u>, ASTM STP 960, Gupta, D.C., and Langer, P. H., Eds, American Society for Testing and Materials, 1986, pp 336-352.

[5]   Tomizawa, K., Sassa, K., Shimanuki, Y., and Nishizawa, J., "Growth of Low Dislocation Density GaAs by As Pressure-Controlled Czochralski Method," <u>Journal of Electrochemical Society</u>, Vol. 131, No. 10, October 1984, pp 2394-2397.

[6]   Yonenaga, I., Sumino, K., and Hoshi K., "Mechanical Strength of Silicon Crystals as a Function of Oxygen Concentration," <u>Journal of Applied Physics</u>, Vol. 56, No. 8, October 1984, pp 2346-2350.

[7]   Suga, H., and Imura, T., "Solid Solution Hardening of Silver Single Crystals By Indium, By Tin and By Antimony," <u>Japanese Journal of Applied Physics</u>, Vol. 14, No. 8, August 1975, pp 1253-1254.

[8]   Yonenaga, I., Onose, U., and Sumino, K., "Mechanical Properties of GaAs Crystals," <u>Journal of Material Research Society</u>, Vol. 2, No. 2, March/April 1987, pp 252-261.

[9]   Swaminathan, N., and Copley, S.M., "Temperature and Orientation Dependence of Plastic Deformation in GaAs Single Crystals Doped with Si, Cr, or Zn, <u>"Journal of The American Ceramic Society</u>, Vol. 58, No. 11-12, 1975, pp 482-485.

[10] Nakada, Y., and Imura, T.,"Influence of Dopants and Deformation Temperature on Strength of GaAs," <u>physica status solidi(a)</u>, Vol. 103, 1987, pp435-442.

[11] Shimanuki, Y., Furuya, H., Suzuki, I., and Murai, K., "Effect of Thermal History on Microdefect Formation in Czochralski Silicon Single Crystals," <u>Japanese Journal of Applied Physics</u>, Vol. 24, No. 12, December 1985, pp 1594-1599.

[12] Suga, H., and Murai, K., "Precipitation Behavior of Deposited Metals in CZ-Si," <u>SemiconductorProcessing</u>, ASTM STP 850, Gupta, D.C. Ed., American Society for Testing and Materials, 1984, pp 241-256.

[13] Swaminathan, V., and Copley, S.M., "Hardening of GaAs by Solute-Vacancy Pairs, <u>"Journal of Applied Physics</u>, Vol. 47, No. 10, October 1976, pp 4405-4413.

Witawat Wijaranakula, John H. Matlock, and Howard Mollenkopf

NUCLEATION AND GROWTH KINETICS OF BULK MICRODEFECTS IN
HEAVILY DOPED EPITAXIAL SILICON WAFERS

REFERENCE: Wijaranakula, W., Matlock, J.H., and Mol-
lenkopf, H., "Nucleation and Growth Kinetics of Bulk
Microdefects in Heavily Doped Epitaxial Silicon
Wafers", Semiconductor Fabrication: Technology and
Metrology, ASTM STP 990, Dinesh C. Gupta, editor,
American Society for Testing and Materials, 1989.

ABSTRACT: Nucleation and growth mechanisms of the
bulk microdefects in oxygen controlled silicon substrate wafers heavily doped with boron and antimony
were studied following pre- and postepitaxial
enhanced precipitation annealing at various temperatures. It was observed that "grown-in" microdefects
in both dopant species are nucleated by a similar
mechanism during the crystal growth cooling period.
Microdefect growth behavior appears, however, to be
different, probably due to differing effects of the
dopant species. It was also observed that the pre-
and postepitaxial annealing as well as the epitaxial
deposition processes have a strong impact on the
growth of the bulk microdefects. Based upon this
study, generic growth characteristics of the bulk
microdefects of both P^+ and N^+ materials are established and a growth kinetics model is proposed.

KEYWORDS: silicon epitaxy, oxygen precipitation,
internal gettering

Thermally induced defects which include oxidation-
induced defects (OSFs and swirls) [1-3] and those induced
by oxygen precipitation [4-5] have been studied for many
years. Defects associated with oxygen precipitation seem
to draw the most attention because well controlled

Dr. Wijaranakula is a senior engineer/R&D Materials
Characterization, Dr. Mollenkopf is the department manager
and Dr. Matlock is the Vice President of Technology at SEH
America, Inc., 4111 SE 112st Avenue, Vancouver, WA 98662

oxygen precipitation with respect to the internal gettering (IG) process could lead to high device performance and yield [6-9]. In epitaxial technology where heavily-doped substrate wafers are used, the difference between precipitation behavior in boron doped P+ and antimony doped N+ silicon is observed [10]. Extensive studies on this subject have been conducted but no clear picture of the nucleation and growth mechanism has yet been reported. The precipitation model [11] based on complex formation between an impurity and a donor-type self-interstitial seems to be plausible. However, a similar argument can also be postulated in the case where a complex between boron and donor-type vacancy is involved. Both acceptor and donor-type vacancies are known to exist at high temperature [12].

In the past, the determination of oxygen precipitation in lightly-doped silicon has been performed by measuring the change in the interstitial oxygen $[O_i]$ concentration using the Fourier Transform Infrared (FTIR) spectrophotometer prior to and after various thermal cycles [13-14]. It was found that reduction of $[O_i]$ concentration after a given thermal cycle could be directly correlated to the initial $[O_i]$ concentration in the silicon matrix [6, 15]. Plots of the reduction of $[O_i]$ concentration as a function of initial $[O_i]$ concentration have recently been used as generic curves [16] for various oxygen precipitate thermal cycles. An unknown factor involving this method is the influence of the oxygen depleted zone, termed the "denuded zone" (DNZ) on the FTIR reading [17]. This can eventually be prevented by removing the oxygen denuded layer prior to measurement [18].

In heavily-doped silicon, determination of the oxygen precipitation rate by IR measurement is not possible. This is because the $[O_i]$ concentration cannot be determined directly by the FTIR due to free carrier absorption. SIMS, (Secondary Ion Mass Spectrometry), which determines the total concentration of oxygen, cannot distingush $[O_i]$ concentration from the oxygen concentration which is incorporated in the form of a solid solution. Therefore, any reduction in interstitial oxygen concentration cannot be quantitatively determined. At the present time, evaluation of the nucleation and growth of bulk defects associated with oxygen precipitation in heavily-doped silicon is relied primarily upon observation of the defect formation.

The demand for epitaxial silicon material for the application of IC devices such as high density CMOS [19-20] and CCD [21] has increased significantly during the past several years. Devices fabricated on epitaxial silicon material have shown superb characteristics (e.g. latch-up prevention and the uniformity of resistivity) [22-23] when compared to devices fabricated on lightly-doped silicon. Despite the abundant research on oxygen precipitation and internal gettering in epitaxial silicon material [24-29], a fundamental understanding of the nucleation and growth of bulk defects and control of the precipitation process is considered to be lacking. Extensive studies were conducted on the following subjects and will be discussed in this paper:

    a. Heterogeneous nucleation of the oxide microprecipitates.
    b. Growth kinetics of bulk defects in epitaxial silicon wafers.
    c. Impact of the epitaxial deposition process on oxygen precipitation.

EXPERIMENTAL PROCEDURES, RESULTS, AND DISCUSSIONS

Heterogeneous Nucleation of the Oxide Microprecipitates

The starting materials were P^+ and $N^+(100)$ substrate wafers, 100 mm in diameter and heavily-doped with boron and antimony (0.01 and 0.025 ohm-cm). In order to prevent a possible fluctuation in the oxygen precipitation rate due to the thermal history effect [30-31] and the crystal growth conditions [32-33], substrate wafers were prepared only from a very short section of fully grown crystals. The length of the sections were between 15 and 30 millimeters. The oxygen content in each section was determined by SIMS because the FTIR cannot be used when the resistivity is lower than 0.1 ohm-cm. Only sections that contained oxygen in the range between 1.45×10^{18} and 1.55×10^{18} atoms/cm^3 (ASTM F121-79) were used.

Isochronal pre-annealing of the substrate wafers was carried out in nitrogen ambient at specific temperatures ranging between 500 and 900°C. Mixed gases (nitrogen + 5% oxygen in volume) were used to prevent "nitrogen" pitting when pre-annealing was performed at temperatures above 750°C. This pre-annealing was necessary to induce heterogeneous nucleation of the "grown-in" microprecipitates. Substrate wafers with no pre-annealing were also set aside and used as the control samples. P^+ substrate wafers were pre-annealed for 3 hours, whereas N^+ substrate wafers were pre-annealed for 24 hours so that sufficient bulk defects could be obtained for this study. After pre-annealing, wafers were processed through the polishing and epitaxial deposition steps. During epitaxial deposition, epitaxial layers of approximately 6 and 13.5 microns thick were deposited. Epitaxial deposition was performed at 1150°C using trichlorosilane as the gas source. Boron and phosphorus were used as the doping species. After epitaxial deposition, the wafers were annealed at 1050°C in dry oxygen ambient for 16 hours. This annealing step would represent the well drive-in step of the CMOS IC fabrica-

tion process. Bulk defects were examined on the (110)
cleaved surface after Wright etch [34]. P/P+ samples were
etched for 1 1/4 minutes, while 2 1/2 minutes were required to etch the N/N+ samples. Extended etching of P/P+
samples results in overetching and the formation of artifacts.

     Figs. 1 and 2 show a series of photomicrographs of
the cross sections of P/P+ and N/N+ samples. It is
observed that the bulk defect size and density are
strongly influenced by the pre-annealing temperature. The
isolated bulk defects in a heavily-precipitated area are

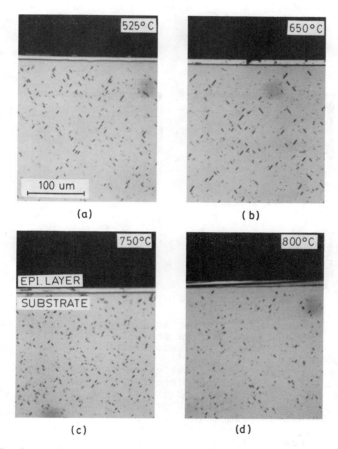

(a)   (b)

(c)   (d)

FIG. 1 -- Cross section optical photomicrographs for
         P/P+(100) wafers preannealed at a) 525,
         b) 650, c) 750, and d) 800°C.

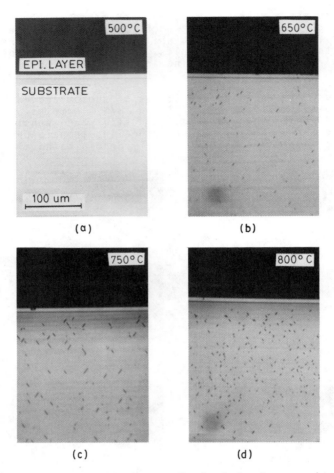

FIG. 2 -- Cross section optical photomicrographs for
         N/N+(100) wafers pre-annealed at a) 500,
         b) 650, c) 750, and d) 800°C.

much smaller than in the lightly-precipitated area. Under
the SEM (Scanning Electron Microscope), two types of bulk
defects   have been identified :   (i) bulk stacking   faults
(BSF's)   and   (ii) small etch pits which are   believed   to
have   originated   from oxide precipitates and   dislocation
loops   [35-37].   Figs.   3a   and   3b   show   the   SEM
photomicrographs of the bulk defects in P/P+ and N/N+
wafers pre-annealed at 750°C.

        The   bulk defect densities counted under the optical
microscope at 200 and 400X magnification are plotted as   a

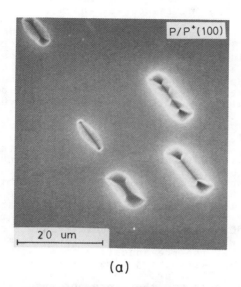

(a)

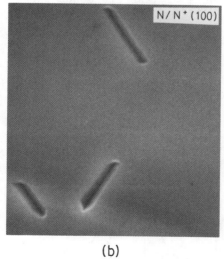

(b)

FIG. 3 -- SEM micrographs of bulk defects in samples
pre-annealed at 750°C a) P/P⁺ and b) N/N⁺(100).

function of pre-annealing temperature in Figs. 4 and 5. Bulk defects were counted at 400X magnification only in the high density region. The curves shown in Figs. 4 and 5 represent the overall transformation [38] of the nuclea- tion and growth of the microprecipitates and their evolu- tion into BSFs. Nucleation of the "grown-in" microprecipi- tates is considered to take place during the crystal growth cooling period whereas their dissolution and growth occur during epitaxial deposition and subsequent high temperature annealing. Heterogeneous nucleation occurs during pre-annealing by utilizing these microprecipitates as nucleation sites.

In Fig. 4, the total bulk defect density in P/P$^+$ wafers increases with increasing pre-annealing temperature and then decreases rapidly when the pre-annealing tempera- ture exceeds 700°C. The peak of the curve lies in the temperature range between 650 and 700°C. This result indicates that the heterogeneous nucleation rate of micro- precipitates at low temperatures is small, probably due to the lowering of the oxygen diffusivity [39]. At tempera- tures above 750°C, the oxygen solubility and the critical radius increase which causes a dissolution of micropreci- pitates. Note that the pre-annealing time was 3 hours. In the case where pre-annealing time is less than 3 hours, less dissolution will occur. Samples pre-annealed at 900°C for less than 3 hours may therefore not show significant reduction in bulk defect density.

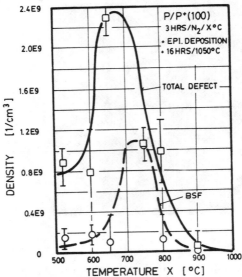

FIG. 4 -- Relationship between bulk defect density and pre-annealing temperature in P/P$^+$ wafers.

As observed in Fig. 4, the generation rate of BSFs in P/P$^+$ wafers appears to follow the same trend as that of the total bulk defects. The peak of the curve for the BSF density lies at a temperature (750°C) slightly higher than that for the total defect density. The growth mechanism of isolated BSFs, which is controlled by both oxygen and self-interstitial diffusion [40-41], is different than that of oxide precipitates. These results agree with data obtained from similar experiments performed on lightly-doped CZ-grown P(100) materials [42]. Another observation shows that the bulk defect density in the control samples is identical to that in the samples pre-annealed at temperatures below 600°C. Bulk defects are observed in the control samples because the "grown-in" microprecipitates pre-existed in the substrate wafers prior to epitaxial deposition. As explained earlier, pre-annealing causes heterogeneous nucleation of the pre-existing microprecipitates and enhances oxygen precipitation. Therefore, the curves shown in Fig. 4 should not lead to a conclusion that the nucleation of bulk defects occurs through a homogeneous process as proposed elsewhere [43].

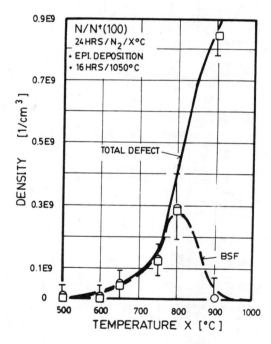

FIG. 5 -- Relationship between bulk defect density and pre-annealing temperature in N/N$^+$ wafers.

In N/N$^+$ wafers, the total bulk defect density is found to be much lower than in P/P$^+$ wafers despite a much longer pre-annealing time. A high bulk defect density is observed in N/N$^+$ wafers pre-annealed at temperatures well above 700°C. This indicates that the heterogeneous nucleation of microprecipitates in antimony doped silicon does not follow the diffusion controlled growth process described by the Zener's theory [44]. In Zener's theory, the dissolution of microprecipitates should occur during pre-annealing at high temperatures. This phenomenon has been interpretated as the result of an interaction between point defects generated at the precipitate and oxygen atoms [45]. An absence of the bulk defects in N/N$^+$ control samples and samples pre-annealed at 500°C implies that only small, thermodynamically unstable microprecipitates pre-existed in the N$^+$ substrate prior to epitaxial deposition.

Growth Kinetics of the Bulk Defects in Epitaxial Wafers

Growth kinetics of bulk defects were determined after annealing the epitaxial samples at a given temperature for various times. P/P$^+$(100) samples were prepared from 100 mm substrate wafers heavily-doped with boron (0.01 and 0.03 ohm-cm). Only one substrate resistivity range was chosen because no strong doping concentration effect of boron on oxygen precipitation was anticipated. The oxygen content in the P$^+$ substrate wafers was in the range between 1.4×10^{18} and 1.6×10^{18} atoms/cm^3. The epitaxial layer was 13.5 microns thick and lightly-doped with boron. N/N$^+$(100) samples were prepared from 100 mm substrate wafers doped with antimony at different concentration levels. They were catagorized according to their substrate resistivity into three groups: a) 0.02, b) 0.06, and c) 0.1 ohm-cm. The oxygen content in all wafers was approximately 1.5×10^{18} atoms/cm^3. The epitaxial layer was lightly-doped with phosphorus and had a thickness of 6 microns. All of the epitaxial wafers were cleaved into four quarter samples. Each individual quarter sample was annealed at 1050°C in dry oxygen ambient for a specific time up to 40 hours. Some P/P$^+$(100) samples received an additional four hour nucleation anneal at 750°C in a nitrogen ambient prior to the high temperature annealing.

Fig. 6 shows isothermal growth curves for bulk defects at 1050°C. In P/P$^+$ samples the growth behavior assumes the sigmoidal shape (S shape) as described elsewhere [39]. The curves were extrapolated under an assumption that some microdefects having a size below the detection limit of the optical microscope exist in an "as-received" epitaxial wafer. In P/P$^+$ samples which had received an additional nucleation anneal, the growth rate of the bulk defects increases significantly. An increase in the microprecipitate size as the result of the nucleation anneal, contributed to an increase in the growth rate.

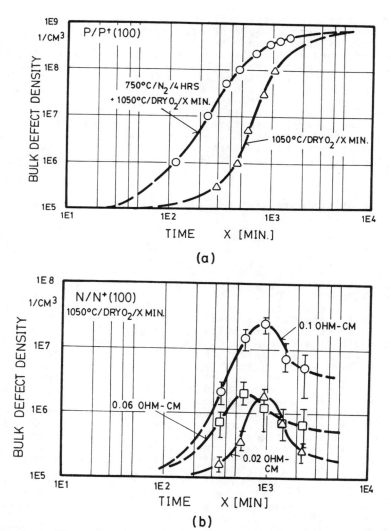

FIG. 6 -- The relationship between bulk defect density
and 1050°C annealing time in a) P/P+ and
b) N/N+(100) wafers.

In N/N+ samples, the bulk defect density increases
with increasing annealing time and then decreases
gradually when the annealing time is extended beyond 1000
minutes. At the present time, this phenomenon is not well
understood. It is suggested that the interaction between
the point defects and antimony could play a significant

role and be responsible for this phenomenon. In Fig. 6b, the dependence of bulk defect growth rate on substrate resistivity and a suppression of oxygen precipitation in heavily-doped samples is observed. In earlier P/P+ samples, the growth rate of microdefects increases with increasing microprecipitate size. It is proposed that the difference in the growth rate of microdefects in N/N+ wafers could be directly related to differences in microprecipitate size. In heavily-doped samples (0.02 ohm-cm), the microprecipitate size must be smaller than in lightly-doped samples (0.1 ohm-cm). The effect of antimony doping level on the suppression of oxygen precipitation is consistent with data reported in the previous experiment [10].

Impact of the Epitaxial Deposition Processes on Oxygen Precipitation

The impact of epitaxial deposition on oxygen precipitation was studied on three different CZ-grown (100) oriented crystals. The first crystal was 150 cm long and heavily-doped with boron (0.02 ± 0.005 ohm-cm). The second and third crystals were doped with antimony at different concentrations. Only sections approximately 35 cm long were cut from the seed-end section of antimony doped crystals because the resisitivity in the section beyond this length decreased below the resistivity range to be tested (0.01 ± 0.005 and 0.53 ± 0.005 ohm-cm, respectively). The oxygen content in the P+ crystal varied in the range between 1.25×10^{18} and 1.4×10^{18} atoms/cm^3. The oxygen content in both N+ crystals was in the range between 1.4×10^{18} and 1.6×10^{18} atoms/cm^3. All substrate wafers were laser marked for identification and divided into two groups. One group was processed through the epitaxial deposition step while the other group was set aside. After epitaxial deposition, the substrate and epitaxial wafers were recombined and then annealed at 1050°C in dry oxygen ambient for times between 16 and 24 hours.

Fig. 7 shows the bulk defect density distribution along the P+ crystal axis. The bulk defect density in the substrate wafers distributes uniformly along the crystal axis while the bulk defect density in the epitaxial wafers decreases with increasing distance from the crystal seed-end. No bulk defects were observed in the epitaxial wafers from the tang end section. The curve for bulk defect density was extrapolated for completion. In the figure, the effect of epitaxial deposition on a dissolution of the microprecipitates, particularly in the tang end section, is observed. This result implies that the microprecipitate size in the crystal tang end is smaller than the critical size at epitaxial deposition temperature [46].

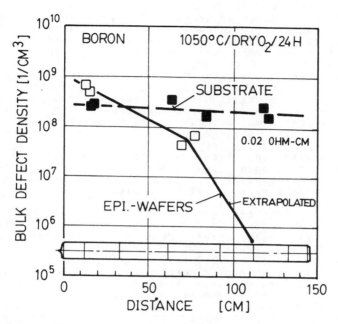

FIG. 7 -- Bulk defect density distribution along the p+
crystal axis.

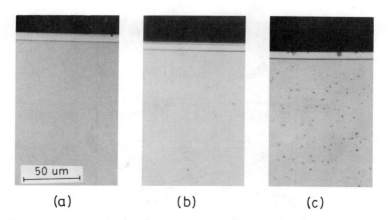

(a)   (b)   (c)

FIG. 8 -- Cross section optical micrographs for
P/P+(100) wafers pre-annealed at 650°C for
a) 0, b) 150, and c) 300 minutes showing
the bulk defects in the wafer right after
epitaxial deposition.

In the seed-end of the P^+ crystal, a slightly higher bulk defect density in epitaxial wafers compared to that in substrate wafers indicates that a microprecipitate growth could occur during epitaxial deposition. More corroborating evidence for a microprecipitate growth is illustrated in Fig. 8. (The cross section photomicrographs were taken from the samples right after epitaxial deposition.) In Fig. 8a, no bulk defect is observed in the epitaxial wafer without pre-annealing. In Figs. 8b and 8c, where samples were pre-annealed for 150 and 300 minutes, an increase in the bulk defect density is observed. It is suggested that a microprecipitate having a sufficiently large size can also grow during epitaxial deposition. After reviewing these results, it is concluded that both dissolution and growth could occur during epitaxial deposition. This depends strongly upon the microprecipitate size prior to epitaxial deposition.

Fig. 9 shows the bulk defect density distribution along the lightly-doped N^+ crystal (0.53 ohm-cm). In this crystal, the bulk defect density in substrate and epitaxial wafers decreases with increasing distance from the seed-end section. The bulk defect density in the epitaxial wafers is approximately two orders of magnitude lower than in substrate wafers. No bulk defects are observed in the heavily-doped N^+ crystal (0.01 ohm-cm) probably because only small microprecipitates pre-existed in the crystal. They dissolved completely during the epitaxial deposition and subsequent high temperature annealing. From this result it is quite clear that the microprecipitate size is affected by the antimony doping concentration.

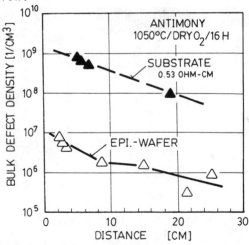

FIG. 9 -- Bulk defect density distribution along the lightly- doped N^+ crystal axis.

By comparing the results for P/P+ with those for N/N+ wafers, it seems quite plausible that the microprecipitate size depends strongly upon the doping species type. It is proposed that the microprecipitate size in N+ crystal is much smaller than that in P+ crystal.

Physical Model of Nucleation and Growth of Oxide Precipitates

In general, oxygen in saturation will not precipitate until embryos (thermodynamically unstable microprecipitates) are nucleated. The nucleation of embryos occurs either through homogeneous or heterogeneous processes. In silicon, nucleation of an "isolated" embryo is considered to be predominantly heterogeneous [47-51]. Agglomerates associated with aggregated vacancy-oxygen complexes are considered to be the preferred sites for this type of nucleation [46]. The formation of a vacancy-oxygen agglomerate or nucleation site of the microprecipitate occurs through a clustering or condensation reaction of vacancy-oxygen complexes and is considered homogeneous.

The nucleation concept for vacancy-oxygen agglomerates in heavily-doped silicon can be described as follows: At temperatures close to the melting point, ionized vacancies predominate and complexing between ionized vacancies and impurities facilitated by the coulombic attracting forces occurs. The evidence for this is the formation of vacancy-oxygen and vacancy-impurity complexes (V^-Sb^+, V^-P^+ and V^+B^-), which are observed from electron paramagnetic resonance (EPR) studies in quenched silicon [52-53]. In p-type silicon, the majority of the vacancies are the positively-ionized vacancies V^+, whereas the negatively-ionized vacancies V^- and $V^=$ predominate in n-type silicon [12]. The concentration of vacancy-oxygen complexes in silicon is strongly dependent upon the negatively-ionized vacancy concentration because the stable configuration of a vacancy-oxygen complex results from the trapping of a negatively-ionized vacancy by interstitial oxygen $(V^-O)^-$ [53].

In silicon heavily-doped with antimony, the concentration of V^-Sb^+ complexes will be high while the concentration of negatively-ionized vacancies as well as V-O complexes is low. A formation of V-O agglometrates with a low concentration of V-O complexes would result in a reduction in the agglomerate size. Therefore, the nucleation annealing period required to grow embryos in silicon heavily-doped with antimony to a size that is thermally stable will be considerably long. A decrease in antimony doping concentration will cause an increase in the concentration of negatively-ionized vacancies. In heavily-doped p-type silicon no strong effect of doping concentration on negatively-charged vacancies is anticipated. The basic concept of this model is illustrated in Fig. 10.

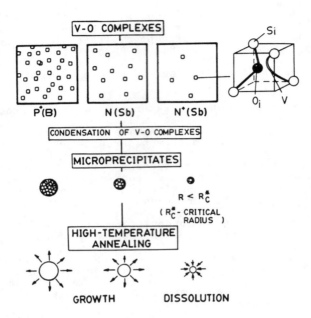

FIG. 10 -- Nucleation and growth models for oxide
microprecipitate in heavily-doped silicon.

Summary

It is proposed that the nucleation of oxygen precipitates in both P+ and N+ wafers occurs through a heterogeneous process ultilizing "grown-in" microprecipitates,
namely V-O agglomerates, as the nucleation sites. The
nucleation of the V-O agglomerates occurs through a
clustering reaction. The size of the V-O agglomerate is
affected by both the doping species and the concentration.
Antimony complexes with vacancies and reduces the concentration of the V-O complexes in silicon. This causes a
reduction in the size of the V-O agglomerate and therefore, "grown-in" microprecipitate. The size of the
microprecipitate is also found to be influenced by pre-
annealing.

Growth of microprecipitates in "as-received" N/N+
wafers does not follow the sigmoidal growth behavior as
observed in P/P+ wafers. Defect shrinkage in N/N+ wafers
after an extended isothermal annealing and suppression of
oxygen precipitation in silicon heavily-doped with antimony is observed. Both phenomena are interpretated as a
result of the interaction between point defects and antimony.

ACKNOWLEDGMENT

The authors would like to thank Mr. K. Mitani for the preparation of the epitaxial samples. The work was performed at SEH America, in Vancouver, Washington.

REFERENCES

[1] Booker, G.R. and Tunstall, W.J., "Diffraction Contrast Analysis of Two-Dimensional Defects Present in Silicon after Annealing", Philosophy Magazine, Vol.13, 1966, pp. 71-83.

[2] Sanders, I.R. and Dobson, P.S., "Oxidation, Defects and Vacancy Diffusion in Silicon", Philosophy Magazine, Vol.20, 1965, pp.881-893.

[3] De Kock, A.J.R., "Point Defect Condensation in Dislocation-Free Silicon Crystals", Semiconductor Silicon 1977, H.R. Huff and E. Sirtl, Eds., The Electrochemical Society, 1977, pp. 508-520.

[4] Patel, J.R., Jackson, K.A., and Reiss, H., "Oxygen Precipitation and Stacking-Fault Formation in Dislocation-Free Silicon", Journal of Applied Physics, Vol. 48, No. 12, December 1977, pp. 5279-5288.

[5] Tan, T.Y., Gardner, E.E., Tice, W.K., "Intrinsic Gettering by Oxide Precipitate Induced Dislocations in Czochralski Si", Applied Physics Letters, Vol.30, No. 4, 15 February 1977, pp. 175-176.

[6] Matlock, J.H., "Material Defect Factors Affect MOS Device Performance", Silicon Processing, ASTM STP 804, D.C. Gupta, Ed., American Society for Testing and Materials, 1983, pp. 332 -361.

[7] Goldsmith, B., Jastrzebski, L., Soydan, R., "Internal Gettering in Bipolar Process: Part I - Effect on Circuit Performance", Defects in Silicon, W.M. Bullis and L.C. Kimerling, Eds., The Electrochemical Society, Vol.83-9, 1983, pp. 142-52.

[8] Soydan, R., Jastrzebski, L., Goldsmith, B., "Internal Gettering in Bipolar Process: Part II - Oxygen Precipitation Kinetics", Defects in Silicon, W.M. Bullis and L.C. Kimerling, Eds., The Electrochemical Society, Vol.83-9, 1983, pp. 153-65.

[9] Jastrzebski, L., Soydan, R., McGinn, J., Kleppinger, R., Blumenfeld, M., Gillespie, G., Armour, N., Goldsmith, B., Henry, W., and Vecrumba, S., "Comparison of Internal Gettering during Bipolar, CMOS, and CCD (High, Medium, Low Temperature) Processes", Journal of Electrochemical Society, Vol. 134, No. 4, April 1987, pp. 1018-1025.

[10] Tsuya, H., Kondo, Y., and Kanamori, M., "Behaviors of Thermally Induced Microdefects in Heavily Doped Silicon Wafers", Japanese Journal of Applied Physics, Vol. 22, No.1, January 1983, pp. L16-L18.

[11] Shimura, F., Dyson, W., Moody, J.W., and Hockett, R.S., "Oxygen Behavior in Heavily Sb-Doped CZ-Silicon", VLSI Science and Technology 1985, W.M. Bullis and S. Broydo, Eds., The Electrochemical Society, 1985, pp. 507-516.
[12] Van Vechten, J.A. and Thurmond, C.D., "Comparison of Theory with Quenching Experiments for the Entropy and Enthalpy of Vacancy Formation in Si and Ge", Physical Review B, Vol.14, No.8, 15 October 1976, pp.3551-3557.
[13] Tempelhoff, K., Spiegelberg, F, and Gleichmann, R., "Precipitation of Oxygen in Dislocation-Free Silicon", Semiconductor Silicon 1977, H.R Huff and E. Sirtl, Eds., The Electrochemical Society, 1977, pp. 585-595.
[14] Huber, D., Stallhofer, P., and Blatte, M., "Process Modelling with High Oxygen Content CZ Silicon", Semiconductor Silicon 1981, H.R. Huff, R.J. Kriegler, and T. Takeishi, Eds., The Electrochemical Society, 1981, pp. 756-765.
[15] Secco d'Aragona, F., Tsui, R.K., Liaw, H.M., and Fejes, P.L.,"Thermal Annealing of Silicon Wafers for Intrinsic Gettering", Defects in Silicon, W.M. Bullis and L.C. Kimerling, Eds., The Electrochemical Society, Vol.83-9, 1983, pp. 166-179.
[16] Chiou, H-D., "Oxygen Precipitation Behavior and Control in Silicon Crystals", Solid State Technology, Vol.30, March 1987, pp. 77-81.
[17] Wijaranakula, W., unpublished data.
[18] Jastrzebski, L., Zanzucchi, P., Thebault, D., and Lagowski, J., "Method to Measure the Precipitated and Total Oxygen Concentration in Silicon", Journal of Electrochemical Society, Vol.129, No. 7, July 1982, pp. 1638-1641.
[19] Mohsen, A., Kung, R., Schultz, J., Madland, P., Simonson, C., Hamdy, E., and Yu, K., "C-MOS 256-K Ram with Wideband Output Stands By on Microwatts", Electronics, Vol. 57, 14 June 1984, pp. 138-143.
[20] Yamaguchi, T., Morimoto, S., Kawamoto, G., and De Lacy, J., "Process and Device Performance of 1 um-Channel n-Well CMOS Technology", IEEE Transaction Electron Devices, Vol. ED-31, No. 2, February 1984, pp. 205-214.
[21] Slotboom, J.W., Theunissen, M.J., and de Kock, A.J.R., "Impact of Silicon Substrates on Leakage Currents", IEEE Electron Device Letters, Vol. EDL-4, No. 11, November 1983, pp. 403-406.
[22] Troutman, B. and Zappe, H., "Layout and Bias Considerations for Preventing Transiently Triggered Latchup in CMOS", IEEE Transaction on Electron Devices, Vol. ED31, No. 3, March 1984, pp. 315-321.
[23] Yamaguchi, T., Morimoto, S., Kawamoto, G.H., Park, H.K., and Eidery, G.C., International Electron Device Meeting (IEDM) 83, Technical Digest Section 24.3, 1983, pp. 522.

[24] Dyson, W., O'Grady, S., Rossi, J.A., Hellwig, L.G., and Moody, J.W., "N+ and P+ Substrate Effects on Epitaxial Silicon Properties", VLSI Science and Technology/1984, K.E. Bean and G.A. Rozgonyi, Eds., The Electrochemical Society, 1984, pp. 107-119.

[25] Dyson, W., and Makovsky, J., "Oxygen Precipitation in N+ Silicon", Oxygen, Carbon, Hydrogen and Nitrogen in Crystalline Silicon, J.R. Mikkelsen, Jr., S.J. Pearton, J.W. Corbett, and S.J. Pennycook, Eds., Materials Research Society, 1986, pp. 293-300.

[26] Borland, J.O., Kuo, M., Shibley, J., Roberts, B., Schindler, R., and Dalrymple, T., "Influence of Epi-Substrate Point Defect Properties on Getter Enhanced Silicon Epitaxial Processing for Advance CMOS and Bipolar Technologies", VLSI Science and Technology/1984, K.E. Bean and G.A. Rozgonyi, Eds., The Electrochemical Society, 1984, pp. 93-106.

[27] Borland, J.O., Kuo, M., Shibley, J., Roberts, B., Schindler, R., and Dalrymple, T., "An Intrinsic Gettering Process to Improve Minority Carrier Lifetimes in MOS and Bipolar Silicon Epitaxial Technology", Semiconductor Processing, ASTM STP 850, D.C. Gupta, Ed., American Society for Testing and Materials, 1984, pp. 49-62.

[28] Wijaranakula, W., Burke, P., Forbes, L., and Matlock, J.H., "Effect of Pre- and Postepitaxial Deposition Annealing on Oxygen Precipitation in Silicon", Journal of Materials Research, Vol. 1, No. 5, September/October 1986, pp. 698-704.

[29] Wijaranakula, W., Matlock, J.H. and Mollenkopf, H., "Retardation of the Oxygen Precipitation Process in N/N+(100) Epitaxial Silicon Wafers", an Extended Abstracts, The Electrochemical Society, Vol.87-1, 1987, pp. 352-353.

[30] Series, R.W., Barraclough, K.G., and Bardsley, W., "Influence of Precipitate Size and Capillarity Effects on the Surface Denuded Zone in Thermally Processed Cz-Silicon Wafers", Semiconductor Silicon 1981, H.R. Huff, R.J. Kriegler, and Y. Takeishi, Eds., The Electrochemical Society, 1981, pp. 304-12.

[31] Tsuya, H., Shimura, F., Ogawa, K., and Kawamura, T., "A Study on Intrinsic Gettering in CZ Silicon Crystals: Evaluation, Thermal History Dependence, and Enhancement", Journal of Electrochemical Society, Vol.129, No. 2, February 1982, pp. 354-379.

[32] Kock, A.J.R. de and Wijgert, W.M. van de, "The Influence of Thermal Point Defects on the Precipitation of Oxygen in Dislocation-Free Silicon Crystals", Applied Physics Letters, Vol.38, No. 11, 1 June 1981, pp. 888-890.

[33] Harada, H., Abe, T., and Chikawa, J., "Oxygen Precipitation Enhanced with Vacancies in Silicon", Semiconductor Silicon 1986, H.R Huff, T. Abe, and B. Kolbesen, Eds., The Electrochemical Society, Vol.86-4, 1986, pp. 76-85.

[34] Wright Jenkins, M., "A New Preferential Etch for Defects in Silicon Crystals", <u>Journal of Electrochemical Society</u>, Vol. 124, No. 5, May 1977, pp. 757-762.

[35] Maher, D.M., Staudinger, A., and Patel, J.R., "Characterization of Structural Defects in Annealed Silicon Containing Oxygen", <u>Journal of Applied Physics</u>, Vol.47, No. 9, September 1976, pp. 3813-25.

[36] Wada, K, Takaoka, H., Inoue, N., and Kohra, K., "Growth of Stacking Faults by Bardeen-Herring Mechanism in Czochralski Silicon", <u>Japanese Journal of Applied Physics</u>, Vol.18, No.8, 1979, pp. 1629-30.

[37] Rozgonyi, G.A., Jaccodine, R.J.,and Pearce, C.W., "Oxygen Precipitation Effects in Degenerately - Doped Silicon", <u>Defects in Semiconductors II</u>, S. Mahajan and J.W. Corbett, Eds., Materials Research Society, 1983, pp. 181-185.

[38] Edelglass, S.M., in Engineering Materials Science: Structure and Mechanical Behavior of Solids, <u>The Ronald Press Company</u>, New York, 1966.

[39] Reed-Hill, R.E., in Physical Metallurgy Principles, D.Van Nostrand Co., New York, 2. ed., 1973.

[40] Freeland, P.E., Jackson, K.A., Lowe, C., and Patel, J.R., "Kinetics of Oxygen Precipitation in Dislocation- Free Silicon", <u>Bulletin of American Physics Society</u>, Vol. 21, No.3, Serie II, March 1976, pp. 226

[41] Goesele, U., "The Role of Carbon and Point Defects in Silicon", <u>Oxygen, Carbon and Nitrogen in Crystalline Silicon</u>, J.C. Mikkelsen, Jr., S.J. Pearton, J.W. Corbett, and S.J. Pennycook, Eds., Materials Research Society, 1986, pp. 419-431.

[42] Kugimiya, K., Akiyama, S., and Nakamura, S., "Denuded Zone and Microdefect Formation in Czohralsky-Grown Silicon Wafers by Thermal Annealing", <u>Semiconductor Silicon 1981</u>, H.R. Huff, R.J. Kriegler, and Y. Takeishi, Eds., The Electrochemical Society, 1981, pp. 294-303.

[43] Inoue, N., Wada, K., and Osaka, J., "Oxygen Precipitation in Czochralski Silicon - Mechanism and Application", <u>Semiconductor Silicon 1981</u>, H.R. Huff, R.J. Kriegler, and T. Takeishi, Eds., The Electrochemical Society, 1981, pp. 282-293.

[44] Zener, C.J., "Theory of Growth of Spherical Precipitates from Solid Solution", <u>Journal of Applied Physics</u>, Vol.20, No.10, October 1949, pp. 950-953.

[45] Wijaranakula, W., Matlock, J.H., and Mollenkopf, H., "Oxygen Precipitation and Bulk Microdefects Induced by the Pre- and Postepitaxial Annealing in $N/N^+(100)$ Silicon Wafers", <u>Journal of Applied Physics</u>, Vol. 62, 15 December 1987, pp. 4897-4902.

[46] Wijaranakula, W., Matlock, J.H., Mollenkopf, H., Burke, P., and Forbes, L., "Oxygen Precipitation in $P/P^+(100)$ Epitaxial Silicon Material", <u>Journal of the Electrochemical Society</u>, Vol. 134, No. 9, September 1987, pp. 2310-2316.

[47] Shimura, F., Tsuya, H., and Kawamura, T., "Precipita-
     tion and Redistribution of Oxygen in Czochralski-
     Grown Silicon", Applied Physics Letters, Vol. 37, No.
     5, 1 September 1980, pp. 483-486.
[48] Shimura, F., Tsuya, H., and Kawamura, T., "Surface-
     and Inner-Microdefects in Annealed Silicon Wafer
     Containing Oxygen", Journal of Applied Physics, Vol.
     51, No. 1, January 1980, pp. 269-273.
[49] Tice, W.K. and Tan, T.Y., "Precipitation of Oxygen
     and Intrinsic Gettering in Silicon", Defects in Semi-
     conductors, J. Narayan and T.Y. Tan, Eds., Materials
     Research Society, 1981, pp. 367-380.
[50] Kishino, S., Matsushita, Y., Kanamori, M, and Iizuka,
     T., "Thermally Induced Microdefects in Czochralski-
     Grown Silicon: Nucleation and Growth Behavior", Japa-
     nese Journal of Applied Physics, Vol. 21, No.1, Ja-
     nuary 1982, pp. 1-12.
[51] Ravi, K.V., "The Heterogeneous Precipitation of Sili-
     con Oxides in Silicon", Journal of Electrochemical
     Society, Vol.121, No.8, August 1974, pp. 1090-1098.
[52] Lannoo, M., and Bourgoin, J., in Point Defects in
     Semiconductors I, Springer-Verlag, Berlin, 1981.
[53] Watkins, G.D., "EPR Studies of Lattice Defects in
     Semiconductors", Defects and Their Structure in
     Nonmetallic Solids, B. Henderson and A.E. Hughes,
     eds., Plenum Press, New York, 1975, pp.203-220.

Harry L. Berkowitz

ON THE APPLICATION OF CALIBRATION DATA TO SPREADING RESISTANCE ANALYSIS

REFERENCE: Berkowitz, H. L., "On the Application of Calibration Data to Spreading Resistance Analysis," Semiconductor Fabrication: Technology and Metrology, ASTM STP 990, Dinesh C. Gupta, editor, American Society for Testing and Materials, 1989.

ABSTRACT: The requirements imposed by microelectronics structures on material characterization by spreading resistance profiling (SRP) have made the development of sound calibration procedures for SRP essential. To this end, the Efficient Multilayer Analysis Program, also known as the Berkowitz-Lux technique, has been adapted to incorporate both variable probe radius and barrier resistance models. Since both models are heuristically based, two versions of each method have been tried. Numerical stability and the ability to produce reasonable results are discussed for each version.

KEYWORDS: spreading resistance, profiling

INTRODUCTION

The need for accuracy in material characterization of microelectronics structures is increasing as device sizes and process tolerances shrink. As a result, it has become essential to develop sound methods of reconciling measured calibration data with procedures for spreading resistance profiling (SRP) analysis. To this end, the Efficient Multilayer Analysis Program (EMAP) [1-3] has been adapted to incorporate both variable effective probe radius and barrier resistance models to analyze spreading resistance profiles.

In section 2, a brief review of the anatomy of an SRP analysis program is given. In particular, those features of the EMAP scheme not previously published are disclosed.

In section 3, the modification of an SRP program to accommodate profiles measured on semiconductor materials is discussed.

Dr. Berkowitz is Chief Scientist at Solid State Measurements Inc., 110 Technology Drive, Pittsburgh, PA 15275.

Implementations of the commonly invoked barrier resistance and variable effective probe contact radius models are described.

In section 4, representative spreading resistance profiles are presented, in which the resistivity and concentration profiles have been calculated using the barrier resistance and variable effective probe contact radius models.

Section 5 is devoted to conclusions and to a discussion of future trends for high resolution electrical profiling of semiconductor device structures.

REVIEW OF CURRENT PRACTICE

Most methods of analyzing spreading resistance profiles are based on the Schumann and Gardner (SG) multilayer solution to Laplace's equation [4] for a probe injecting current into a conducting slab, where the resistivity of the slab is assumed to be a function of depth only. Over the years much effort has been expended to reduce the time and computer resources needed to evaluate the SG integral, and several successful methods have been published [1,5-7]. This section describes the elements, in addition to an SG integrator, which are required to deconvolve a resistivity profile from a measured spreading resistance profile. As an example, the techniques used in the EMAP program are described.

The calculation of spreading resistance given a resistivity profile is straightforward and is described in Reference 1. To calculate resistivities given spreading resistances, however, involves the inversion of a highly nonlinear system. Assuming that spreading resistances are measured atop sublayers of constant resistivity and thickness, the calculation is made as follows. Starting at the deepest point, the value of a trial sublayer resistivity is adjusted (and the SG correction factor recalculated) until the calculated sublayer spreading resistance agrees with the measured sublayer spreading resistance to within the desired tolerance. The resistivities thus obtained are then used in the calculation of the resistivities of higher sublayers until the surface sublayer is reached. The process used for ohmic material is outlined in the flow chart in Figure 1.

Efficient methods for estimating the initial sublayer resistance and refining the estimate can significantly reduce the number of SG integrals needed to achieve convergence. The method used to choose a trial sublayer resistivity depends on the position of the sublayer in the profile. On the substrate or junction, i.e. the lowest level, the resistivity ρ is calculated using the equation:

$$\rho = 2aR_m/C_{sub}$$

where C_{sub} is the SG correction factor for an infinite substrate R_m is the measured spreading resistance, and a is the probe contact radius. If the layer is within three layers above the substrate (or junction) then

$$\rho_i = \rho_{i+1}.$$

For other layers the initial guess is made by extrapolating $Ln(\rho)$ for the three previously calculated resistivities with a parabola:

$$\rho_i = \rho_{i+3}(\rho_{i+1}/\rho_{i+2})^3$$

This appeal to continuity for the first guess of the sublayer resistivity frequently results in convergence in one or two iterations.

Commonly used methods to improve the sublayer resistivity estimate include regula falsi, the secant method, or other zero finders which are readily available [8]. For the purposes of this paper, programs prefixed with "TST" use the plodding but robust step and bisection method, while those prefixed with "EMAP" employ the method described below.

To efficiently interpolate the SG correction factor as a function of ρ, a function with the following properties was sought: (i) it had to behave like the SG correction factor at large and small values of the resistivity; (ii) it had to lead to a numerically simple method of calculating the improved sublayer resistivity estimate. At large and small values of the resistivity, the SG correction factor approaches constants C_1 and C_0 respectively, which depend only on geometry [1]. An approximate correction factor C_a is defined by a simple Pade approximation:

$$C_a = (C_0 + AC_1\rho/a)/(1+A\rho/a)$$

The parameter A is adjusted so that the last calculated SG correction factor agrees with C_a when the last estimated ρ is inserted into the above equation. By setting R_m equal to $\rho\, C_a/(2\,a)$ and finding the positive root of the quadratic equation,

$$\frac{A\,C_1}{2}(\rho/a)^2 + \frac{(C_0-R_mA)}{2}(\rho/a) - R_m = 0$$

the next estimate of ρ, is obtained.

As with most superlinear interpolation schemes, oscillations can sometimes occur during which convergence is very slow. Therefore EMAP... programs test for oscillatory behavior and use an averaging technique to damp the oscillations and restore rapid convergence. Oscillations are detected by noting the trend of three consecutive estimates of ρ : r_1, r_2, and r_3. If $(r_3-r_2)(r_2-r_3)$ is negative then r_3, the most recently calculated value of ρ, is replaced with the value of the expression:

$$(r_3r_1-r_2^2)/(r_3+r_1-2r_2)$$

and the calculation continues. Both EMAP... and TST... programs require that $|(1-R_c/R_m)|$ be less than .0001 to terminate the calculation of a sublayer resistivity.

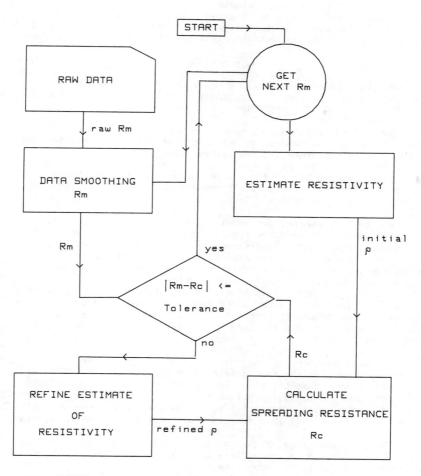

NOTE! Unlabeled lines are signal lines

Figure 1 - Flow chart for a multilayer analysis program.

APPLICATION of SRP to NON-OHMIC MATERIAL

It is well known that a simple ohmic theory of conduction is inadequate to calculate spreading resistances as a function of resistivity (in semiconductor materials). Resistance measurements on uniform slabs of silicon deviate significantly from the simple formula

$$R_m = \rho/(2a).$$

In fact, the spreading resistance measured on uniform resistivity bulk silicon depends on conductivity type and crystallographic orientation in addition to the bulk resistivity.

Several empirical models have been advanced to reconcile totally ohmic theory and experiment by assuming that effects at the interface between the metal probe and the semiconductor can explain all discrepancies [2,3]. Because of the great complexity of the combined effects of interfacial charge and piezo-electricity/resistance in the vicinity of a metal-semiconductor contact under ~10^6 psi pressure, the models thus far advanced are largely based on heuristic arguments.

We have implemented two versions each of the variable effective contact radius model and the barrier resistance model. The first pair of models assumes that the discrepancy between a simple Ohmic theory and experiment is due to surface effects. In these models, the variable effective radius or barrier resistance is assumed to be a function of the surface resistivity only. In the second pair of models, the discrepancies are assumed to be due to some functional of the entire resistivity profile beneath the contact. For these models we assume, in the absence of better theoretical guidance, that the effective radius or barrier resistance is a function of the spreading resistance rather than the resistivity.

Separate versions of the EMAP program have been written to accommodate each of the four models under consideration. TSTBR and TSTVA implement, respectively, the barrier resistance and variable effective contact radius as a function of surface resistivity. EMAPBR and EMAPVA implement, respectively, the barrier resistance and variable effective contact radius as functions of sublayer spreading resistance.

The implementation of the two surface effect models, TSTBR and TSTVA, requires that a new surface layer barrier resistance or effective contact radius be chosen each time a new sublayer resistivity estimate is chosen. As this process tends to minimize the speed advantage·of the superlinear interpolator, a simple step and bisection zero finder was employed instead. A further advantage of this simple robust method is that searching for multiple roots is straightforward. (The existence of more than one undetected root could, in the worst case, result in a misleading resistivity profile. At best, it would produce obvious numerical trash). Both TSTBR and TSTVA issue warnings if more than one value of resistivity satisfies the convergence test for any sublayer.

As the measured resistance is not changed during the search for the

sublayer resistivity, the barrier resistance or variable effective
radius is calculated once by EMAPBR and EMAPVA. Thus, operationally,
these programs differ little from the original EMAP scheme.

To use the above programs, the spreading resistance probe should be
calibrated using the methods of American Society for Testing and
Materials F672. The resistance as a function of resistivity (or vice
versa as required) is obtained by interpolating the measured points with
the following:

$$\text{With } \rho_i <= \rho < \rho_{i+1},$$

$$\log (R) = M[\ \log(\rho/\rho_i)\ ] + \log(\rho_i)$$

$$M = \log(R_{i+1}/R_i)/\log(\rho_{i+1}/\rho_i)$$

$$a(\rho) = C_{sub}\ \rho/(2R) \qquad \text{for variable a}$$

$$R_{barrier} = R - C_{sub}\ \rho/(2a) \qquad \text{for barrier resistance}$$

C_{sub} is the correction factor for an infinite substrate with the desired
probe spacing as calculated using EMAP.

Each time a new radius is called for, the SG function and the
integration mesh are recalculated. Each time a new barrier resistance
is called for, the spreading resistance is taken to be $R_m - R_{barrier}$.
Where R_m again, is the measured resistance.

EXPERIMENTAL RESULTS

Each of the EMAP-derived programs have been used to analyze
spreading resistance profiles measured on a variety of common device
structures. We will compare the concentration and resistivity profiles
calculated with the new algorithms with those produced by the multilayer
analysis code M2 supplied by Solid State Measurements Inc. (SSM). The
samples chosen include a double drift IMPATT diode, a shallow P implant,
and two same type epitaxial samples, N on N^+ and P on P^+.

In testing the EMAP-derived programs, we have found that the use of
EMAPVA on P-type layers and TSTBR on N-type layers produces the most
plausible results. TSTVA is usually a noise generator, exhibiting
multiple roots and wild oscillations. EMAPBR, while numerically well
behaved, yields unconvincing results. For the most part, results from
TSTBR and EMAPVA, used as above, will be shown.

A functioning IMPATT usually means that the dopant concentration
profiles in the vicinity of the junction where avalanche takes place
were done correctly. A good SRP scheme should be able to confirm the
concentration profile for a properly functioning IMPATT. In Figure 2,
we show the spreading resistance profile for an IMPATT diode. Also
shown are the concentration profiles calculated by the SSM M2 code and
selected EMAP-derived programs. In this case, the rather unappealing
profiles produced by TSTVA on the P-layer and EMAPBR on the N-layer are
also shown.

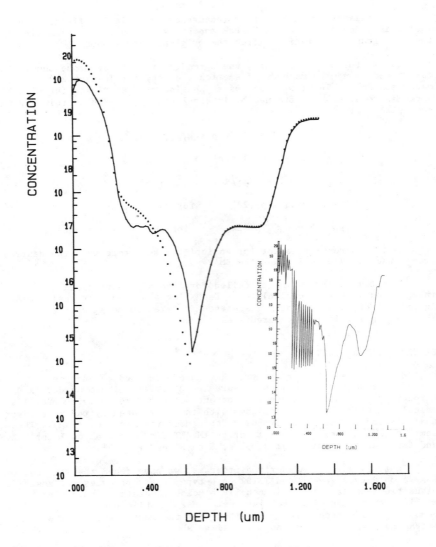

Figure 2 – IMPATT concentration profiles. Plateaus on either side of
the junction are designed to have the same concentration. Left layer
is P-type, right layer is N-type. Solid curve: left layer EMAPVA
used, right layer TSTBR used. Dotted curve M2 used on both layers.
The inserted graph was calculated using TSTVA on the P layer and EMAPBR
on the N layer.

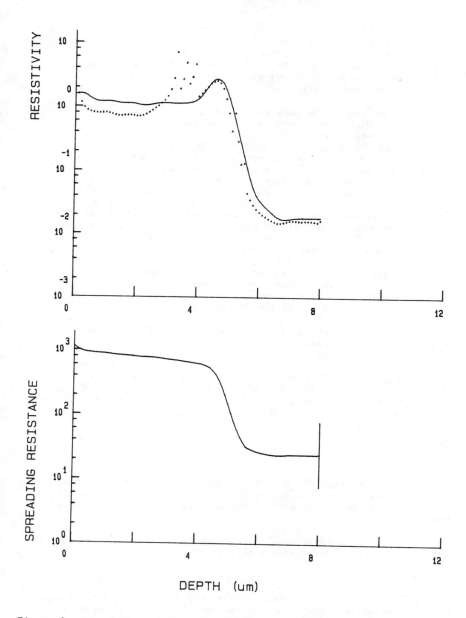

Figure 3 —Top graph P on P+ epi. Points: M2 calculated resistivity.
The spikes are thought to be due to an attempt to use the variable
radius as a function of surface resistivity model. Line: same profile
calculated using EMAPVA Bottom graph: input spreading resistance.

For some time it has been known that the M2 program may produce unstable results in profiling P on P$^+$ epitaxially grown silicon. We now believe that the cause of the instability is the use of a surface effect variable radius model in that program. In Figure 3, we display resistivity profiles for M2 and EMAPVA derived from the SR profile of the P on P+ epitaxial sample.

The existence of the peak in the resistivity profiles of Figure 3 requires some discussion. When we invited expert epi-growers who are also expert users of the spreading resistance technique to speculate on the origin of the peak, it was suggested that: (i) "The profile was taken with to much light on the sample", (ii) "The peak is an artifact of the SG method if no barrier resistance is included in the correction of spreading resistance profiles with abrupt transitions", (iii) "There may have been a limited supply of a compensating contaminant in the epi reactor when the P-layer was grown". To elucidate the situation, the spreading resistance profiles were calculated from resistivity profiles using the methods of EMAP with a fixed effective probe contact radius. The results of these calculations for resistivity profiles with and without the peak are shown in Figure 4. It is clear that the Schumann and Gardner method expects a far gentler transition in the spreading resistance profile for a resistivity profile without a peak. It is also clear that it is unlikely that this or other difficult situations can be definitively resolved without extensive collaboration between people who do fabrication and the people who do characterization.

The resistivity and spreading resistance profiles for an N on N$^+$, calculated using the barrier resistance model are plotted in Figure 5 for comparison with the P on P$^+$ results.

In Figure 6, the calculated concentration profiles for a shallow boron implant are plotted, along the measured spreading resistance profile. Here, we compare the measured sheet resistance with the sheet resistance calculated for the P-layer by M2 and EMAPVA.

CONCLUSIONS

We have presented the results of coupling variable effective contact radius and barrier resistance models to an accurate realization of Schumann and Gardner's multilayer analysis scheme using programs derived from EMAP.

We have compared the results produced by the above scheme with the SSM program M2 on a wide variety of samples.

We observe that:

a.   The SSM program M2 tends to be less responsive to rapid changes in input spreading resistance data than the EMAP derived programs. Concentration profiles produced from noisy spreading resistance data by M2 appear smoother than EMAP derived profiles because of M2's apparent internal damping. On implant samples this damping leads M2 to over estimate the implant dose or to under estimate the sheet resistance compared to the EMAP derived results.

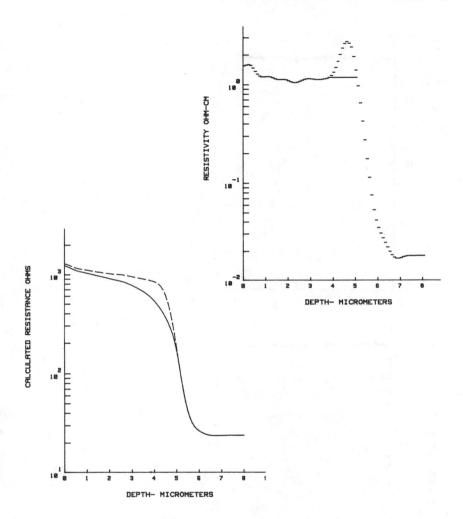

Figure 4 —Spreading resistance profiles were calculated from
resistivity profiles using the methods of EMAP and a fixed effective
contact radius model. The two resistivity profiles shown in the upper
graph are the resistivity profile of Figure 3 and this same profile
with the peak removed. These resistivity profiles were used to
calculate the SRPs shown in the lower graph, with the solid curve
representing the expected SRP associated with the resistivity profile
with no peak.

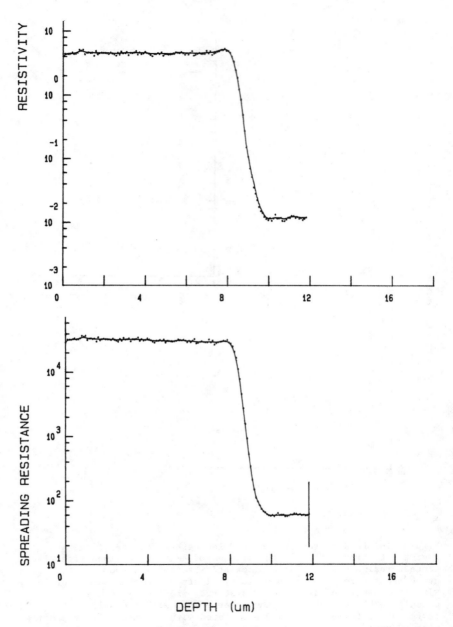

Figure 5 –N on N+ epi.   Top graph: Resistivity calculated for N-type sample M2 (points) and TSTBR (line) usually calculate similar results. Bottom graph: Measured spreading resistances, raw data (points), smoothed data (line).

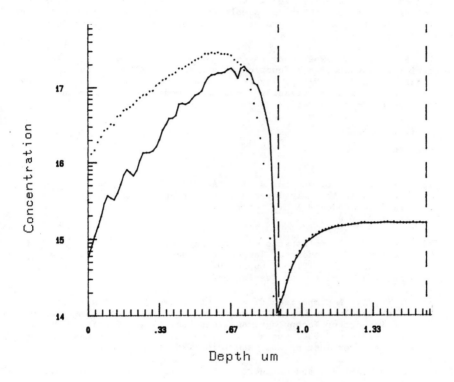

Figure 6 –Shallow Boron implant into N type silicon. Concentration
profiles calculated by M2 (points), EMAPVA (line, left layer) and TSTBR
(line, right layer). Agreement in the N layer (right) between TSTBR
and M2 is excellent. In the P layer (left), EMAPVA predicts more rapid
changes than does M2. Sheet resistances for the P layer are:
    M2:   calculated 2167 Ω,
  EMAPVA: calculated 3742 Ω,
           Measured ~ 3400 Ω.

b. To produce plausible results using the EMAP derived programs, it is required that the input spreading resistance data be smoothed. Concentration profiles calculated from smoothed data tends to remain within the envelope of the concentration profiles derived from raw data to the same extent that the smoothed spreading resistance data is within the envelope of the raw spreading resistance data.

c. In order to obtain anything resembling quantitative results, it is necessary that every step in the procedure be carefully controlled including probe conditioning, sample preparation, and calibration using calibration blocks of the proper conductivity type and crystallographic orientation.

Based on our experience to date, we are recommending that a a barrier resistance, as a function of surface resistivity, model be used on data measured on N-type layers and that a variable radius, as a function of measured spreading resistance, model be used for data measured on P-type layers.

REFERENCES

[1] Berkowitz, H. L. and Lux R. A., "An Efficient Integration Technique for use in the Multilayer Analysis of Spreading Resistance Profiles," Journal of Electrochemical Society., Vol. 128 No. 5, p. 1137 (1981).

[2] Albers, J., "Some Aspects of Spreading Resistance Profile Analysis," Emerging Semiconductor Technology, American Society for Testing and Materials STP 960, Gupta, D. C., and Langer, P. H., Eds. American Society for Testing and Materials (1986).

[3] Pawlik, M. "A Comparison of Sampling Volume Correction Factors in High Resolution Quantitative Spreading Resistance," Emerging Semiconductor Technology, American Society for Testing and Materials STP 960, Gupta, D. C., and Langer, P. H., Eds. American Society for Testing and Materials (1986).

[4] Schumann, P. A., and Gardner, E. E., Solid State Electronics., Vol. 12, p. 371 (1969).

[5] Choo, S. C., Leong, M. S. Solid State Electronics., Vol. 22, p. 405 (1979).

[6] Choo, S. C., M. S. Leong and Sim, J. H. Solid State Electronics., Vol. 26, p. 723 (1980).

[7] Piessens, R., Vandervorst, W. B., and Maes, H. E., Journal of Electrochemical Society., Vol. 130 No. 2, p. 468 (1983)

[8] For example see "Numberical Recipes", Press, W. H., Flannery, B. P., Teukolsky, S. A., Vettering, W. T., Cambridge University Press, New Rochelle, NY (1986).

David J. Ruprecht, Lance G. Hellwig, and Jon A. Rossi

EPITAXIAL SILICON QUALITY IMPROVEMENT BY AUTOMATIC SURFACE INSPECTION

REFERENCE: Ruprecht, D. J., Hellwig, L. G., and Rossi, J. A.,
"Epitaxial Silicon Quality Improvement by Automatic Surface
Inspection," Semiconductor Fabrication: Technology and Me-
trology, ASTM STP 990, Dinesh C. Gupta, editor, American
Society for Testing and Materials, 1989.

ABSTRACT: With increasing demands on epitaxial wafer surface
quality, automated inspection is necessary. The results from
automatic wafer inspection equipment are ambiguous without
careful examination of the detected defects. To facilitate
microscopic verification of automatically detected defects,
we have designed a system for matching flaw counts to actual
defects. Using this system, the epitaxial deposition process
has been optimized to reduce surface defects.

KEYWORDS: silicon epitaxy, defect inspection, microscopic
inspection, automated inspection, surface quality

INTRODUCTION

The field of defect inspection on epitaxial silicon wafers has
been changing over the past several years. Larger diameters and more
perfect surfaces make detection of defects increasingly difficult.
Despite the fact that defect densities are lower, however, their
detection is still critical because die sizes are increasing, even up
to full wafer scale. For a good wafer, it is no longer feasible to sit
at a microscope and count the number of flaws in a field of view. Even
an ultra-wide eyepiece on a microscope covers only about 20 mm² at
50X magnification, or 0.1% of a 150 mm diameter wafer. Thus automated
surface inspection is rapidly becoming a necessity.

Our automated wafer inspection equipment has exhibited several
problems in defect detection on epitaxial silicon wafers. Some defects
simply can not be detected using the signal from scattered laser light.
Other defects scatter the light to such an extent to be counted several
times by the system. Only by making a map of the wafers and finding

David Ruprecht, Lance Hellwig, and Jon Rossi are at Monsanto
Electronic Materials Company, 501 Pearl Drive, Saint Peters, Missouri.

the reported defects in the microscope can we be sure of the identification and quantity of actual defects on the wafer. To alleviate
the tedium and uncertainty of such a task, a system was developed
that stores a wafer map on disk for retrieval by a computer capable
of driving a microscope stage to each reported flaw.

With a clearer understanding of the defects being reported, the
automated inspection system is providing valuable feedback to the epi
reactor. By including measurements of flaw counts in experiments
that determine optimum epitaxial deposition parameters, processes
that generate fewer surface defects have been developed. Combining
the throughput of automated surface inspection with the verification
of accuracy from the microscopic system, epitaxial wafers with high
quality surfaces are consistently being produced.

EXPERIMENTAL METHOD

Conditions

   Material: The material we typically inspect is epitaxial silicon
with thicknesses ranging from 5 to 20 microns. The epitaxy is deposited on polished silicon substrates with (100) orientation and
diameters of 100, 125, and 150 mm.

   Equipment: Epitaxial silicon films are deposited in either an
Applied Materials 7800 series or a Gemini reactor operated at atmospheric pressure and growth temperature between 1050 and 1150 C. The
wafers are inspected on an Estek (formerly Aeronca) WIS 150 SI. An
HP 9816 computer receives the data from the WIS and stores it on an
HP Shared Resource Management (SRM) system. The SRM consists of a
disk drive, printer, and plotter driven by a computer that acts as
a file server, enabling easy access to data and output devices by
many users. The maps are retrieved from the SRM by an HP 9836
computer which drives a Semprex X-Y stage under the Nomarski differential interference contrast optics of a Nikon Optiphot microscope.

WIS Operation

   The Estek WIS 150 SI is a pixel based, laser scanning wafer
inspection system. Figure 1 shows a schematic of its operation.
Light from a 10 mW He-Ne laser is folded onto a multi-faceted rotating mirror. This mirror sweeps the beam across a wafer which moves at
a fixed rate perpendicularly to the beam, thus covering the entire
wafer surface. When the beam is on the wafer, light is reflected by
the wafer's surface directly into the light channel photomultiplier
tube (PMT). Any defect or particle in the path of the beam will
scatter some of the light into the dark channel PMT. If the scattering object is large enough, there will also be a significant decrease
in the intensity at the light channel PMT.

   Electronics in the WIS amplify and process the signals from the
PMTs and compare the intensity levels with operator entered
thresholds. The levels and frequencies of the signals are used to

determine a flaw category for each defect. The values 1, 2, 3, 5 and 6 are dark channel flaws, 7, 9 and B are light channel flaws, and 8, A, C and G are flaws generated by a combination of light and dark channel signals. The distribution of flaw counts with respect to flaw categories gives an indicator of wafer quality. We primarily monitor a category called flaw type 4 (F4) which is defined as the sum of flaw types 2, 3, A and C.

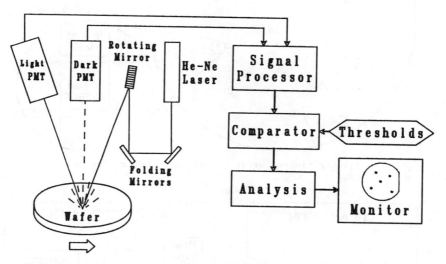

FIG. 1 -- Schematic drawing of WIS automated inspection system.

Further analysis builds a map of the wafer for display on a monitor. Figure 2 is an illustration of a wafer map showing one of the 12 flaw categories at each location of a defect. For clarity, the numbers are shown larger than normal. (The actual pixel density results in 172 pixels across the diameter of a 150 mm wafer.) The inset drawing shows the relative sizes of the pixels in a microscope field of view at 100X magnification. For comparison, a 100 micron defect is shown in one of the pixels, which are approximately 900 microns across.

Microscopic Verification

One problem with automated wafer inspection systems such as the WIS is the uncertainty involved in flaw counts. For example, what defects do the different flaw categories represent? Are the defects structural or only removable particles? How accurate are the total counts? Attempting to locate defects in a microscope, even with a wafer map is not a practical procedure because of the positional uncertainties. To accomplish the direct comparison of WIS flaws to actual defects, we designed a Defect Analysis and Verification System illustrated in Figure 3.

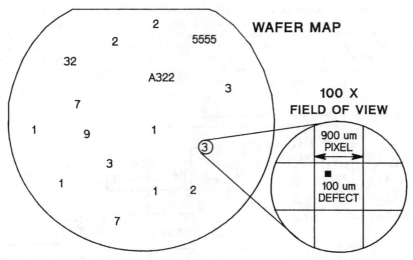

FIG. 2 -- Illustration of wafer map showing 100X microscope field of
view.

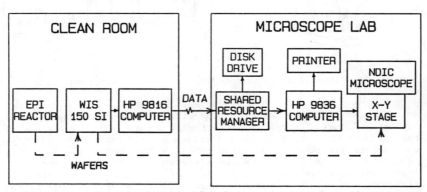

FIG. 3 -- Schematic drawing of Defect Analysis and Verification
System.

After epitaxial deposition, wafers are taken from the reactor
and scanned by the WIS 150 in a clean room.   An HP 9816 computer
receives the wafer maps from the printer port on the WIS and stores
the data on a remote Shared Resource Manager (SRM). Each mapped wafer
is then taken to the microscope lab and placed on the motorized X-Y
stage of a Nikon Nomarski differential interference contrast microscope.   The map for each wafer is retrieved from the SRM disk and
printed by an HP 9836 computer.

Custom software in the computer translates the WIS coordinates
into the microscope stage coordinates using reference points on the
edge of the wafer. The program steps through the flaw types, starting

with the most severe, and drives the stage to the corresponding location on the wafer. The operator centers each of the first few
defects in the field of view and instructs the computer to adjust the
translation coefficients using a Simplex algorithm [1] until an
optimal fit is obtained. While the program automatically steps the
microscope stage to each flaw coordinate, the observer examines and
photographs each particular defect that triggered the WIS response.
In this fashion we build up a collection of flaws, as registered by
automatic inspection, with corresponding photographs of the actual
defects. In addition, a manual scanning mode is used to note and
photograph any defects which did not appear on the map and therefore
escaped detection by the WIS.

RESULTS AND DISCUSSIONS

Typical Defects

    Combining the speed of the automated wafer inspection system
and the accuracy of the microscopic verification system has given us
an opportunity to examine a great number of epitaxial defects (over
six thousand). A summary of those results is shown in Table 1. The
left hand column lists the source of the detected signal. The table
entry gives the percentage of the time that the particular defect
triggered the source. For example, the epitaxial stacking fault with
an associated hillock (column 4), registering as a dark channel flaw
(row 1), accounted for 26.1% of the total number of defects recorded.
The last column shows that most defects (49.6%) are detected by the
dark channel and that some defects (14.4%) go undetected, triggering
neither channel.

TABLE 1 -- Epitaxial defects verified in the microscope (%).

PMT signal	ESF	Hillock	ESF with hillock	Other	Total/ signal
Dark channel	5.7	15.9	26.1	1.9	49.6
Light channel	1.2	12.8	4.5	0.5	19.0
Both	1.6	4.0	9.5	1.9	17.0
Neither	0.4	11.9	0.9	1.2	14.4
Total/type	8.9	44.6	41.0	5.5	100.0

    The microphotographs in Figure 4 are examples of typical epi-
taxial defects found using this system. By marking the position of
the defect on the wafer during microscopic verification, each defect
was located in a WYKO profilometer for dimensional measurements. The
defects in Figure 4 are examples of (a) a normal epitaxial stacking
fault (ESF), (b) a smooth hillock, (c) an ESF with an associated

hillock (the hillock is barely discernible on the upper right corner of the square ESF), (d) a compound ESF or 'sparkle', (e) a faceted hillock, and (f) a compound ESF with a depressed region of surface roughness. Table 2 lists the dimensions of these defects as determined by the profilometer along with the registered flaw type from the WIS. These microphotographs were selected because they are by far the most common epitaxial defects; the dimensions of these defects are proportional to epi layer thickness.

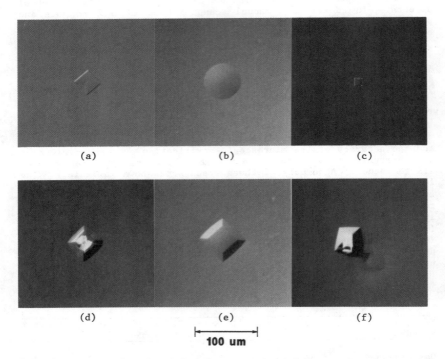

```
      (a)              (b)              (c)



      (d)              (e)              (f)
                 |——————————|
                    100 um
```

FIG. 4 -- Typical epitaxial defects include (a) normal epi stacking fault (ESF), (b) smooth hillock, (c) ESF with a hillock, (d) compound ESF, (e) faceted hillock, and (f) compound ESF with surface roughness.

TABLE 2 -- Dimensions and WIS flaw types for the defects shown in Figure 4.

Defect	Width, um	Height, nm	WIS flaw type
(a) ESF	30	50	32
(b) Hillock	60	10	None
(c) ESF with hillock	12	7	2
(d) Compound ESF	45	900	AA22
(e) Faceted hillock	55	150	9
(f) Compound ESF with roughness	45	600	A322

Inspection Discrepancies

Another application of the microscopic verification system is the analysis of surface inspection problems. Some defects cannot be detected by the WIS. Others result in discrepancies between hand held, bright light inspection and automatic inspection which can only be resolved by identifying actual defects in the microscope.

Three examples of problems encountered when using an automated inspection system can be illustrated using photographs in Figure 4 and the WIS results in Table 2. The smooth hillock (b) is not detected by either the WIS or visual, macroscopic inspection. The ESF with a hillock (c) on a thin epi layer registers as a flaw type 2 in the WIS but is not visible in the bright light, resulting in disagreement between the two inspection methods. The compound ESFs (d) and (f) are easily detected by both visual and automated inspection. The problem with these large defects is that the WIS registers each single defect as a string of 4 pixels even though they are only 1/16th as wide as one pixel.

Analysis of thousands of defects have led to several conclusions about the operation of the WIS. First, the WIS classifies epitaxial defects by brightness, not by size. Many papers [2-4] have investigated the relationship between size and light scattering by particles or spheres, but the crystallographic planes present on epi defects violate the necessary conditions for correlation. Second, the WIS overcounts bright epi defects by as much as 4 times. The problem was first thought to be cases where a defect lies on the boundary between two or more pixels, but a pattern in the observations contradict that hypothesis. The most common feature of a large, bright defect is a 'large' flaw type followed (in the direction of the path of the laser beam) by several dark channel flaws (eg A322). Analysis with the microscopic verification system shows the defect to be in the first pixel, indicating that the tail is a failure of the signal to return to a quiescent state. Third, the WIS simply misses shallow, non-crystallographic defects. However, it is entirely probable that these latter two observations will be prevented in future inspection equipment.

Epitaxial Quality Improvement

Despite the shortcomings of the automated inspection system, its use as a process development tool is invaluable. Measuring the effects of process changes on surface quality, along with checks for validity with the microscopic verification system, have led to substantial improvements in our epitaxial depositions.

An example of the gains possible with these systems is shown in the bar chart in Figure 5. The vertical axis is the percentage of wafers with the corresponding number of flaw type 4 (F4) counts. Our initial distribution, labeled "BEFORE" is Gaussian with an average of 10 counts per wafer and a standard deviation of 5. After making process changes to the reactor, we were able to achieve a much better distribution, labeled "AFTER" that is more Poisson-like with an average of 3 counts per wafer. (Each of these distributions represent more than 1000 wafers of 100 mm diameter). The latter distribution should be typical of present day commercially available epitaxy; the work presented here shows that most of those detected flaws are stacking faults and/or hillocks of one variety or another.

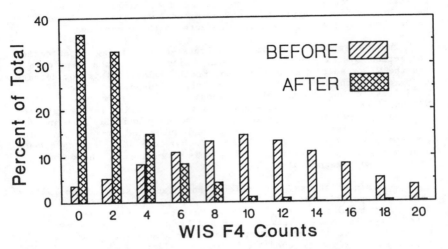

FIG. 5 -- Bar chart of progress made using automated inspection.

CONCLUSIONS

The WIS (and, no doubt, other automatic inspection units [5]) is a good, nondestructive tool for measuring epitaxial silicon surface quality. However, it is not without limitations which must be understood when trying to interpret flaw count data or compare counts with other techniques. Combining this tool with a microscope for defect verification and analysis provides the necessary level of understanding and, more importantly, reveals what type of defects are being grown in the epitaxial process. Knowing which defects are present enables the development of processes that produce higher quality surfaces. Finally, the WIS and microscopic verification systems are not limited to epitaxial deposition and probably can be expanded to many downstream processes where defect analysis is important.

ACKNOWLEDGMENTS

The authors would like to thank P. Doerhoff, R. Caldwell, J. Harmon, and L. Lauer for technical assistance, P. A. Tierney for support of this work, and P. Fehr for preparation of the manuscript.

REFERENCES

[1] Caceci, M. S. and Cacheris, W. P., "Fitting Curves to Data,"
     BYTE, Vol. 9, No. 5, May 1984, pp. 340-362.
[2] Locke, B. R. and Donovan, R. P., "Particle Sizing Uncertainties
     in Laser Scanning of Silicon Wafers," Journal of Electrochemical
     Society, Vol. 134, No. 7, July 1987, pp. 1763-1771.
[3] Tullis, B. J., "Measuring and Specifying Particle Contamination
     by Process Equipment: Part III, Calibration," Microcontamina-
     tion, Vol. 4, No. 1, January 1986, pp. 50-55, 86.
[4] Bohren, C. F. and Huffman, D. R., Absorption and Scattering of
     Light by Small Particles, John Wiley & Sons, New York, 1983.
[5] Liaw, H. M., Rose, J. W., and Nguyen, H. T., "Characterization
     of Silicon Surface Defects by the Laser Scanning Technique,"
     Emerging Semiconductor Technology, ASTM STP 960, D. C. Gupta
     and P. H. Langer, Eds., American Society for Testing and
     Materials, 1986.

Robert G. Mazur and Robert J. Hillard

SPREADING RESISTANCE PROFILES IN GALLIUM ARSENIDE

REFERENCE: Mazur, R. G., Hillard, R. J., "Spreading Resistance Profiles in Gallium Arsenide," Semiconductor Fabrication: Technology and Metrology, ASTM STP 990, Dinesh C. Gupta, ed., American Society for Testing and Materials, 1989.

ABSTRACT: The spreading resistance technique is widely used for profiling carrier concentration and resistivity in a variety of silicon structures. Several authors have reported some success in applying the spreading resistance technique to profiling doped GaAs samples. However, the use of spreading resistance measurements on GaAs is not widespread. The primary reasons for this are experimental problems with sample surface preparation and the very high values of contact resistance found in point contacts to GaAs. This paper details modifications to the spreading resistance technique to obtain reproducible and stable results on a variety of GaAs structures. It also discusses the current limits of such measurements.

KEYWORDS: Spreading resistance, gallium arsenide, resistivity profiling, dopant profiles, bevel sample preparation.

INTRODUCTION

The spreading resistance technique is widely used for measuring both resistivity and carrier concentration profiles in a variety of as-grown and processed silicon structures. Several attempts [1-3] to extend the spreading resistance technique to GaAs have been made, but with limited success. Queirolo [1] measured both bulk samples and diffused samples as processed for GaAs LEDs. He found it possible to get usable depth profiles for carrier concentrations exceeding about 5×10^{17} cm^{-3} (N-type) and about 1×10^{17} cm^{-3} (P-type). Ehrstein [2,3] measured P-type (zinc-doped) bulk samples with carrier concentrations in the range of 4.5×10^{16} cm^{-3} to 1.5×10^{18} cm^{-3}. He also obtained a measurable spreading resistance of about 1×10^{8} ohms for an N-type sample with a carrier concentration of about 7×10^{17} cm^{-3}, and success-

R. G. Mazur is President and R. J. Hillard is a Senior Engineer at Solid State Measurements Inc., 110 Technology Drive, Pittsburgh, PA 15275.

fully profiled a 5×10^{13} cm^{-2}, 100 keV beryllium implant. In addition, in 1983 the authors had good results in using spreading resistance to profile GaAs solar cell samples. The samples consisted of N-type layers greater than 1×10^{18} cm^{-3} and P-type epitaxial layers doped to various carrier concentrations greater than 1×10^{17} cm^{-3}. Based on the results of these earlier efforts, the authors decided to further explore the use of spreading resistance measurements in GaAs. In particular, the limitations cited by both Queirolo and Ehrstein were addressed. They found that application of the spreading resistance technique to GaAs was restricted by two factors:

1. the sensitivity of measurements to the surface finish on the beveled sample, and

2. the high spreading resistance values obtained during measurements on GaAs, even for relatively high carrier concentration material.

The current work suggests that these limitations are at least partially surmountable, and that the spreading resistance technique can produce useful measurements in GaAs. The following sections detail experimental procedures developed, and present results obtained on several N-type and P-type GaAs samples.

MEASUREMENT PROCEDURES

Sample Preparation

Since the spreading resistance technique is a strict comparison method, test samples must have surfaces that are highly reproducible and that have a high recombination velocity. Experience has shown that the only way to obtain correct surfaces is to generate them mechanically in a chemically neutral environment. Therefore, a sample preparation technique for silicon based on grinding bevels on a frosted glass plate with diamond and oil was used. This technique produces excellent results in silicon, and has been widely adopted throughout the world.

In 1983 work on GaAs solar cell material, the authors prepared reproducible bevel surfaces using the same bevel-grinding method. However, during several later attempts at profiling GaAs, the authors could not obtain suitable bevels using this method. Most of the surfaces were so badly torn that measurements were impossible. Therefore, the present work began by focusing on the technique to be used for beveling test samples.

Initial attempts at improving GaAs surface quality suggested an increase of pressure during bevel grinding. To test this, a series of variously sized samples were prepared using grinding pressures ranging from about 55 to 700 g/mm^2. It was found that grinding pressures higher than 500 g/mm^2 significantly degrade surface quality. It was also found that grinding pressures lower than 125 g/mm^2 also degrade surface quality, although to a lesser degree. The end result was that a standard piston weight of 233 g produced the best bevel surface quality for sample widths in the range of 2 to 3 mm and bevel lengths from 0.3 mm to 1.7 mm.

During the course of experiments with grinding pressure, it was discovered that bevel surface quality actually depends primarily on the cleanliness of the sample preparation apparatus. In particular, silicon debris on the grinding plate ruins the GaAs surface; therefore the frosted glass plate must be thoroughly cleaned before grinding GaAs samples (or else reserved exclusively for GaAs sample preparation). Figure 1 shows typical surface damage caused by silicon contamination.

Figure 1.   Typical bad bevel surface caused by silicon-contaminated glass plate used during preparation.

The current procedure for preparing GaAs samples is as follows:

1. Obtain a circular glass plate for a Buehler Ecomet III or similar rotating wheel grinder/polisher. Frost the plate by lapping with a glass tool and an abrasive slurry of 5 μm alumina and water. The final finish should be translucent when backlit, but nearly transparent when laid on a surface.

2. Clean the frosted glass plate thoroughly with warm water and soap. Charge it with a slurry of 0.25 μm diamond in oil. Condition the plate by bevel grinding a number of silicon samples. A plate that is <u>not</u> freshly ground provides the best sample bevels.

3. After conditioning, thoroughly clean the plate with warm water and soap to remove all traces of silicon debris. Recharge the plate with fresh 0.25 μm diamond abrasive and oil.

After preparing the plate with this procedure, reserve the plate for GaAs samples only.

4. Use a standard 233 g piston in a beveling jig. Reserve this jig for use with GaAs only.

5. Maintain plate speed at one revolution per second.

6. Grind the bevel in the direction shown in Figure 2. For details on beveling, see reference [4].

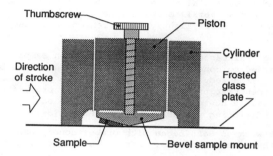

Figure 2.   Typical beveling jig illustrating the position of the sample on the bevel sample mount.

While the authors continue to explore further improvements in GaAs sample preparation, it is clear that the current technique produces surfaces that meet both the requirements of being highly reproducible and having a high surface recombination velocity. Figure 3 shows a good bevel surface produced with this technique.

Figure 3.   Typical good bevel surface.

Probe Conditioning

Proper probe conditioning is a very important aspect of the spreading resistance technique.[5,6]. Since the probes used in spreading resistance measurements do not move laterally on contact, they cannot break through surface insulating layers by "scrubbing." Instead, each probe must be "conditioned" by grinding the probe tip with the proper diamond abrasive. The goal is to create a large number of microscopic protrusions, or "asperities," over the contact area. The asperities are small enough to fracture the surface insulating layer by pressure alone, generating a micro-contact at each asperity. Because the overall shape of the probe tip is also controlled, the micro-contacts are tightly clustered and act electrically as a single contact.

In spreading resistance measurements on silicon samples, the authors had learned to condition probes to increase the number of micro-contacts. This reduces the pressure at each micro-contact, and minimizes probe penetration. The result is better profiling of the extremely thin layers now common in silicon technology. For details of the probe conditioning process, see references [5-7].

The current work on GaAs began with probes conditioned for use on silicon using the same procedures. After conditioning, the probes

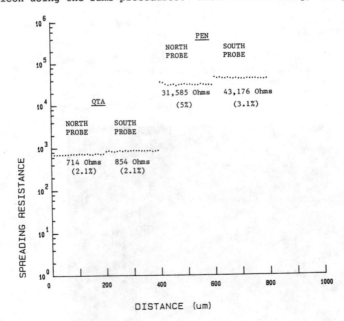

Figure 4.   Results of probe qualification after conditioning probes. Probe qualification samples: QTA ≈ 1-Ωcm P-type silicon; PEN 1μm N on N⁺ epitaxial silicon. Probe load 10 g.

were tested using standard silicon probe qualification samples (see figure 4).[7].

Probe Stabilization

In addition to being conditioned, spreading resistance probes must also be "stabilized" before use. For silicon, stabilization is usually done by running 100 to 200 measurement points on a ground bevel surface. For GaAs, it is necessary to stabilize by running between 500 to 1000 points. Figure 5 shows a series of depth profiles (the first eight of 23) on a P into P$^-$ implant. Note that the measured spreading resistance values change considerably on re-profiling, but that the average measured spreading resistance in the substrate stabilizes after about 600 points.

Figure 6 is partially derived from the data shown in figure 5, and extended to include a summary of the measured resistance values over a total of 2,300 points. The data points are calculated as the

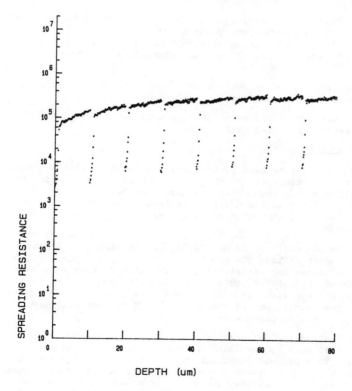

Figure 5.   Results from running a set of newly conditioned probes on a 0.25 μm diamond ground GaAs surface. Note the initial instability. This is an implanted sample mounted on a 1°9′ bevel sample mount.

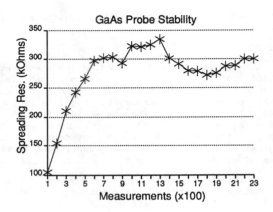

Figure 6.   Plot of measured resistance on a P-type GaAs surface
             after running twenty-three sets of 100 points each.
             Each data point corresponds to one set of measurements
             in the series.   Note that stabilization occurs after
             about 600 points.

average measured spreading resistance in the substrate region, and do
not include the implanted layer.

     After conditioning and stabilizing probes for use on GaAs, they
are then reserved for GaAs exclusively.

Short Term Stability

     In addition to long term probe stability there is also a question
about short term stability, as shown in the earlier publication by
Ehrstein[3]. Ehrstein found that the spreading resistance value shows
a pronounced minimum in the measured resistance versus time curve,
and remains unstable through the actual measurement interval (see
figure 7).

     Therefore, in addition to qualifying probes by making measure-
ments on standard silicon QTA and penetration samples, the authors
also measured spreading resistance as a function of time on a GaAs
sample.   These are referred to as probe settling curves.   Based on
previous experience with silicon, the probe descent and load transfer
parameters involved in making the metal to silicon contact were optimized before taking measurements.

     Figure 8 shows typical results.   The shape of the curve is
similar to that seen by Ehrstein, but the minimum is much less
pronounced.   This probably occurs because the current practice is to
adjust the system to minimize probe descent and load transfer rates.
Also note that the instability remaining at measurement time does not
seriously affect the data. While the mechanism that causes the minimum in the curve is not fully understood, it can probably be further
reduced by lowering probe pressure.

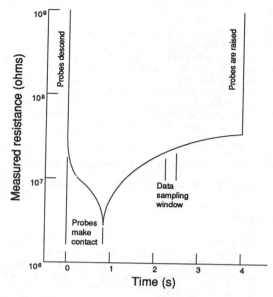

Figure 7.   Representation of measured resistance as a function of
time, as obtained by J. Ehrstein during a single
measurement cycle for probes in GaAs.

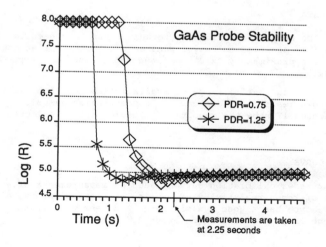

Figure 8.   Plot of measured resistance on P-type GaAs as a function of time, obtained at two different probe descent
rates.   Probe descent flowmeter readings were 0.75 and
1.25 cubic feet per hour (actual probe descent rates approximately 0.45 mm/s and 1.0 mm/s respectively).

Probe Loading

Queirolo[1] suggested that higher probe loads would increase the contact size and thus reduce overall resistance. To determine if this is a valid approach, probe loads in the range of 10 to 45 g were evaluated. The results showed that while higher loads do produce a lower measurement resistance, they also cause extensive subsurface damage (to the extent that regrinding cannot completely remove probe marks). Therefore, while higher probe loads might be practical for samples with very thick layers, they are totally inappropriate for the thin layers common in GaAs device structures.

Key findings in the probe loading experiments were:

• 10 g probes produce the best measurements on thin layers.

• Proper probe conditioning is a very important factor.

MEASUREMENT ENVIRONMENT

Low frequency vibration affects both spreading resistance stability and probe conditioning in silicon measurements. Since GaAs is softer than silicon, it could be expected that GaAs measurements might be even more sensitive. Therefore, all measurements were made on a vibration damping table to minimize the effects of vibration.

Measurements were made in the dark to avoid spurious voltages resulting from ambient light.

MEASUREMENT DATA

To date, the spreading resistance technique has been used to obtain reproducible profiles on P-type GaAs samples with carrier concentrations of approximately 1×10^{15} cm^{-3} and above, and on N-type GaAs of about 2.4×10^{17} cm^{-3} or higher.

Table I shows the entire range of available samples with corresponding known resistivity and carrier concentration values. Figures 9 through 17 show the results of measurements on selected samples.

CALIBRATION CURVE

Figure 18 shows calibration curves based on measurements of available samples of known resistivity or carrier concentration. Note that while P- type has a good dynamic range and sensitivity, for N-type the range only extends down to about 2.4×10^{17} cm^{-3}.

CONCLUSIONS

Meaningful spreading resistance measurements on GaAs can be performed using the sample and probe preparation procedures outlined in this paper. To date, successful measurements have been taken on a number of GaAs samples. These include a variety of bulk and

Table 1: GaAs Measurement Results (10 Gram Load)

Sample #	Orientation	Type	Process	Dopant	Layer thick.	Resistivity Ohm-cm	Carrier Concentration cm^{-3}	Figure number
D1	<100>	P	Epi	--	--	--	--	9
D2	<100>	P	Implant	--	--	--	--	10
A1	<100>	P	Bulk	Zinc	--	--	$3x10^{16}$ [1]	11
C78	<100>	P	MBE Epi	Silicon	5μm	15.6	$9.8x10^{14}$ [2]	12
C68	<100>	P	MBE Epi	Be	2μm	$9.02x10^{-2}$	$2.57x10^{17}$ [2]	13
#204	<100>	N	MOCVD Epi	Silicon	2μm	--	$2.4x10^{17}$ [2]	14
#207	<100>	N	MOCVD	Silicon	1μm	--	$1x10^{18}$ [2]	15
C88	<100>	N	MBE Epi	Silicon	.5μm	$1.08x10^{-3}$	$3.22x10^{18}$ [2]	16
#239	<100>	N	MOCVD Epi	Silicon	1μm	--	$5.6x10^{18}$ [2]	17
#212	<100>	N	MOCVD Epi	Silicon	1μm	--	$N1=3.2x10^{16}$ [2] $N2=8.2x10^{16}$ [2]	N/A
C87	<100>	N	MBE Epi	Silicon	.5μm	$2.64x10^{-2}$	$6.43x10^{16}$ [2]	N/A
#39-54	<111>	N	Bulk	Silicon	--	--	$0.9-1.8x10^{17}$ [1]	N/A
G611-029P	<100>	N	Bulk	Silicon	--	--	$1.5x10^{17}$ [1]	N/A

[1] Nominal values
[2] Carrier concentration value established by Hall or C-V measurements.

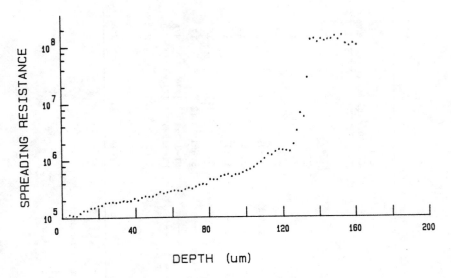

Figure 9.   Spreading resistance profile of GaAs P-type epi on a high resisitivity substrate.

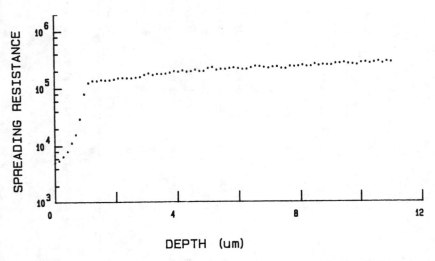

Figure 10. Spreading resistance profile of P-type GaAs implant.

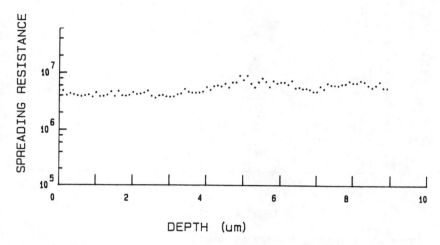

Figure 11. Spreading resistance profile of P-type GaAs bulk sample doped with zinc. Dopant density is $3x10^{16}$ cm^{-3}.

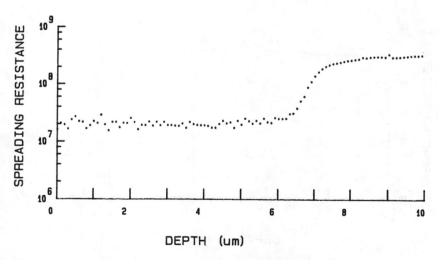

Figure 12. Spreading resistance profile of MBE P-type epi on high resistivity substrate. Dopant density is $9.8x10^{14}$ cm^{-3}.

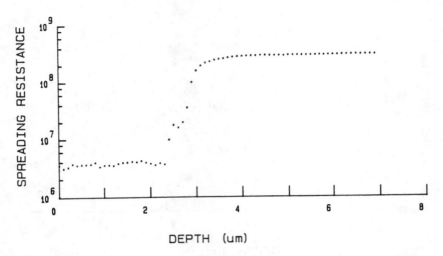

Figure 13. Spreading resistance profile of GaAs MBE P-type epi on
high resistivity substrate. Dopant density of epi is
2.57×10^{17} cm^{-3}.

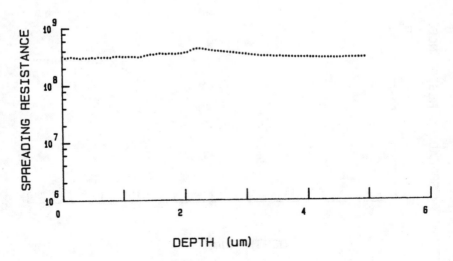

Figure 14. Spreading resistance profile of GaAs MOCVD N-type epi.
Dopant density is 2.4×10^{17} cm^{-3}.

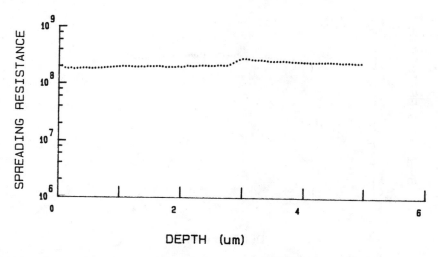

Figure 15. Spreading resistance profile of GaAs MOCVD N-type epi.
            Dopant density is 1×10^{18} cm^{-3}.

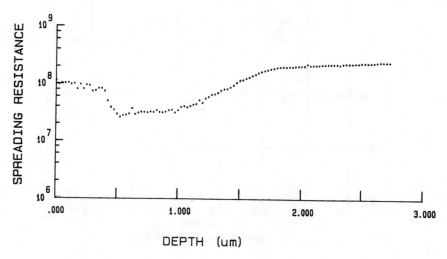

Figure 16. Spreading resistance profile of GaAs MBE N-type epi.
            Dopant density is 3.22×10^{18} cm^{-3}.

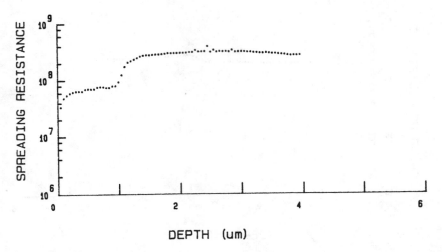

Figure 17. Spreading resistance profile of GaAs MOCVD N-type epi.
Dopant density is 5.6×10^{18} cm^{-3}.

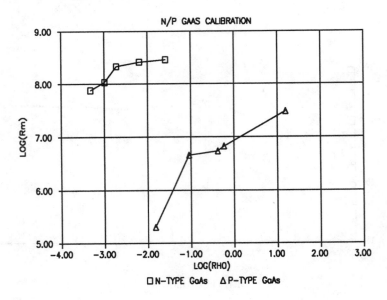

Figure 18. Calibration curve for GaAs based on SSM's present collection of samples.

epitaxially deposited structures and a P-type ion implant. The spreading resistance values obtained range up to about 5×10^8 ohms and are experimentally reproducible.

Spreading resistance measurements in GaAs do not have the same sensitivity as in silicon. However, the technique can certainly be used to generate dopant profiles for samples over the range of about 9.8×10^{14} cm^{-3} and higher for P-type and greater than approximately 2.4×10^{17} cm^{-3} for N-type. Spreading resistance profiles can also produce accurate measurements of layer thickness in many GaAs structures.

As the spreading resistance technique is a comparison method, the ability to produce quantitative measurements in GaAs depends on the development of adequate calibration samples. Since there are significant variations in mobility in GaAs structures grown by different processes, it is possible that separate calibration curves may be required for each type of process.

Additional efforts to apply the spreading resistance technique in GaAs are planned; these will focus on:

- Improving the procedures for sample preparation and probe conditioning, with special attention to increasing the stability of point contacts and developing GaAs probe qualification samples.

- Testing the technique against more and better characterized GaAs samples, especially epitaxial structures. The authors would certainly welcome any such samples that readers may care to send for evaluation.

- Further developing the use of the technique for quantitative measurements. This requires locating GaAs samples whose electrical properties have been well characterized using Hall-effect or C-V measurements. These will be used in developing a more extensive calibration curve.

- Experimenting with a number of chemical techniques intended to passivate GaAs surfaces. It is hoped that this will increase the dynamic range of spreading resistance measurements, particularly in N-type material. Currently, several chemical compounds reported in the literature to be effective in GaAs surface passivation are being evaluated.

REFERENCES

[1] Queirolo, G., "Spreading Resistance Measurements on Gallium Arsenide," J. Electrochem. Soc., Vol. 125, No. 10, 1672-76, 1978.

[2] Ehrstein, J. R., "Spreading Resistance Measurements," Semiconductor Technology Program Progress Briefs, NBSIR 80-2006-4, National Technical Information Service, Springfield, VA 22161, 1980.

[3] Ehrstein, J. R., and Seabaugh, A. C., "Gallium Arsenide Materials Characterization: Annual Report, Oct. 12, 1978 to Oct. 12, 1979," NBSIR 81-2403 National Technical Information Service, Springfield, VA 22161, 1981.

[4] SSM Technical Publications, _Bevel Sample Preparation Instructions_, Solid State Measurements, Inc., Pittsburgh, PA 15275, 1987.

[5] Mazur, R. G., "Dopant Profiles by the Spreading Resistance Technique," _Symposium on Materials Characterization in Microelectronics Processing_, American Chemical Society, St. Louis, MO, 1984.

[6] Mazur, R. G., and Gruber, G. A., "Dopant Profiles on Thin Layer Silicon Structures with the Spreading Resistance Technique," _Solid State Technology_, Vol. 24, 69, 1981.

[7] SSM Technical Publications, _Probe Conditioning Instructions_, Solid State Measurements, Inc., Pittsburgh, PA 15275, 1987.

Fabrication Technology

Carlos L. Ygartua and Robert Swaroop

HIGH DOSE ARSENIC IMPLANT FOR BIPOLAR BURIED LAYERS

REFERENCE: Ygartua, C.L. and Swaroop, R.B., "High Dose Arsenic Implant for Bipolar Buried Layers", Semiconductor Fabrication: Technology and Metrology, ASTM STP 990, Dinesh C. Gupta, editor, American Society for Testing and Materials, Philadelphia 1989.

ABSTRACT: The use of arsenic ion implant for a low sheet resistance and deep junction buried layer process was investigated. Appropriate ion doses and energy were found to obtain the desired buried layer profile using a pre-implant oxide. A low temperature (1050°C) oxidation was employed to remove the highly damaged surface region after diffusion/anneal of the arsenic implant. Damage was characterized after the buried layer process and epitaxial growth. The electrical performances and relative yield of the bipolar devices made from implanted and deposited (solid-source) arsenic buried layer were compared. The results indicated that implanted buried layer produced almost defect free epitaxial layer in the subsequent processing.

KEY WORDS: Arsenic Implant, Buried Layer, Epitaxial Defects.

A buried layer process in silicon wafers must result in a surface that is free of crystallographic defects for a high quality epitaxial film to be deposited. Metallic precipitates in the buried layer will cause stacking faults in the epi layer and dislocation loops will be propagated into the Epi layer, i.e. any disorder or contamination will cause disorder in the epi layer that could eventually result in failure of a device (1). The major failure mechanism is due to metallic precipitation at the point detects if these defect precipitation

Mr. Ygartua is a Senior Engineer at National Semiconductor (formerly Fairchild) 545 Whisman Rd., (M/S 2-200), Mountain View, California 94039. Dr. Swaroop is Director of Technology at ASYST Technologies Inc., 1745 McCandless Dr., Milpitas, CA 95035. Formerly he was with National Semiconductor (Fairchild) when this work was performed.

115

clusters happen to be in an active region of a device such as p-n junction depletion region.

The high diffusivity (and possible good crystal fit factor) of arsenic makes it desirable for a low sheet resistance deep junction buried layer. It is heavy enough ion to cause extensive damage to the implanted region if the buried layer is achieved via implant method. Annealing and/or removal of the damaged layer is therefore necessary. Some annealing takes place during implantation due to heating of the wafers from stopping of the ion beam (2). This generally results in partial annealing which is not desirable since re-crystallization by epitaxial type growth in the damaged layer occurs optimally when the implanted layer is completely amorphous.

An energy of 80 KEV was chosen to maximize damage to the silicon, since at this energy nuclear stopping predominates for Arsenic. We have investigated the use of a pre-implant oxide in order to trap metallic impurities. The source of metallic impurities trapped by the pre-implant oxide is conjectured to be sputtered ions from the implant chamber. The disadvantage of the pre-implant oxide is recoil-implanted oxygen (3), but the damage resulting from this is shallow enough (less than $1200A°$ (3)) to be removed during the post-diffusion oxidation. In order to compensate for the arsenic that is stopped by the oxide a significantly higher dose: (1.0×10^{16}) cm^{-2} vs. (5.0×10^{15}) cm^{-2} is used to obtain the same sheet resistance.

Oxidation during annealing was kept to a minimum to prevent excessive oxide-defect complexes and formation of oxidation induced stacking faults (SF) (3). This study indicates that using the proper pre-implanted oxide thickness and damage anneal removal method, we are able to produce a defect free silicon epitaxial film over a heavily doped implanted arsenic buried layer.

EXPERIMENTAL PROCEDURE AND EVALUATION

The silicon wafers used for these experiments were P-type <111> with resistivity of (1.5-3) ohm-cm. Wafers were implanted with a Varian CF 3000 implanter with electrostatic scan at 80 KEV with Way-Flow cooling. Implant current was approximately 350μA, with doses varying between $5.0X10^{15}$ cm^{-2} to $1.0X10^{16}$ cm^{-2}. Wafers were implanted both with and without a pre-implant oxide. The pre-implant oxide thickness was either $300A°$ or $600A°$. The details of experimental process steps are given in Figure 1.

After implantation wafers with pre-implant oxide were etched with HF to remove the oxide in some cases. In

other cases the oxide was left on. Wafers then received
a diffusion/anneal process to obtain the desired sheet
resistance and junction depth.

Diffusion/anneal consisted of 400 min. dry N_2 cycle
at 1250°C which was more than sufficient for re-crystallization of the damaged layer. The actual ramping was
done in N_2/O_2 environment in order to avoid the N_2
pitting (see Figure 1).

After diffusion/anneal a lower temperature 1050°C dry
O_2 oxidation was performed to remove the remaining
damage. Oxide was then removed and an epitaxial layer
was deposited using a barrel type radiation heated reactor at 1200°C with $SiCl_4$ as a deposition source in H_2
carrier. The epitaxial layer was doped with phosphorous
and a two minutes insitu HCl etch was performed prior to
epi deposition. The epitaxial layer thickness used for
study of defects was ~15μm with 3 - 5 ohm-cm resistivity.

A buried layer with a junction depth of 6-8μm was obtained after the high temperature (1250°C) diffusion/
anneal. Implantation damage was examined using a preferential etch after diffusion/anneal and after the low
temperature oxidation. Epitaxial defects associated with
implant damage and/or anomalous metallic contamination
were also examined with preferential etch. The buried
layer dopant profile was evaluated using spreading resistance profile (SRP) method. The latter measures carrier
distribution (on a bevelled specimen) associated with the
atomic profile.

The remaining bipolar device process steps were then
performed and the finished devices were tested. Device
yield was compared to an established process using a solid
source (AS_2O_3) process.

RESULTS

1. Sheet Resistance Uniformity
    Table 1 shows the results of sheet resistance uniform-
    ity across the wafer and wafer to wafer obtained
    through implant and solid-source deposition processes.
    The sigma (δ) value given in this table is a standard
    deviation calculated for 5 positions on each wafer. A
    sample of 25 wafers was used. The within wafer δ is
    the standard deviation of the averages of each wafer.
    The wafer to wafer δ is the standard deviation of the
    average of each wafer. The % variance within wafer is
    the ratio of the δ within wafer to the average of all
    the measurements. The % variance wafer to wafer is
    the ratio of the δ wafer to wafer to the average of
    all the measurements. It is apparent that the implant
    method produces excellent uniformity compared with the

solid-source deposition process.

2. Post Anneal/Diffusion
    Extensive surface damage was observed both with and
    without pre-implant oxide after anneal/diffusion in
    the buried layer areas. Sirtl etching resulted in
    numerous etch pits of various sizes. The etch pits
    tended to be larger for the process without a pre-
    implant oxidation (Figure 2) than for the process
    with 600 A° pre-implant ox (Figure 3).

3. Post Oxidation:
    A 2000 A° dry O_2 oxidation (at 1050°C) following the
    high temperature (1250°C) diffusion/anneal was suf-
    ficient to essentially consume the damaged silicon
    surface. Very few etch pits (after Sirtl etching)
    were observed for wafers with or without a pre-implant
    oxidation (Figures 4 and 5). This indicated that the
    damaged region extended less than 1000 A° into the
    silicon.

4. Post Epi:
    Stacking faults were observed most frequently with the
    process that has no pre-implant oxide (Figure 6).
    Wafers that had 300 A° and 600 A° pre-implant oxide
    but deglaze after implant also produced SF in the
    epitaxial layer (deglaze is etching of oxide in a
    diluted (6:1) HF solution for a given time). Figure 7
    shows an example with a 600 A° pre-implant oxide that
    had no post implant deglaze. The least occurrence of
    SF were found with the process that had a 600 A° pre-
    implant oxide with the implant followed by a deglaze
    (Figure 8). An unacceptable number of SF were found
    with the 300 A° pre-implant oxide that also had a post
    implant deglaze (Figure 9). An acceptable number of
    SF for the product line investigated was less than
    200 per cm^2.

Figure 10 shows the dopant profile of the Epi-buried
layer structure obtained with the arsenic implant process for a 3μm epi process. The profile shows minimal
autodoping with a sharp transition region.

In Table 2 the approximate defect density after epi
deposition for each process is shown. Devices were
fabricated with the processes that had 300 A° and 600
A° pre-implant oxide with a deglaze following the implant. Table 3 shows a summary of the relative yield
compared to the standard process (solid-source deposition). The 600 A° pre-implant oxide process resulted in a yield that was equivalent to the
standard yield which correlates with the lower
defect density.

CONCLUSIONS

A low defect density epitaxial layer with a high dose arsenic implanted buried layer can be produced. The results of this investigation indicate the following:

1. Using a pre-implant oxide that is removed after implant reduces SF in the epi that are probably due to metallic precipitates which act as nucleation sites for SF.

2. A dry O_2 oxidation after diffusion/anneal at relatively low temperatures is necessary to remove implant surface damage that appears as etch-pits using a pre- ferential etch.

ACKNOWLEDGEMENTS

The authors wish to thank Josie Bungcayao, Jo Miller, and Don Whiteside for assistance with experimental work.

Table 1:   Sheet Resistance Uniformity

	Implant	Solid Source
Within Wafer δ	.56	1.40
Wafer to Wafer δ	.64	1.75
% Variance Within Wafer	4.1	10.9
% Variance Wafer to Wafer	4.7	11.7

Table 2:   EPI Defect Density

Pre-Implant Oxide (A°)	Deglaze	Defect Density (cm^{-2})
0	N/A	~2400
300	No	~1800
300	Yes	< 600
600	No	<1200
600	Yes	< 200

Table 3:   Relative Yield

Product Group	Pre-Implant Ox (A°)	Relative Yield *
Op Amp	600	100.5
Voltage Regulator	300	97.8
Voltage Regulator	600	99.7
Interface	600	99.3

*1.   Relative Yield = $\dfrac{\text{Implant yield}}{\text{Standard yield}}$ X 100

*2.   Average for all split lots for each product group is shown.

Experimental Matrix

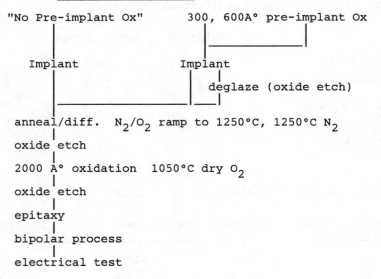

Figure 1.   Experimental Matrix Indicating, Process Steps

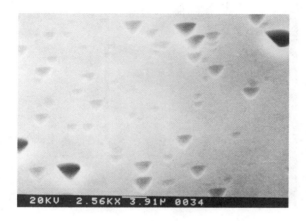

Figure 2   0 A° Pre-implant ox, after
              diffusion/anneal

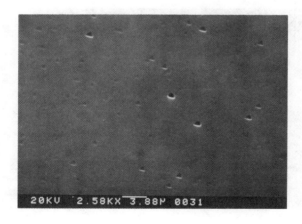

Figure 3   600 A° Pre-implant ox, no
              deglaze, after diffusion/anneal

Figure 4   0 A° Pre-implant ox, after
              diffusion/anneal + oxidation

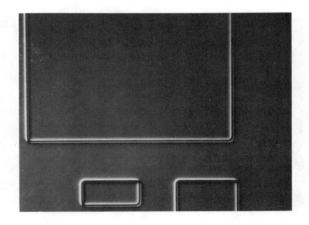

Figure 5   600 A° Pre-implant ox, no deglaze
              after diffusion/anneal + oxidation

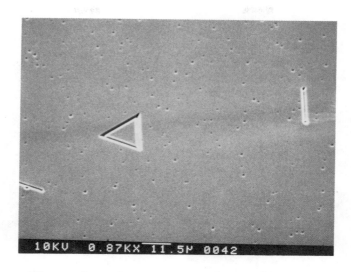

Figure 6   0 A° Pre-implant ox, diffusion/
                anneal + oxidation, after Epi

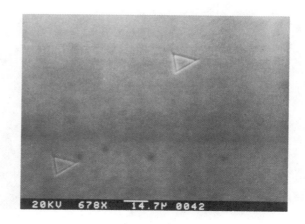

Figure 7   600 A° Pre-implant ox, no deglaze
                diffusion/anneal + oxidation, after
                Epi

Figure 8   600 A° Pre-implant ox, deglaze,
             diffusion/anneal + oxidation after
             Epi

Figure 9   300 A° Pre-implant ox, deglaze
             diffusion/anneal + oxidation, after
             Epi

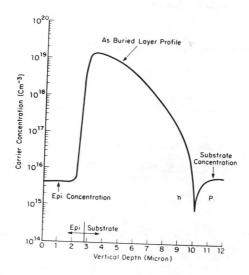

Figure 10   Profile of Epi-buried layer structure

REFERENCES

(1)   A. Dreeban and A. Schajko "On a Relationship Be-
       tween Substrate Perfection and Stacking Faults in
       Homo Epitaxial Silicon", RCA Review, Vol. 44,
       p. 217, 1983

(2)   S. Prussin, D.I. Margolese, and R.N. Tauber "The
       Nature of Defect Layer Formation for Arsenic Ion
       Implantation", J. Appl. Phys., Vol. 54, No. 5,
       p. 2316, 1983

(3)   T. Hirao, G. Fuse, K. Inoue, S. Takayanagi,
       Y. Yaegashi, and S. Ichikawa "The Effect of the
       Recoil-Implanted Oxygen in Si on The Electrical
       Activation of As After Through-Oxide Implantation",
       J. Appl. Phys., Vol. 50, No. 8, p. 5251, 1979

Ravi Subrahmanyan, Hisham Z. Massoud, and Richard B. Fair

ACCURATE   JUNCTION-DEPTH   MEASUREMENTS   USING   CHEMICAL
STAINING

REFERENCE:Subrahmanyan, R., Massoud, H. Z., and Fair, R. B., "Accurate Junction-Depth Measurements Using Chemical Staining," Semiconductor Fabrication: Technology and Metrology, ASTM STP 990, Dinesh C. Gupta, editor, American Society for Testing and Materials, 1989.

ABSTRACT: The techniques of chemical staining, spreading resistance, and secondary-ion mass spectrometry (SIMS) have been used in the determination of the depth of diffused and ion-implanted junctions in an effort to estimate the accuracy of the staining method. Computer simulations were also used to study the behaviour of charge carriers in the semiconductor under illumination, and the accuracy of the junction depth obtained from raw spreading resistance data. It was observed that it is possible to measure junction depth reproducibly, to within 200 Å of the metallurgical junction depth, by carefully controlling the surface preparation of the sample and the lighting conditions under which the staining takes place.

KEYWORDS: chemical staining, junction depth, spreading resistance, SIMS.

The method of chemical staining of doped silicon layers for the determination of junction depths has been known since the early days of the semiconductor industry [1–4]. The technique has often been applied to the study of dopant diffusion in silicon [5–7] and is the subject of an ASTM standard [8] which estimates the accuracy of the technique to be ~ 0.2 µm [6,8]. Wu et al. [6] have shown that by following strict experimental procedures, it is possible to obtain junction depths to an accuracy of 200 Å. However, staining is generally known to be highly dependent on experimental conditions and, as a result, its accuracy and reproducibility for junction-depth measurement are still questioned.

This paper reports the results of a detailed study of the staining method. Questions about the accuracy and reproducibility of the method are answered by using a large variety of stains under various conditions and by carrying out marker-layer experiments. Staining is then compared with other techniques such as spreading resistance [9] and SIMS [10]. Computer simulations of spreading resistance and the effect of illumination on the distribution of charge carriers in the silicon substrate are carried out to further explain the observed effects.

Ravi Subrahmanyan, Hisham Z. Massoud, and Richard B. Fair are with the Department of Electrical Engineering, Duke University, Durham, North Carolina, 27706.

JUNCTION STAINING

The determination of junction depth by staining is generally carried out as follows: the sample is beveled at a shallow angle to mechanically magnify the junction depth. The magnification along the beveled surface is $1/\sin\theta$, where θ is the bevel angle, and it can be made large by choosing a suitably small angle. Magnifications up to 200× are easily obtained. A drop of the staining solution is then placed on the sample, which is strongly illuminated for a period usually less than 1 min. The staining solution is then quickly washed off, and the sample is examined to see if a stain has formed. If the staining is unsuccessful, the sample is either stained for a longer or shorter time, under different conditions of illumination, or by using a different staining solution. Finally, the junction depth is determined by measuring the length of the stained section, taking into account the mechanical magnification due to beveling. The success of the staining procedure depends on various conditions such as surface preparation, the composition and volume of the staining solution, nature and intensity of illumination, and the staining time.

Various solutions have been described for use in staining junctions [4,6]. These solutions fall into two basic categories: metal-ion-based solutions that stain by electrodeposition of the metal on the n-type region [11], and HF-based solutions that delineate the junction by preferentially etching the p-type region [4]. In the case of metal ion solutions, which are typically solutions of salts containing metals like Sb, Ag, Cu, Pt, and Au, staining occurs as a result of an electrochemical displacement reaction in which the metal is deposited onto the doped semiconductor [11]. Differences in the electrochemical potentials in the n-type and p-type regions lead to different deposition rates, causing different amounts of plating on the two regions.

Staining by HF-based solutions occurs by a differential etching of the n-type and p-type regions. The exact nature of the stain is unknown, but it is thought to consist of silicon monoxide, or amorphous silicon formed by the etching of the silicon surface. These solutions generally consist of mixtures of HF and an oxidizing agent such as nitric acid (1-3-10 stain) or potassium dichromate (Secco etch) [4]. The different oxidation rates in the n-type and p-type regions lead to regions of varying oxide thicknesses, which are etched differently by HF, resulting in a delineation of the n-type and p-type regions. These regions are observed by viewing with a Nomarski phase-contrast microscope or an interference microscope.

The staining reaction is also known to be influenced strongly by illumination of the sample during staining [12]. In the absence of strong illumination, factors such as surface preparation, the concentration of the solution, staining time, the volume of solution on the sample, and ambient lighting play exaggerated roles in the staining process. While factors such as staining time can be controlled accurately, it is much more difficult to control surface preparation, solution volume, and ambient temperature. As a result, staining done under uncontrolled conditions of illumination is imprecise and is usually not reproducible with a great degree of precision. The presence of strong illumination causes the effects of extraneous factors to be greatly reduced, giving sharp stains and consistent results [13,14]. Wu et al. [6] observed that the use of ultraviolet illumination is helpful in staining lightly doped samples. The shorter wavelength u.v. light is absorbed to a much greater extent on the silicon surface, causing a much greater surface response, which in turn enhances the staining reaction.

SAMPLE PREPARATION

The samples to be stained were broken into rectangular pieces roughly 2 mm × 4 mm by cleaving. These pieces were mounted singly on 1°9' or 34' beveling blocks using quartz-type adhesive wax. The amount of wax under the sample was minimized to get the sample surface as parallel as possible to the surface of the block. The samples were mounted with the smaller side parallel to the ridge on the beveling block, and care was taken to get the cleft edge as close and parallel to the ridge as possible. The beveling block was then attached to the piston of a stainless steel lapping jig manufactured by Solid State Measurements. The cylinder of the lapping jig was placed on a preconditioned glass plate [15] covered with a paste consisting of $1/4$ μm diamond paste and a few drops of isocut fluid (Buehler No. 11-1193-032). The piston was then inserted into the cylinder slowly, and care was taken to ensure that there was enough damping grease on the piston walls that the piston did not quickly fall down into the cylinder and smash the sample on the glass plate. This is an important consideration because the sharp, freshly cleft edge on the sample is likely to shatter on impact, leaving tiny pieces of silicon on the plate which will scratch the surface during subsequent lapping. The entire jig was then moved in a circular fashion on the glass plate, until ~ 1 mm of the lapped surface was exposed. The sample was then thoroughly cleaned with deionised water. It is essential to remove all the oil and diamond paste at this point. If necessary, the sample should be cleaned repeatedly in acetone and water until all residual oily films are removed.

Grinding using diamond paste is commonly used for lapping silicon prior to spreading resistance measurements. This method has the advantage that the sample is ground in an inert non-aqueous slurry, such that lapping is fully mechanical in nature and non-stable surface charges are minimized [16]. However, it was found that the surface may still be rough, with fine scratches, after lapping in diamond paste. This is acceptable for samples prepared for spreading resistance, but makes the interpretation of staining results difficult. The samples were therefore lapped further in an SSM Model No. 7 L/P machine using a filtered 1:1 solution of colloidal silica (Ludox) in water. The sample was lapped at slow speed, and was examined every 5 min to check the condition of the surface. Lapping was stopped when the surface displayed a clean, scratch free, mirror-like finish. The sample was then thoughroughly cleaned with deionised water while still on the beveling block.

Some important recommendations concerning lapping were made by Pawlik [17] and followed in this study. Starting with an absolutely clean glass plate is necessary. In addition to particles and silicon chips which can scratch the lapped surface, smears and stains on the glass may rub off on the sample, making it impossible to get a good stain. The glass plates used for lapping should be frosted by polishing with 3 μm alumina powder and a polishing wheel. This produces small scratches on the plate surface which hold the lapping compound during sample preparation, making it easier to grind the silicon. It is also desirable to move the lapping jig such that the sample is lapped up the bevel, however this is difficult if the lapping is done by hand. The lapping jig should also be as massive as reasonably possible to prevent rocking of the jig during lapping. Finally, if the sample does not already have a protective oxide layer, it is essential to deposit a layer of SiO_2 about 2500 Å thick on the sample before beveling. This serves to minimize errors due to edge rounding during beveling, and also helps to delineate the edge of the bevel after staining [6]. It was found that by observing these recommendations, smooth, flat, and scratch-free beveled surfaces could be obtained reproducibly. Figure 1 shows a profile of a bevel taken with a Tencor AlphaStep 100 surface profilometer, and it can be seen that there is no noticeable rounding of the bevel surface.

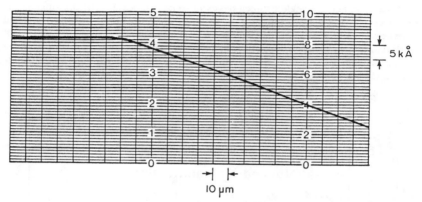

Fig. 1. Profilometer trace of beveled surface showing absence of curvature.

The setup used for staining consisted of a stand supporting a Westinghouse 275 Watt Sun Lamp and a Blacklite 75 Watt UW lamp attached to a timer with a resolution of 0.01 sec. The block holding the lapped sample was placed at a distance of about 1 inch under the lamps, and a drop of the staining solution was carefully placed on the sample using a Teflon dropper. The excess wax on the beveling block prevented damage to the block from the staining solution. This allowed the sample to be kept on the block during staining, which had the important advantage of not contaminating the sample by wax during removal from the block. Normally, removing the sample requires heating the block to melt the wax, and it is difficult to avoid contamination of the sample by the liquid wax during removal of the sample, which substantially reduces the quality of the obtained stain.

The lamps were switched on by turning on the timer, and the timer was switched off after times ranging from 10 sec to several minutes. The sample was immediately rinsed in water to wash off the staining solution and then examined under a microscope to check the stain quality and to measure the length of the stained region. Because the sample was still mounted on the beveling block, the beveled and stained surface was parallel to the bottom of the block, making it easy to examine the sample under the microscope. Examining a beveled sample at an angle other than 90° to the beveled surface would make it difficult to measure distances on the beveled surface.

Uncertainty in measurement of the bevel angle is a major source of error in staining measurements, especially when blocks with very small angles, typically less than 1° are used to obtain a large magnification. The error is caused by unevenness in the layer of wax used to attach the sample to the beveling block, which causes the actual bevel angle to deviate from the nominal block angle. It is therefore essential to precisely measure the bevel angle on each sample. This was done using the small-angle measurement setup of Tong *et al.* [18], using an attachment to an ASR100-C spreading resistance measurement unit [18,19,20], which gives results accurate to well within 5% [17]. In this method, an image from a thin wire is simultaneously projected on to the beveled and the top surfaces of the sample, and the angle between the two surfaces is measured by determining the seperation between the two images. The measurement procedure is described in detail elsewhere [18,19]. Figure 2 shows a plot of several measurements carried out with a 1°9' block for different samples. It can be seen that there is a variation of up to 20% from the nominal magnification of 50x, underscoring the importance of measuring the bevel angle on each sample.

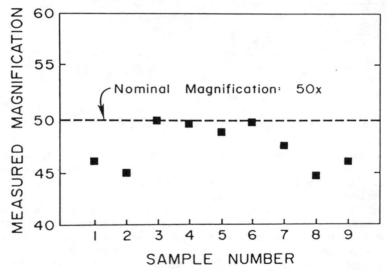

Fig. 2.   Variations in the measured magnification for a block with a nominal bevel angle of 1°9' and nominal magnification of 50.

The staining procedure described above was applied to a set of eight samples prepared by implanting and diffusing boron, arsenic, or phosphorus into (100) silicon (Table 1), and using four different staining solutions (Table 2). The copper solutions preferentially stain the n-type layers, while the HF solutions preferentially stain the p-type layer. The samples were stained with both kinds of stains, and the junction depths, obtained by staining both the n-type and the p-type layers on the same sample, were measured. Each sample was stained for times ranging from 5 sec to 1 min under three conditions of illumination: no illumination, under white light, and under white and ultraviolet light. The bevel angle was measured for each sample, and the junction depth was calculated by measuring the width of the stained region on a photograph taken with an optical microscope under magnifications ranging from 340 to 1720×. This procedure allowed the junction depth to be measured to within 100 Å, with an accumulated error of ± 5%. It was found that staining is extremely unpredictable and inaccurate without illumination as discussed earlier and the results described in Figs. 3–8 are all for stains carried out under ultraviolet illumination.

Sample I.D.	Dopant Atom	Junction Type	Processing Temperature	Approx. Junction Depth
B1	Boron	p^+-n	1000°C	1.0 μm
B2	Boron	p^+-n	1100°C	1.5 μm
B3	Boron	p^+-n	1150°C	3.0 μm
P1	Phosphorus	n^+-p	1000°C	3.5 μm
P2	Phosphorus	n^+-p	900°C	1.0 μm
A2	Arsenic	n^+-p	1000°C	0.4 μm
A11	Arsenic	n^+-p	1100°C	0.7 μm
DNA-1	Boron	p^+-n	1100°C	2.0 μm

Table 1. Samples used in the chemical staining experiments.

Name	Composition	Type
Copper	8 g/liter $CuSO_4.5H_2O$ 10 cc/liter 49% HF	Cu
1-3-10	1 ml HF, 3 ml HNO_3, 10 ml CH_3COOH	HF
1-3-10 Cu	10 ml (1-3-10) + 2 drops of 20 g $Cu(NO_3)_2$, 80 ml H_2O, 1 ml 49% HF	HF, Cu
Secco	1 vol. 44 g $K_2Cr_2O_7$, 1 lit. H_2O, 2 vols. 49% HF	HF
SirtlA	50 g CrO_3, 100 ml H_2O, 75 ml 49% HF	Cr

Table 2. Composition of staining solutions.

STAINING RESULTS

Figure 3 shows the stained junction depth as a function of time for the p^+-n samples B1, B2, and B3 for Copper and 1-3-10 solutions. The sample identification in this and the following figures are given in Table 1. Details of the composition of the different staining solutions are given in Table 2. The nominal mechanical magnification is also shown. In most cases, samples were beveled using a 1°9' beveling block which corresponds to a nominal magnification of 50×. Figure 4 shows the stained junction depth vs staining time for samples B1, B2, and B3 for Secco and SirtlA stains. Figures 5 and 6 show the stained junction depth as a function of staining time for the n^+-p samples P1, P2, A2, and A11. These plots show that a staining time of 30 sec is required for the stain to form completely for the HF-based solutions. It is important to note that there is agreement between junction depths obtained using copper and 1-3-10 solutions for both p^+-n and n^+-p solutions. As mentioned earlier, the copper solution preferentially stains the n-type layer, and the (1-3-10) solution stains the p-type layer. The agreement in the junction depths shows that both solutions stain up to the same point regardless of whether the staining is carried out on the high-concentration side or the low-concentration side. The same conclusion may also be drawn by comparing the junction depths obtained using copper and Secco solutions. Finally, Figs. 7 and 8 show the measured junction depths for different samples obtained with different staining solutions. The staining time was determined individually for each sample and staining solution to get optimal staining results. It can be seen that the different solutions give results that agree within experimental error.

Once the procedure for staining was determined, many measurements were taken for each sample over a three-month period, and it was found that the results were highly repeatable. It was observed that staining works best under ultraviolet light. The copper solution is most accurate for times under 15 sec. Overexposure causes overplating for n^+-p junctions, making delineation difficult. However, exposures of up to 30 sec may be required for staining the higher resistivity n-layers on p^+-n junctions. Heavily overplated regions may wash off of the sample during rinsing and caution must be exercised while rinsing n^+-p samples. All other solutions require longer exposures of ~ 30 sec. The Secco solution shows irregular bands in 10 sec which develop into one or two distinct bands in 25 sec. Prolonged exposure can wipe out the stain completely. SirtlA stains have a very complex structure and are difficult to interpret. In general, n^+-p junctions stain better than p^+-n junctions. However, p^+-n junctions can be stained accurately in individual cases. Finally, all stains considered are equally accurate under conditions suited to the particular solution. The best approach was determined by trying out all of them on a sample and comparing the results with spreading resistance. The one most suited to that sample, as shown by the most accurate stain, was then chosen.

SPREADING RESISTANCE RESULTS

Spreading resistance [9,21–23] was also used to determine the junction depth for all the samples described above. The junction depths obtained using the two methods were compared to calibrate the staining and to determine its accuracy. Detailed reviews of the

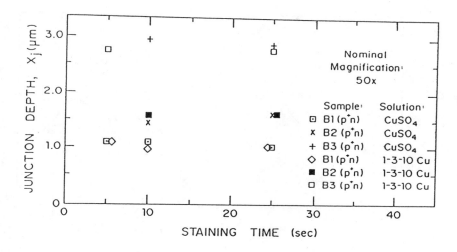

Fig. 3.   Delineated junction depth as a function of staining time for p^+-n samples stained with copper and (1-3-10) solutions.

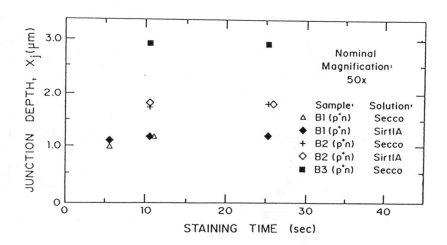

Fig. 4.   Delineated junction depth as a function of staining time for p^+-n samples stained with Secco and SirtlA solutions.

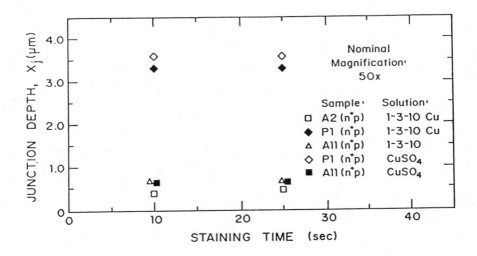

Fig. 5.   Delineated junction depth as a function of staining time for n^+-p samples stained with copper and (1-3-10) solutions.

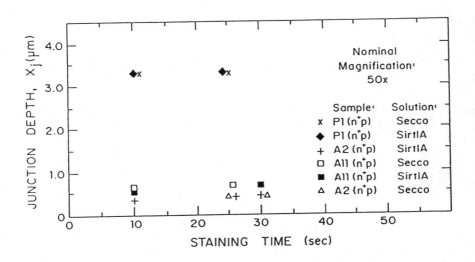

Fig. 6.   Delineated junction depth as a function of staining time for n^+-p samples stained with Secco and SirtlA solutions.

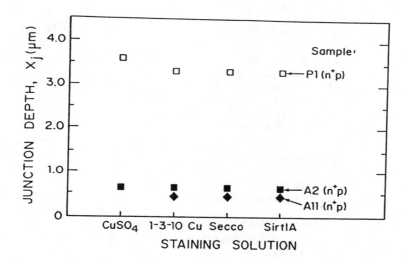

Fig. 7. Comparison of staining solutions in delineating n^+-p samples.

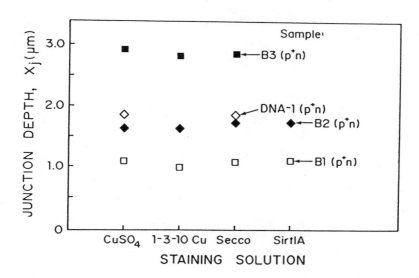

Fig. 8. Comparison of staining solutions in delineating p^+-n samples.

technique have been given by Mazur [9] and Ehrstein [22] and may be referred to for further details. The spreading resistance measurements described below were carried out using an ASR-100C spreading resistance unit manufactured by Solid State Measurements [15]. The samples to be analyzed were mounted on beveling blocks and beveled as described earlier. The beveled samples were mounted on the ASR-100C and the small-angle-measurement setup on the optical microscope attached to the ASR-100C was used to measure the bevel angle [15,19]. Spreading resistance readings were then taken on the samples, by choosing the x-step distance in such a way that the 25–50 steps would be taken to reach the junction. The junction depth was then calculated from the distance between the surface and the peak in the raw spreading resistance data, taking into account the actual bevel angle and x-step distances.

The samples described in Table 1 were all analyzed using spreading resistance, and their junction depths were determined. In many cases, the same mounted sample was used for spreading resistance as well as staining. Figure 9 shows the ratio of junction depth measured using spreading resistance to that obtained by staining, for the various samples. It can be seen that there is good agreement within ± 5% in all cases. The n^+-p samples agree better overall, but p^+-n samples can be stained as accurately in individual cases. The agreement between staining and spreading resistance can also be noted by looking at samples on which the staining has been carried out after spreading resistance analysis; the spreading resistance probe marks in the stained layer may be counted by viewing the sample under oblique illumination, and the number of points in the raw spreading resistance data between the surface and the peak corresponds exactly to the probe marks counted in the stained layer.

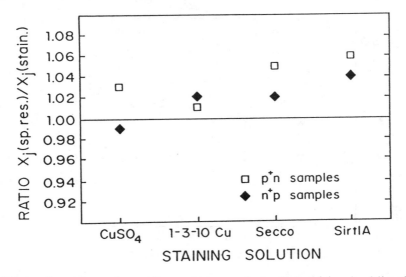

Fig. 9.   Comparison of spreading resistance and chemical staining in delineating junction depths for different staining solutions.

A MARKER–LAYER EXPERIMENT

The accuracy of chemical staining was independently checked by an experiment in which the location of the junction in a doped sample was indicated by an oxide marker layer, as illustrated in Fig. 10. This experiment was originally performed by Wu *et al.* [6] who found that the n-type epilayer could be stained completely up to the surface of the p-type substrate using a copper solution. This experiment clearly demonstrated that the copper solution stains up to the electrical junction.

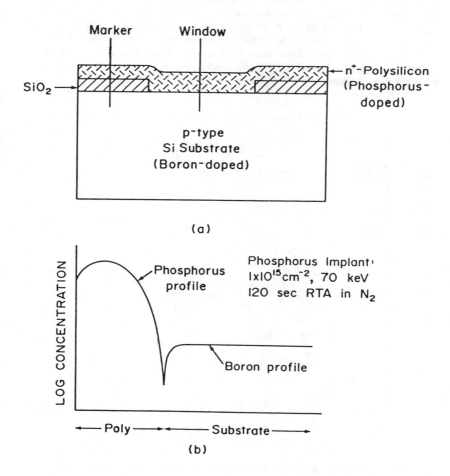

Fig. 10. Marker-layer experiment used in this study. (a) Structure, and (b) Dopant profiles in the polysilicon layer and the single-crystal silicon substrate.

This experiment was repeated in a modified form as shown in Fig. 10. Approximately 9000 Å of oxide was grown on a 10^{15} cm^{-3} boron-doped wafer. Windows were etched in the oxide, and 1 µm of polysilicon was deposited. The wafer was given a 15 min *in situ* HCl clean to remove the native oxide from the open windows prior to the polysilicon deposition. The wafer was then implanted with 10^{15} cm^{-2} phosphorus at 70 keV and given a 120 sec rapid-thermal anneal in a nitrogen ambient at 1000°C. This was considered to be sufficient to redistribute the phosphorus within the polysilicon layer, without causing significant diffusion of phosphorus from the doped polysilicon layer into the substrate. It was also assumed that the polysilicon/single-crystal interface would form an electrical junction. The windowed areas were then angle-lapped and stained from both the n-type side and the p-type side, and it was found that both stains extended exactly up to the interface between the polysilicon and substrate as indicated by the buried oxide layer. Spreading resistance was measured on these samples, both in the windows and over the marker. Figure 11 shows the raw spreading resistance data as a function of depth for the two regions.

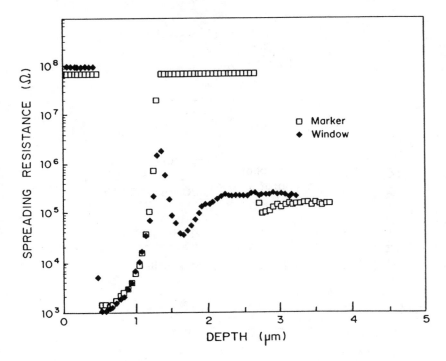

Fig. 11. Spreading resistance *vs* depth in the window and marker regions.

The plot for the marker region initially shows high resistivity from the oxide layer covering the sample. The resistivity then drops as the probes move into the phosphorus-doped polysilicon. The resistivity rises as the phosphorus concentration falls off in the polysilicon layer, and becomes extremely high in the oxide-marker layer. The resistivity remains high throughout the marker layer, and drops down to a constant value in the substrate beyond the marker. The plot for the window region follows a similar pattern. The resistivity is high in the surface oxide layer, then drops down in the phosphorus-doped polysilicon layer. The resistivity again rises as the phosphorus concentration drops off in the polysilicon, and the results are very close to the plot of resistivity in the polysilicon layer over the marker. The thickness of the polysilicon layer in the center of the window region is the same as that over the marker, since the windows were many millimeters wide, such that the start of the second high resistivity region in the plot over the marker layer indicates the polysilicon/substrate interface in the window region. The peak in the resistivity coincides with this point, indicating that the junction is at the polysilicon/substrate interface.

COMPARISON OF JUNCTION-DEPTH MEASUREMENT TECHNIQUES

It was shown earlier that there is good agreement between junction depths determined using chemical staining and spreading resistance. However, differences between dopant profiles obtained using SIMS and spreading resistance have been reported in the literature [24–26]. This difference is usually attributed to the fact that SIMS measures the total chemical concentration of the dopant, while spreading resistance measures the electrically active fraction of the dopant. It is expected that SIMS and spreading resistance will agree best when full activation of dopant atoms takes place [24]. Phenomena such as clustering or precipitation of dopant atoms would reduce the electrically active fraction of dopant atoms and create differences between the SIMS and spreading resistance profiles. However, such phenomena occur primarily at higher concentrations, and it seems reasonable to assume that in the region near the junction, all atoms are sufficiently activated provided the sample has been subjected to suitable heat treatment. Also, comparisons of doping profiles from SIMS and spreading resistance generally use reduced spreading resistance data. The process of reduction of raw spreading resistance data to profile is an empirical one, and it is possible that errors in the calibration and reduction process causes errors in the profile. In summary, the region near the junction is an area in which both methods approach their limits. Therefore, while comparisons between SIMS and spreading resistance show that there is a difference between the profiles, they do not reveal much about the accuracy of junction depths obtained from spreading resistance.

The key question is whether raw spreading resistance data accurately give the metallurgical junction depth. This question may be answered by comparing the metallurgical junction depth obtained by performing SIMS on a sample with an accurately known substrate concentration, with raw spreading resistance data. No such comparison is available in the literature. The issue is complicated by the need to know the substrate concentration accurately in order to obtain the true junction depth from the SIMS profile. A simple experiment was carried out in which the substrate concentration in a relatively highly doped substrate was measured by the SIMS beam at the same time that an implanted dopant distribution was being profiled. Boron was implanted and driven into a wafer uniformly doped with $\sim 10^{18}$ cm^{-3} antimony. The peak boron concentration was calculated to be 10^{19} cm^{-3}. The high background concentration was well above the SIMS limit of 10^{15} to 10^{16} cm^{-3}, and the small range of concentrations of interest allowed the SIMS measurement process to be optimized for sensitivity at the cost of reduced dynamic range. This was important because boron and antimony are dopants of opposing polarities, and the use of an oxygen primary ion beam beam, which is frequently used in the measurement of boron profiles, would reduce the sensitivity of the measurement of the antimony concentration. Figure 12 shows the measured boron and antimony profiles, with the raw spreading resistance data plotted to the same depth scale. It can be seen that the junction depths measured by the two methods are in good agreement.

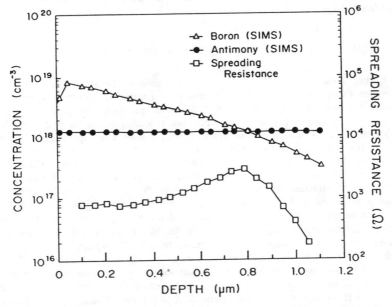

Fig. 12. Comparison of junction depths measured with SIMS and spreading resistance.

COMPUTER SIMULATION OF STAINING AND SPREADING RESISTANCE

The spreading resistance measurement process was also simulated using the two-dimensional device simulator PISCES-II [27]. It must be noted that there are limitations in this simulation. A true simulation of the spreading resistance measurement process would require the use of a three dimensional device simulator, which is not presently available. The simulation was carried out by defining a surface with a certain boron profile and a background n-type concentration, and defining two point contacts parallel to the junction at various distances from the interface. The resistance between the contacts was measured by assuming a voltage at the contacts and solving for the current, and a simulated spreading resistance profile was built up by calculating the resistance at various distance from the junction on either side. Ohmic contacts were assumed, and the contact spacing and the applied voltage were similar to conditions used in spreading resistance measurements. It was assumed in this simulation that the doping profile vertically into the silicon maps linearly on to the bevel surface, and surface effects such as surface charges and leakage currents were ignored. In spite of these limitations, the simulations were useful in showing that the apparent location of the junction as indicated by the peak in the spreading resistance data is not shifted from the true location of the junction due to shunting from the high concentration areas, and that for a fully activated sample, which can be assumed at the low concentrations close to the junction, only a nonlinear mapping of the vertical concentration profile onto the bevel can cause the junction depth shown by spreading resistance to be different from the true junction depth. Figure 13 shows the doping profile and measured spreading resistance along the bevel. It can be seen that the peak in the calculated spreading resistance profile closely matches the location of the junction indicated by the doping profile.

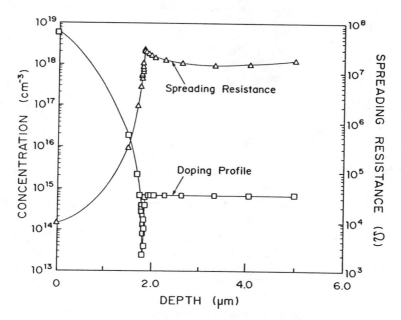

Fig. 13. Plot of doping profiles and spreading resistance data calculated using PISCES–II.

The observed lack of dependence of junction staining measurements on the depletion region width will now be briefly discussed. It has been observed that the depletion region width has no effect on the width of the stained layer, which extends over the depletion region to the junction [6]. This study confirms that observation. A qualitative explanation was given by Wu *et al.* [6] who observed that the plating reaction for copper depends on the free electron concentration, and that plating therefore takes place wherever electrons are the majority carriers. For a p^+-n junction under illumination, it was found that the measured photovoltage of about 0.5 V is not affected significantly by the presence of the staining solution, which shows that the solution is highly resistive [6]. For such a bias, the point where the quasi-Fermi level passes through the center of the bandgap is much closer to the junction than in the unilluminated case, hence the region in which electrons are the majority carriers also extends closer to the junction. This interpretation stresses the importance of the effect of illumination on the electron and hole concentrations, the location where the quasi-Fermi level crosses the center of the bandgap, and the shift in that location with illumination. Difficulty is encountered here because of the lack of quantitative understanding of the chemical aspects of the staining process, such as the electron concentration necessary to cause plating with the copper solution, and the effect of variables such as the volume of the staining solution. The forward bias on the junction caused by the illumination also depends on the wavelength and intensity of the illumination, and the degree to which it is absorbed by the staining solution.

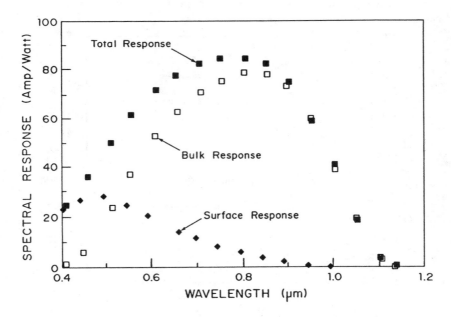

Fig. 14. Spectral response of silicon as a function of wavelength [6].

In order to understand further the effect of illumination on the carrier concentrations at the p-n junction, a series of simulations was carried out using a one-dimensional device simulator [28]. The effect of illumination was included by providing the simulator with carrier generation rates calculated from the intensity of illumination and the absorption of light in silicon. Figure 14 shows the dependence of the responsivity or spectral response of silicon on wavelength [6]. Assuming a uniform distribution of incident optical power with wavelength, the approximate carrier generation due to incident illumination was calculated by numerically integrating the data in Fig. 14 to obtain the number of generated hole-electron pairs as a function of the incident optical power. The approximate carrier generation rate was calculated using estimated values of the power per unit area at the sample provided by the illumination sources used in the staining experiments, and was found to be $\sim 10^{20}$ electron-hole pairs/cm^{3}sec. This value of generation rate was used in calculations of carrier concentrations in a representative p-n junction.

The effect of the conductance of the staining solution on the carrier concentrations was estimated by performing simulations for various values of conductance and comparing the calculated photovoltage with the values reported by Wu *et al.* [6]. A detailed description of these simulations is given elsewhere [30]. Figure 15 shows the calculated photovoltage as a function of the resistance, assuming the generation rate calculated above. It is seen that the photovoltage is almost independent of the resistance across the p-n junction for high values of resistance. The measured photovoltage across a stained junction has been found by Wu *et al.* [6] to be of the order of $0.4 - 0.5$ V, implying that the staining solutions is highly resistive, and all simulations were carried out assuming a value of resistance equal to 100 kΩ.

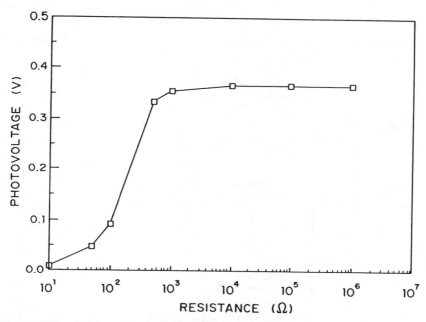

Fig. 15. Photovoltage generated under illumination as a function of resistance across the p-n junction.

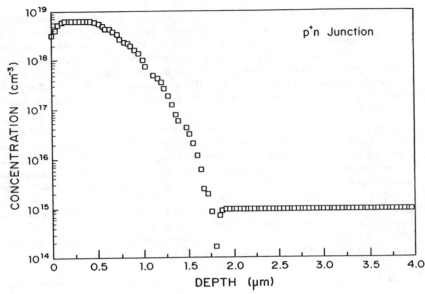

Fig. 16. Doping profile in pn junction used for calculations of carrier concentrations under illumination.

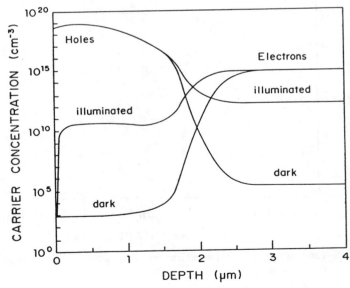

Fig. 17. Effect of illumination on carrier concentrations in a p-n junction.

Figure 16 shows the doping profile in a p^+-n diode, obtained by SIMS profiling, which was used in the calculation of carrier concentrations. The junction depth is 1.8 μm. Figure 17 compares carrier concentrations in the vicinity of the junction with and without illumination, and shows the significant increase in the minority carrier concentrations under illumination. It is especially important to note that the region near the junction sees an increase of three orders of magnitude in the carrier concentrations, which means that a significantly greater number of carriers are available for the staining reaction. Equally importantly, the extra optically generated carriers probably serve to stabilize the reaction, reducing the effect of experimental variations such as surface condition upon the staining reaction. The effect of carrier spilling on the location of the electrical junction [25] is also reduced by the illumination, as shown in Fig. 18 which shows a magnified plot of the region near the junction from Fig. 17. The topmost line shows the doping profile, with the dip in the profile indicating the junction. The electrical junction is assumed to be at the intersection of the hole and electron concentrations for a given illumination. It can be seen that the location of the electrical junction is shifted closer to the metallurgical junction by almost 0.1 μm.

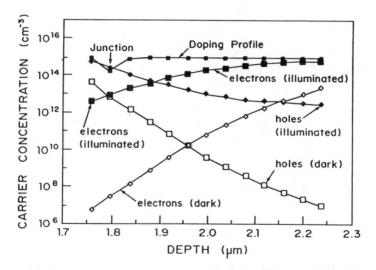

Fig. 18. Magnified view showing relative locations of the electrical and metallurgical junctions in a p-n junction under illumination.

In summary, the illumination of samples during staining improves the accuracy of the results by sharply increasing the number of carriers available for the reaction in the vicinity of the junction, the illumination allows the staining to occur closer to the junction, and possibly also stabilizes the reaction, and by reducing the concentration gradient of carriers, the illumination reduces the effects of carrier spilling which can cause the electrical junction to move away from the metallurgical junction. Hu [25] has shown that the effects of carrier spilling can cause significant differences between electrical and metallurgical junction depths on the bevel for junctions shallower than 0.2 μm. None of the samples studied in this work were shallower than 0.3 μm, however, there is some evidence that staining under strong illumination gives good results for shallower junctions also [31]. Hu's work has shown that the deviation of the electrical junction from the metallurgical junction decreases as the surface and substrate concentrations increase [25]. Illumination effectively adds a large number of carriers to the existing concentration levels, which results in an increase in those levels, reducing deviations from the metallurgical junction depth.

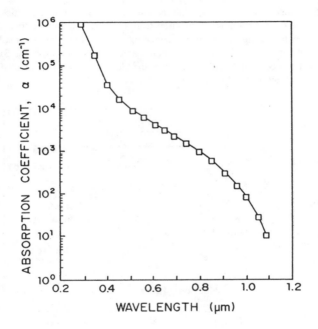

Fig. 19. Optical absorption coefficient of silicon as a function of wavelength [32].

It must be noted that the generation rate of 10^{20} electron-hole pairs/cm^{3}sec calculated earlier is conservative, and the actual levels may be an order of magnitude higher. Figure 19 shows the optical absorption coefficient α for silicon as a function of wavelength [32], and it can be seen that the values of absorption coefficient become extremely high as the wavelengths approach the ultraviolet region. In the case of bulk devices and solar cells, the short wavelength cutoff value for α depends on the value of α at which the light penetration into the silicon is so small that recombination prevents generated carriers from reaching the junction. In the case of staining, where the surface is the region of interest, however, these carriers increase the total number of carriers available for the staining reaction. Because of the lack of data, our calculation of the generation rate only included wavelengths up to the near ultraviolet region for wavelengths down to 0.4 μm. However it is probable that there is a significant contribution due to the far ultraviolet wavelengths. This would make the overall concentration levels higher, further reducing the difference of electrical and metallurgical junction depths.

CONCLUSIONS

Chemical staining experiments were carried out with a variety of staining solutions on junction ranging in depth from 0.3 μm to 3 μm. Accurate and reproducible results were obtained. The experimental conditions under which staining takes place such as the staining solution, staining time, illumination, and type of junctions were optimized. Under strong illumination, successful staining was carried out using both copper and HF-based solutions. Samples were stained from both the n-type side and the p-type side, and the results were in good agreement. The junction depths were measured with a resolution of better than 200 Å. The results obtained from staining were compared with spreading resistance and secondary-ion mass spectrometry used in junction-depth determination in order to evaluate the accuracy and resolution of the staining technique. Good correlation was found between the junction depths measured by the different methods. Previous studies have shown that doping profiles obtained using SIMS and spreading resistance differ in the region near the junction. No systematic variation has been observed; the SIMS profiles are found to be deeper, shallower, or coincidental with the spreading resistance profiles. To check the possibility that shunting due to the high-concentration region may shift the apparent location of the electrical junction as determined by spreading resistance, a simulation of the spreading resistance process was carried out using a two-dimensional device simulator. The results of the simulations indicate that the spreading resistance peak occurs at the junction, and that the location of the junction is not shifted. Therefore, assuming complete electrical activation near the junction, the raw spreading resistance data also show the metallurgical junction.

ACKNOWLEDGEMENTS

This work was supported by the Semiconductor Research Corporation. Additional support for characterization equipment was granted by the North Carolina Board of Science and Technology. The authors would like to thank Profs. U. Gösele, Duke University, and G. Rozgonyi, North Carolina State University, and Mr. B. Rogers for many helpful discussions, and Dr. Ali Salih for his help with the experimental characterization.

REFERENCES

[1]   P. J. Archer, J. Phys. Chem. Solids, Vol. 14, p. 104, 1960.

[2]   R. Memming and G. Schwandt, Surf. Sci., Vol. 4, p. 109, 1966.

[3]   D. R. Turner, J. Electrochem. Soc., Vol. 105, p. 402, 1958.

[4]   See W. R. Runyan, Semiconductor Measurements and Instrumentation, McGraw Hill, New York, 1975, and D. Schimmel and M. J. Elkind, J. Electrochem. Soc. Vol. 125, p. 152, 1978.

[5]   C. Hill, "Measurement of local diffusion coefficients in planar device structures," in Semiconductor Silicon 1981, H. R. Huff, R. J. Kriegler, and Y. Takeishi, Eds., The Electrochemical Society, Princeton, New Jersey, 1981.

[6]   C. P. Wu, E. C. Douglas, C. W. Mueller, and R. Williams, J. Electrochem. Soc., Vol. 126, p. 1982, 1979.

[7]   C. H. Carter, W. Maszara, G. A. Rozgonyi, and D. K. Sadana, "Comparison of damage profiles obtained by angle lapping/staining and cross-sectional transmission electron microscopy," SPIE Conference 1984, p. 463.

[8]   ASTM Standard F-110, Revision, American Society for Testing and Materials, February 1975.

[9]   R. G. Mazur, "The Effects of RF Electromagnetic Radiation on Spreading Resistance Measurements," in Semiconductor Processing, ASTM STP 850, Dinesh C. Gupta, Ed., American Society for Testing and Materials, 1984.

[10] D. E. Newbury and D. Simon, in SIMS IV, A. Benninghoven, J. Okano, R. Shimizu, and W. H. Werner, Eds., Springer Verlag, Berlin, 1984.

[11] D. R. Turner, J. Electrochem. Soc., Vol. 106, p. 701, 1959.

[12] D. E. Davies, Solid-State Electron., Vol. 13, p. 229, 1970.

[13] P. J. Whoriskey, J. Appl. Phys., Vol. 126, p. 867, 1958.

[14] S. J. Silverman and D. R. Benn, J. Electrochem. Soc., Vol. 105, p. 170, 1958.

[15] Solid State Measurements, "ASR-100 C Spreading Resistance Measurement Unit, Operator's Manual," Pittsburhg, PA.

[16] R. Brennan and D. Dickey, Solid-State Technol., Vol. 27(12), p. 125, 1984.

[17] M. Pawlik, "Dopant Profiling in Silicon," in Semiconductor Processing, ASTM STP 850, Dinesh C. Gupta, Ed., American Society for Testing and Materials, 1984.

[18] A. H. Tong, E. F. Gorey, and C. P. Schneider, Rev. Sci. Inst., Vol. 43, p. 320, 1972.

[19] Solid State Measurements, "Small-Angle Measurement," Pittsburgh, PA.

[20] D. C. D'Avanzo, R. D. Rung, and R. W. Dutton, "Spreading Resistance For Impurity Profiles," Tech. Rep. 5013-2, Stanford Electronics Laboratories, Stanford University, Stanford, CA, February 1977.

[21] R. G. Mazur and G. A. Gruber, Solid-State Technol., Vol. 24(11), p. 64, 1981.

[22] J. R. Ehrstein, "Spreading Resistance Measurements — An Overview," in Emerging Semiconductor Technology, ASTM STP 960, Dinesh C. Gupta and P. H. Langer,

Eds., American Society for Testing and Materials, 1986.

[23] ASTM Standard F674-80, part 43, American Society for Testing and Materials, 1980.

[24] J. R. Ehrstein, R. G. Downing, B. R. Stallard, D. S. Simmons, and R. F. Fleming, "Comparison of Depth Profiling ^{10}B in Silicon Using Spreading Resistance Profiling, Secondary-Ion Mass Spectroscopy, and Neutron Depth Profiling," in Semiconductor Processing, ASTM STP 850, Dinesh C. Gupta, Ed., American Society for Testing and Materials, 1984.

[25] S. M. Hu, J. Appl. Phys., Vol. 53, p. 1499, 1982.

[26] J. George, W. Banke, K. Varahramyan, and G. J. Slusser, "Analysis of Boron Profiles As Determined by Secondary-Ion Mass Spectroscopy, Spreading Resistance, and Process Modeling," in Emerging Semiconductor Technology, ASTM STP 960, Dinesh C. Gupta and P. H. Langer, Eds., American Society for Testing and Materials, 1986.

[27] M. R. Pinto, C. S. Rafferty, and R. W. Dutton, "Pisces II: Poisson and Continuity Equations Solver," Tech. Rep., Stanford Electronics Laboratories, Stanford University, Stanford, CA, September 1984.

[28] U. Gösele, Private Communication.

[29] S. M. Sze, VLSI Technology, McGraw Hill, New York, 1983.

[30] R. Subrahmanyan, Ph.D. Thesis, Department of Electrical Engineering, Duke University, Durham, North Carolina, 1988.

[31] G. A. Rozgonyi, Private Communication.

[32] S. M. Sze, Semiconductor Devices — Physics and Technology, John Wiley, New York, 1985.

Vladimir Starov and Larry Lane

USE OF POLYSILICON DEPOSITION IN A COLD-WALL LPCVD REACTOR
TO DETERMINE WAFER TEMPERATURE UNIFORMITY

REFERENCE: Starov, V. and Lane, L.R., "Use of
Polysilicon Deposition in a Cold-Wall LPCVD
Reactor To Determine Wafer Temperature
Uniformity", Semiconductor Fabrication:
Technology and Metrology, ASTM STP 990, Dinesh C.
Gupta, editor, American Society of Testing and
Materials, 1989.

ABSTRACT: In the Varian 5101 LPCVD reactor
operating in a Rapid Thermal Processing (RTP)
mode the wafer is heated directly by a radiant
heater. The wafer temperature in this case is
measured by a pyrometer pointing at its center.
To obtain a temperature map of the entire wafer,
we have developed and characterized a polysilicon
deposition process. Using the polysilicon
thickness as a "chemical thermometer" [1], we
have been able to improve the radiant heater
design to obtain a temperature uniformity of 0.2%
across a 100 mm wafer and 0.5% on wafers up to
150 mm. As an example of application of our
study, the optimized design was used to deposit
selective tungsten with thickness uniformity of
4% across 140 mm scan on 150 mm wafer.

KEYWORDS: chemical thermometer, chemical vapor
deposition, activation energy, polysilicon growth

One of the most important problems associated with
cold-wall Chemical Vapor Deposition (CVD) reactors is
achieving good coating uniformity. Large temperature
differences between the heated wafers and the rest of the
reactor create generally non-isothermal environment. Since

Dr. Starov is President of Applied Photonics Research
Inc., 421 Grand Street, Redwood City, CA 94062; Mr. Lane
is Senior Process Technician at Varian Associates Inc.,
48664 Milmont Drive, Fremont, CA 94538. The work presented
in this paper was performed at Varian during Dr. Starov's
affiliation with the company.

thickness of the deposited films depends on the substrate temperature exponentially (for surface-reaction limited processes), variations of several degrees can result in 20-30% thickness non-uniformities. The higher the activation energy for the deposition process, the greater thickness variations will be observed, see below.

Precise temperature control can readily be achieved when the wafer is in intimate contact with a massive heated chuck whose temperature uniformity is assured by design. In newer CVD systems, such as Varian's single-wafer 5101 reactor, the wafer is heated directly by a radiant light source, Fig. 1 (also see Ref. 2). This RTP capability enables the operator to heat and cool the wafer very rapidly, opening the doors to new applications, e.g., in situ annealing of the freshly deposited films.

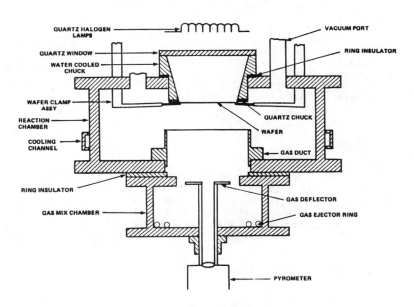

FIG. 1 -- Varian 5101 Rapid Thermal CVD deposition chamber.

In such reactors, however, temperature control becomes tricky. First, wafer temperature measurement must be accomplished by a remote means since a thermocouple in contact with the back of the wafer would be irradiated by the heater directly. Frontside contact is obviously unacceptable due to interference with the deposition process. Usually, an infrared pyrometer sensing emission from the center portion of the wafer is used [2]. This setup does not allow an easy measurement of the wafer temperature uniformity and one must resort to other techniques. An additional complication arises from the fact that the surface emissivity of the substrate changes continuously during the initial phase of the deposition to the emissivity of the deposited material.

An alternative technique used in this study is based on "chemical thermometry". Using yields of chemical reactions with known activation energies to estimate system temperature has been suggested previously by Steel et al. [1]. Such calibrated reactions can be used as a "chemical thermometer" where other methods prove impractical or impossible. For example, in Ref.1, the temperature of a laser heated gas is determined by monitoring decomposition of a "thermometer" compound added to the mixture. Using a thermocouple in that case would be impossible because of its large thermal mass and slow response.

In a similar spirit, to determine the wafer temperature at any point on the wafer, we have developed and characterized a polysilicon deposition process. In this case, the deposited film thickness variations manifest wafer temperature non-uniformities and thus act as a "thermometer".

EXPERIMENTAL

The 5101 test-bed reactor used in our experiments had the configuration shown in Figure 1; it was also described in Ref. 2. Throughout most of the study, we used 100 mm Si wafers with 1000 A oxide. These substrates allowed an easy determination of the deposited polysilicon thickness with standard optical instruments such as a Nanospec automated reflectometer. Several samples were also measured by a Prometrix SpectraMap 200 to get detailed polysilicon thickness maps.

Several heating configurations were tried to optimize the irradiation geometry. One or more samples were deposited using each heating arrangement and the poly-Si thickness was measured at 21 points inside a 90 mm diameter on each 100 mm wafer. Each wafer was thus characterized by the p-Si thickness in the center, the average thickness and the standard deviation.

Most depositions were carried out at 700 C as measured by a calibrated pyrometer at the wafer center. The wafer temperature was controlled by adjusting the lamp power and was kept constant throughout the deposition. The reactor pressure was in the range 80-400 mTorr. Nearly 100% silane was used at the flow rates of up to 100 sccm.

To estimate the temperature dependence of the growth rate we carried out several depositions at 650-800 C, keeping the rest of the conditions unchanged.

RESULTS AND DISCUSSION

Thickness Uniformity Profiles

The polysilicon uniformity on the 100 mm wafers processed with non-optimized irradiation geometry is in the range of 13-65% (1 sigma). The uniformity was calculated as the standard deviation of the 21 thickness measurements taken for each wafer in two directions: parallel and perpendicular to the flat.

A typical normalized uniformity profile of such a sample is shown in Fig. 2. Only scan in direction parallel to the wafer flat (11 points) is shown; the perpendicular scan is essentially the same. The thickness measurements are taken 1 cm apart, except for those at the edges which are 0.5 cm away from the neighboring points. All the measurements are divided by the wafer-center thickness to yield a profile independent of the overall film thickness. The profile shows a significant dip in the center of the wafer and a roll-off at the wafer edge. For this particular sample the uniformity is 20%.

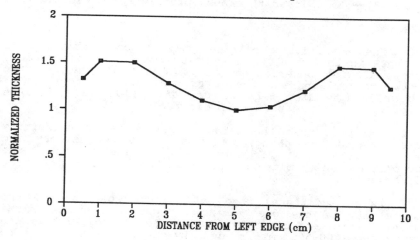

FIG. 2 -- Normalized thickness profile for the initial heater design.

After a considerable optimization of the irradiation geometry (mainly shapes of the reflecting surfaces and distance between the wafer and the heater lamps), a substantially improved poly-Si thickness profile can be obtained, Fig. 3. The standard deviation for this sample is 3.6% and, in general, the uniformity of films deposited with the optimized setup is in the range 3.6-6.5%.

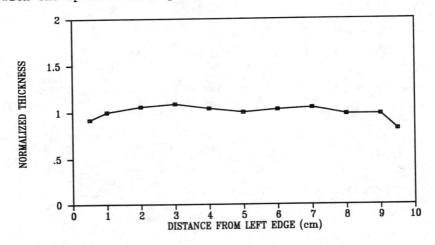

FIG. 3 -- Normalized thickness profile for the optimized heater design.

The sensitivity of the polysilicon uniformity to changes in the irradiation geometry can be illustrated by the following observation: a 5% change in the distance between the lamps and the wafer can cause an improvement in uniformity from 6-8% to ca. 4%. This is a 50-100% improvement in the film uniformity.

The fact that the large improvements in uniformity are obtained by changing the irradiation geometry and keeping the gas flow constant indicates that the deposition uniformity is not limited by the gas flow dynamics.

As an additional check of this independence of the uniformity of the gas flow, we deposited several films under static conditions by filling the reactor with silane to about 200-300 mTorr and by rapidly bringing the temperature to 700 C and keeping it at that temperature for several minutes. The uniformities obtained by this static method are essentially the same as in the flow system. This indicates that the silane flow pattern is not a limiting factor under our experimental conditions.

Activation Energy of The Deposition Process

To estimate the wafer temperature variations corresponding to the observed thickness distributions we have analyzed the dependence of the deposition rate on temperature over the range 650-800 C. Figure 4 shows the results in the form of an Arrhenius plot for samples produced at the silane flow rate of 100 sccm and the reactor pressure of 80-120 mTorr. Under these conditions the rates range from 60 to 1400 A/min.

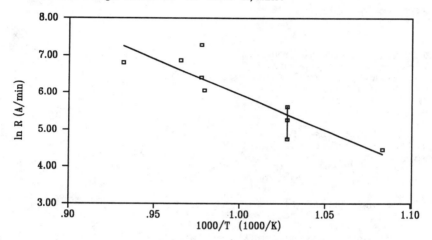

FIG. 4 -- Average deposition rates in the range 650-800 C.

The average deposition rate is defined as the average thickness divided into the deposition time. The linear regression line is also shown. The slope of the line gives the activation energy, Ea, of 38 kcal/mole, with the error range of 30-46 kcal/mole. The error bars shown for the 700 C points are representative of the poor repeatability attainable in this test-bed reactor.

A similar plot for the wafer-center deposition rates yields an identical range for the activation energy, 30-46 kcal/mole, with the same mean, Ea=38 kcal/mole. This value compares very well to the literature data: ~ 36 kcal/mole [3] obtained both in a conventional hot-wall and a vertical-flow reactor; the range of 32-40 kcal/mole [4] for a hot-wall system; and a cold-wall, atmospheric pressure reactor range of 32-38 kcal/mole [5].

Temperature vs. Thickness Uniformity

We can now use the activation energy value to estimate the temperature gradients across the wafers.

Indeed, the deposition rate, R, is related to the temperature through the Arrhenius equation

$$\ln R = A - B/T \qquad (1)$$

where

A = pre-exponential factor,
B = Ea/k, k being the Boltzman constant,
T = the absolute temperature in Kelvin.

Differentiating (1) gives

$$dR/R = B/T \, (dT/T) \qquad (2).$$

For a typical CVD temperature range, 300-800 C, and Ea=40 kcal/mole, the factor B/T in (2) is in the range 19-35 since k=2 cal/mole/degK. Equation (2) explains why relatively small temperature variations, dT/T ~ 1%, across the wafer result in large thickness non-uniformities, dR/R ~ 20-30%.

In our specific example, polysilicon deposition at 700 C, the factor B/T=20 since Ea=38 kcal/mole. Thus, the lowest uniformity observed, ~40-60%, corresponds to dT/T ~ 2-3% or dT ~ 20-30 C; the best uniformity of 3.6% corresponds to dT/T = 0.18% or dT ~ 2 C.

Within the temperature range of our experiments, the B/T factor varies only slightly, decreasing from 21 at 650 C to 18 at 800 C. Therefore, the polysilicon deposition serves as a very sensitive thermometer of the wafer surface throughout the whole temperature range.

Applications To Other Processes

The major objective of this investigation was to optimize the heater design to achieve highly uniform depositions of selective tungsten (sel-W) and other important materials.

The activation energy for the growth of sel-W has been reported [6,7] in the range 9-16 kcal/mole. Taking a mid-range value of 13 kcal/mole and a typical deposition temperature of 550 C, we estimate the B/T factor at around 8. Further, by depositing polysilicon on a 150 mm wafer with the heater optimized for 100 mm wafers, we have found p-Si thickness uniformity ~ 10% across the larger wafers and thus dT/T in this case is ~ 0.5%. Combining this with the B/T = 8 value for the sel-W and using (2) we can predict that the W deposit uniformity should be ~ 4%.

As a check, selective tungsten plugs were grown on a 150 mm wafer coated with 1 micron thick oxide. Windows of various sizes were etched in the oxide down to silicon prior to the sel-W deposition. Dektak measurements of 24 tungsten plugs in oxide holes inside 140 mm diameter on a 150 mm wafer yield the W deposit uniformity of 4.4%, in very good agreement with our estimate based on p-Si deposition.

Note that the Dektak measurements require a height comparison of the before and after deposition oxide-steps, and hence the same oxide holes must be measured twice. The difference gives the height of the W plug inside the hole. This is dictated by the fairly large variations in the oxide thickness, ~ 2.5%, comparable to the variations in the W thickness themselves. The W characterization process is thus rather laborious; in addition, it requires patterned substrates. The polysilicon deposition, on the other hand, is much simpler and requires simpler thickness measurements and inexpensive substrates.

SUMMARY AND CONCLUSIONS

Temperature measurements of the wafer heated directly by a radiant heater in a cold-wall CVD reactor are difficult. A good estimate of the average wafer temperature can be obtained by pointing a calibrated pyrometer at the wafer center. However, a reliable measurement of temperature uniformity across the entire wafer requires an alternative approach.

One possibility is using a simple, well-studied deposition process. Exponential dependence of the growth rate on substrate temperature can make deposition reaction very sensitive to temperature non-uniformities. Polysilicon deposition is particularly useful as such a "thermometer". Measurements of p-Si film thickness are routine and fast. Inexpensive Si wafers coated with 0.1 micron oxide can be used as substrates. The process has relatively high activation energy and, hence, is very sensitive to temperature variations: non-uniformities of the latter are amplified about 20 times and result in easily detectable thickness gradients.

We have applied this method to optimization of the radiant heater used in the Varian 5101 reactor and have improved its performance from 2-3% heating uniformity to better than 0.2% across a 100 mm wafer. The optimized heater can be used for wafers up to 150 mm in diameter with temperature uniformity ~ 0.5%. Owing to relatively low temperature dependence of the selective tungsten process, the optimized heater design yields W uniformity of ~ 4% on 150 mm wafers.

REFERENCES

[1]   Steel, C., Starov, V., Leo, R., John, P., and
Harrison, R.G., "Chemical Thermometers in Megawatt
Infrared Laser Chemistry: The Decomposition of
Cyclobutanone Sensitized by Ammonia", Chemical
Physics Letters, Vol. 62, 1979, pp. 121-124.

[2]   Foster, R.F., Brors, D.L., and Tseng, S., "Selective
Tungsten Deposition in a Varian/Torrex 5101 Cold Wall
CVD Reactor", in Tungsten and Other Refractory Metals
for VLSI Applications, Eliot K. Broadbent, editor.
Proceedings of the 1986 Workshop held at Xerox Palo
Alto Research Center, Palo Alto, CA, November 12-14,
1986.   Published by Materials Research Society,
Pittsburgh, PA.

[3]   Foster, D., Learn, A., and Kamins, T., "Silicon Films
Deposited in a Vertical-Flow Reactor", Solid State
Technology, May 1986, pp. 227-232.

[4]   Harbeke, G., Krausbauer, L., Steigmeier, E.F., and
Widmer, A.E., "Growth and Physical Properties of
LPCVD Polycrystalline Silicon Films", Journal of the
Electrochemical Society, Vol. 131, No. 3, March 1984,
pp. 675-682.

[5]   Beers, A.M., and Bloem, J., "Temperature Dependence
of the Growth Rate of Silicon Prepared Through
Chemical Vapor Deposition from Silane", Applied
Physics Letters, Vol. 41, No. 2, July 1982, pp. 153-
155.

[6]   Kusumoto, Y., Takakuwa, K., Ikuta, T., and Nakayama,
I., "High-Rate and Encroachment-Free Contact Filling
with Selective Tungsten", in Tungsten and Other
Refractory Metals for VLSI Applications, Eliot K.
Broadbent, editor.   Proceedings of the 1986 Workshop
held at Xerox Palo Alto Research Center, Palo Alto,
CA, November 12-14, 1986.   Published by Materials
Research Society, Pittsburgh, PA.

[7]   Broadbent, E.K., and Ramiller, C.L., "Selective Low
Pressure Chemical Vapor Deposition of Tungsten",
Journal of the Electrochemical Society, Vol. 131, No.
6, June 1984, pp. 1427-1433.

Jyoti K. Bhardwaj, Adrian Kiermasz, Michael A. Stephens,
Sarah J. Harrington, and Andrew D. McQuarrie

DRY ETCHING TECHNIQUES FOR MMIC FABRICATION ON GaAs

REFERENCE: Bhardwaj,J.K., Kiermasz,A., Stephens,M.A., Harrington,
S.J., and McQuarrie,A.D., "Dry Etching Techniques for MMIC
Fabrication on GaAs,"Semiconductor Fabrication: Technology
and Metrology, ASTM STP 990,Dinesh C. Gupta, editor, American
Society for Testing and Materials, 1989.

ABSTRACT: During the fabrication of a GaAs monolithic microwave
integrated circuit, there are a number of steps which necessitate
the etching of GaAs, namely; mesa etching (for device isolation),
gate recessing (to control the saturation current levels), substrate
thinning for (transmission line impedance control), through
substrate via holes (to reduce interconnection inductances) and
scribe-line etching (for yield enhancement). Reproducible dry etch
processes have been developed for these steps. However, the
diversity of the process constraints imposed by these fabrication
steps has led to a number of process operation regimes: for example,
resulting in average etch rates ranging from less than 1000Å/min up
to 10u/min for 2" GaAs substrates. The process details are
discussed with particular emphasis on the rate limiting steps and
the factors governing the reactive gas/surface reaction rates.

KEYWORDS: plasma processing, dry etching, gallium arsenide

The discrete MESFET (Metal Semiconductor Field Effect Transistor)
is the fundamental building block of the GaAs MMIC (Monolithic
Microwave Integrated Circuit). Over the past decade there have been
significant advances in the development of the discrete MESFET [1,2]
which has led to present era devices operating up to tens of GHz.
Presently, below approximately 5 GHz discrete silicon bipolar
transistors form the basis of the silicon bipolar MMIC, which is
commonly used in microwave systems operating at such frequencies.
Above 5 GHz or so, GaAs MMICs have begun to challenge the market of

Dr Bhardwaj, Mr Stephens, Mr McQuarrie and Miss Harrington are
process and application engineers at Electrotech Special Research
Systems Ltd., Thornbury Laboratories, Littleton-upon-Severn, Bristol
BS12 1NP U.K.; Dr Kiermasz is process manager at E.T. Plasma
Developments Ltd., Unit 1a Oldmixon Cresent, Oldmixon Trading Estate,
Weston-super-Mare, Avon. BS24 9AX.

159

the hybrid circuit in terms of both cost and performance [3]. This
event is based on the technological advancement in the discrete GaAs
MESFET.

During the fabrication of a GaAs MMIC there are a number of steps
which necessitate the etching of GaAs. Generally, the majority of
this processing has, to date, been carried out using wet chemistry,
such as an acid-peroxide solution for example (where the peroxide
oxidises the GaAs surface and the acid dissolves the oxide layers)
[4]. Wet processing techniques, however, have inherent limitations
such as the inability to control the degree of etch anisotropy,
difficulty in controlling micron and sub-micron feature etching,
relatively poor uniformity across the wafer with select areas of
significantly reduced etch rate due to bubble formation. Optimised
dry etch processing can overcome all of these difficulties, thereby
increasing the performance and cost competitiveness of the MMIC.

Dry etching essentially refers to processing using the reactive
species supplied by a homogeneous gas phase in close proximity to the
wafer. The dry etching of Si has become a well established technique
and significant advances in yield and scale of integration have been
achieved [5]. Whereas Si can be readily etched using fluorine
chemistry, the fluorides of Ga are relatively involatile at practical
temperatures [6]. Thus the developed Si processing techniques do not
readily lend themselves to the etching of GaAs. Instead, GaAs etching
relies on inert gas sputtering or the formation of volatile chloride,
bromide or trimethyl/hydride complexes [7-12]. Although there are
numerous publications relating to GaAs using these chemistries, it has
been found that the process developed for a particular plasma or RIE
(Reactive Ion Etch) machine are essentially non-transferable to one of
a different configuration. However, the etch chemistries generally
still apply, that is, while the process gas chemistry and desired etch
products do not essentially vary between dissimilar RIE systems, the
optimised r.f. power, pressure, gas flow rate etc., will differ.
Hence the individually characterised GaAs etch processes (relating to
r.f. power, pressure etc.) for the MMIC fabrication stages are not

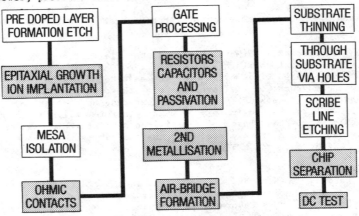

FIG 1 Process steps for MMIC fabrication

discussed in great detail herewith. Instead the important trends are
presented and the discussion concentrates on the etch mechanisms and
rate limiting conditions.

The fabrication steps for GaAs MMICs are illustrated in Fig.1,
highlighting those associated with GaAs etching.

EXPERIMENTAL APPARATUS

The present investigations have been carried out on an Electrotech
Special Research System PF 340 [13]. This has a diode configuration
RIE chamber with a nominal 3:1 anode to cathode area ratio. The
cathode is driven at 13.56 MHz and can either be heated or cooled in
the 75-5°C range. A schematic of the etch chamber is shown in Fig.2.
The etch samples are placed on a platen which is in intimate contact
with the cathode. Etch experimentation was carried out on either
<100> n type (Sn doped, 10^{18} cm-3) GaAs, or on <100> semi-insulating
GaAs. Investigations have shown that there is no evidence for GaAs
etch rate and profile variations with changes in the substrate doping
level [14].

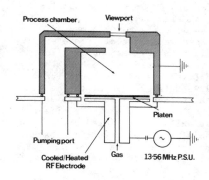

FIG 2   Schematic of RIE chamber

During the etch experiments
measurements of the chamber
pressure (p), gas flow rate (Q),
r.f. power (P), plasma dc self bias
(V), peak to peak voltage and the
process time were made using the
methods described in reference 13.
The etch depth and profile were
measured using a mechanical stylus
(Tencor Instruments alpha-step) and
both optical and scanning electron
microscope techniques.

The effect of equipment related
process variables on the measured
parameters were investigated and
suitable additions made to the
etching system to ensure
reproducible performance.

RESULTS

The first step in GaAs MMIC fabrication, is a pre-doped layer
formation etch (see Fig.1). This is carried out to remove the damaged
substrate surface and contamination resulting from the polishing
procedure. Typically 5-10um are etched without roughening the
polished face. The process developed for this etch is discussed in
conjunction with the substrate thinning results. The remaining steps
involving GaAs etching are discussed in the order of fabrication.

Mesa Isolation

The mesa etch is required to electrically isolate the GaAs MESFET.
Following the formation of the active GaAs region by epitaxial growth

or ion implantation, isolation is achieved by simply etching through the active region into the semi-insulating GaAs. The subsequent processing step is to provide ohmic contacts to the various device regions. Thus the requirements for a mesa isolation etch are typically a sloped wall etch to a depth of 4000Å to 1 um, without any damage to the resist mask. Clearly a sloped profile will aid metallisation over the n type to semi-insulating GaAs step.

Wet etching techniques result in preferential etching along the crystallographic planes giving a sloped profile in the 0° plane and a re-entrant profile in the 90° plane [4]. Metallisation tracks are taken off the mesa via the sloped profile. These wet etch profiles have been mimicked using CCl_2F_2/Cl_2 RIE. The typical etch profiles (exaggerated by increasing the etch depth) are shown in Fig. 3 (a) and (b), while Fig. 3 (c) illustrates the surface topography for P <20W, p <25mTorr and Q <25 sccm. The effect of r.f. power variations on the etch rate is shown in Fig. 4 using 1 cm^2 samples. Although the etch rate does increase with power, variations in the etch profile are observed. While etch rates of ~4.5um/min are obtained for the 1cm sample at P = 20W, these decrease to <1.5um/min for a 2" GaAs wafer. Ideally however, it would seem advantageous for the process engineer to be able to metallise tracks over both the 0° and 90° plane edges of the mesa. Without changing the metallisation technology, this would require the mesa walls to be sloped at ~45° in both planes. Such profiles have been achieved using an Ar/Cl_2 gas mixture. At low values of p, Q and P a 45° – 55° sloped wall, residue free and microscopically smooth etch is obtained. Above P = 20W, surface residues are observed to increase with etch rate, as shown in Fig. 5 for 1 cm^2 GaAs samples. The approximate 500–750Å /min etch rate at 20W decreases to nearly 250Å /min for a 2" GaAs wafer.

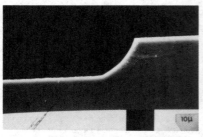

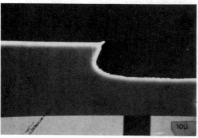

FIG 3 Micrographs of mesa etch profile and surface topography using CCl_2F_2/Cl_2

Both of the above mesa etch processes limit the device packing density to some extent by virtue of the sloped profile. Nevertheless this may be necessary when the mesa etch depth approaches 1um. However as the n doped

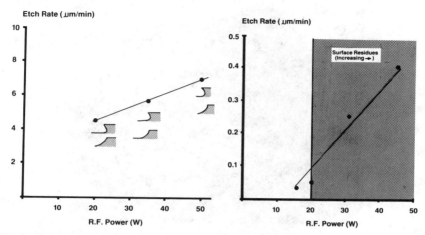

FIG 4   Etch rate as a function of r.f. power   FIG 5   Etch rate versus r.f. power
for CCl_2F_2/Cl_2 RIE   for Ar/Cl_2 RIE

region is typically 1500Å thick,
providing the doping and etch
uniformity can collectively be
controlled within +10%, sufficient
device isolation will be provided
by etching to a depth of 3000Å.
As this is in the region of the
metallisation track thickness, it
is conceivable that an anisotropic
mesa isolation etch can be used to
eliminate the sloped wall profile
and hence increase the packing
density. Using $SiCl_4$ RIE,
anisotropic mesa isolation etching
has been obtained. At moderate
flow rates and pressures (Q < 100
sccm, p <50mTorr) the anisotropic
etch is residue free at P < 27.5W
as shown in Fig. 6. The etch
rates reported refer to sample areas of
approximately 7.5 cm^2. Figure 7
shows a typical scanning electron

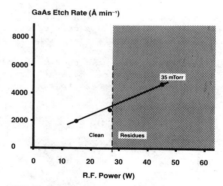

FIG 6   Etch rate versus r.f. power for
$SiCl_4$ RIE

micrograph (SEM) of the anisotropic etch, the depth has been increased
to ~5um to illustrate the side wall profile.

Gate Recess

     The gate of the MESFET is recessed to control the saturation
current levels and to minimise the parasitic capacitance between the
gate and ohmic contacts. This is one of the most critical MMIC
fabrication steps as the uniformity has direct implications on the
variation in active device parameters across the wafer. Taking into
account the gate channel sheet resistivity (after a deep channel

FIG 7 Micrograph of an anisotropic mesa etch using $SiCl_4$ RIE

implant activation) being typically within $\pm$ 5% across a 2" wafer, it
is apparent that gate recessing can introduce a further spread in the
dc device characteristics. Thus it is vital to accurately control
the etch dimensions and also obtain a low damage etch of the sensitive
GaAs active region with good uniformity. A CH_4/H_2 based process has
been successfully used as a gate recess etch, providing both low
controllable etch rates (to realise typical 1000 – 2000Å etch depths

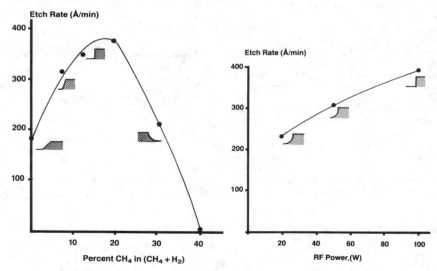

FIG 8 Etch rate versus the percentage of
CH_4 in the CH_4/H_2 process gas
mixture

FIG 9 Etch rate as a function of r.f.
power for 17% CH_4/H_2 RIE

in practical time scales) and more importantly, a low damage etch
surface. The maximum etch rate and anisotropy has been observed with
approximately 17% CH_4/H_2 (see Fig. 8). Higher CH_4 concentrations
result in surface depositions of hydrocarbon based polymeric films,
whilst lower CH_4 concentrations reduce the etch rate (probably by
reactive species depletion). Generally the etch rate increases with
r.f. power as shown in Fig. 9 (for 17% CH_4/H_2). At r.f. powers in
excess of 100W reticulation of the resist mask has been observed.
The optimum process typical yields etch rates of 100Å/min for a 2"
GaAs wafer (P= 100W, 17% CH_4/H_2) and an etch selectivity of GaAs to
resist of 1:4, that is, in order to recess 1000Å of GaAs, a resist
thickness of a least 4000Å is required. A uniformity of $\pm$ 5% has been
obtained across a 2" wafer. The low damage aspect of this process is
covered in the discussion.

Substrate Thinning

    The back surface of the wafer (opposite to the MMIC device side)
is thinned to control the transmission line impendance on MMICs. As
there is no masking of the GaAs during this process, a considerable
area of material is exposed. This results in a loading effect by
virtue of reactive species depletion. Hence the requirement is a
process which yields a high proportion of etchant species (to enable a
high etch rate to be realised), while maintaining a relatively smooth
surface with good uniformity across the wafer. High etch rates of
GaAs have been reported using pure Cl_2 and Br_2 RIE [9,10], with a
crystallographic etch prevailing under certain conditions [22].

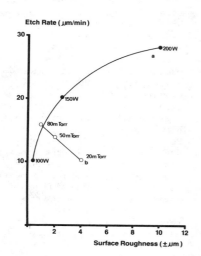

FIG 10   Etch rate as a function of
          surface roughness for
          (a) r.f. power and
          (b) pressure using Cl_2 RIE

Investigations have been
carried out using Cl_2 and etch
rates in excess of 28um/min
have been obtained for $1.25cm^2$
samples, operating at P> 100W
and p> 50mTorr. However such
etch rates have resulted in
particularly rough surfaces ($\pm$
10um). Investigations of the
surface roughness (SR) have
shown it to be affected by both
power and pressure as shown by
Fig. 10, where the etch rate
is plotted as a function of SR
for both power (a) and pressure
(b) variations. Curve (b)
shows the etch rate decreasing
with both increasing SR and
pressure. Thus high pressures
and low powers favour a reduced
SR. This result becomes
particularly important in the
case of utilising the process
for the pre-doped layer
formation etch, where 5-10um
need to be etched leaving a
polished front wafer surface.
Figure 11 shows the loading

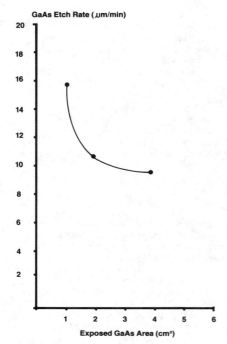

FIG 11   Etch rate versus exposed GaAs area
of Cl_2 RIE

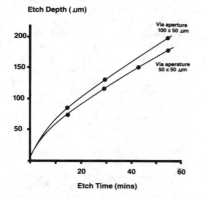

FIG 12   Via hole etch depth as a function
of etch time

effect, manifested as a
decrease in the etch rate as
the exposed GaAs area is
increased (for a surface
roughness of $\leq \pm$ 0.5um). Thus
the etch rate for the 2" wafer
will be somewhat lower than
that observed for 1cm^2
samples. By operating at low
powers and high pressures (in
accordance with Fig.10),
polished GaAs wafers have been
etched (without degrading the
front surface finish) to a 20um
depth at a rate of 2um/min.

Via Hole Etching

In the high frequency MMIC
it is important to reduce
losses arising from stray
circuits inductances. In the
case of circuit interconnects
to ground, the provision
of a ground plane on the
backsurface of the wafer
(connecting to device
structures on the front surface
using through substrate via
holes), can significantly
reduce such losses. Dry
etching offers a means of
forming the via holes without
excessive lateral etching and
enlargement of the hole
diameter (suffered by wet
etching [4]); this enables the
use of smaller chip area and a
higher packing density.
Development of the through
substrate via hole etch process
has been described elsewhere
[16]. The process requirements
are to etch through 200 um GaAs
substrates with limited via
hole apertures obtaining
tapered profiles and minimum
mask undercut in a practical
timescale.

CCl_2F_2 RIE has been
used to develop the via hole
etch. Operating at 70mTorr, 100W and 25 sccm of CCl_2F_2, the etch
depth as a function of time is shown in Fig. 12 for 100x50um^2 and 50 x
50um^2 via apertures. Thus the via hole etch depth appears to be a
function of the via aperture and a diminishing etch rate is observed

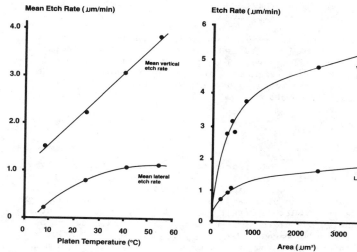

FIG 13 Mean etch rate versus platen temperature for a 40um x 40um via hole aperture

FIG 14 Variation of etch rate with via hole aperture area

with time. In order to reduce the amount of undercutting of the Ni mask [16], the substrate temperature was increased to 55°C (see Fig. 13), such that the etch depth of the via hole was a factor of 3.5 greater than the undercut; resulting in an undercut of <57um per mask edge. If the mean vertical and lateral etch rates are plotted as a funtion of via hole aperture size (Fig. 14), it is apparent that the etch rate does increase with aperture area. The selectivity of the

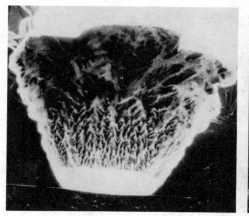

FIG 15 Micrographs of through substrate via holes showing the tapered profile in the 0° plane and re-entrant profile in the 90° plane

etch rate of GaAs to Ni (mask) is >1000 : 1. The SEMs in Fig. 15 show the tapered via hole profile in the 0° plane and the re-entrant profile in the 90° plane. Although initially it may seem that this profile is undesirable for metallisation, it has been demonstrated however, that sputtering will coat the complete via hole surface. The via hole etch process yields a 60 minute process time for 4 x 2" batch of 200 um thick GaAs substrates. Discrete MESFETs and ICs which have been fabricated with through substrate via holes for grounding show a gain increase of 2 dB above 10 GHz [15, 17] compared to conventionally grounded devices.

Scribe-Line Etching

The final stage of MMIC fabrication is chip separation. Typically this procedure involves diamond sawing to remove excess GaAs from the scribe channels, followed by scribing to separate individual circuits. Inevitably, as the saw procedes along the channels it can cause damage to nearby devices and thus result in yield degradation. By etching scribe channels to a depth of 20 – 40um prior to chip separation there are a number of advantages. Firstly, damage to adjacent MMICs will be negated as the saw is below the level of active device depth and secondly, the wafer is less prone to flaws and microcrack migration into the devices during scribing. A scribe line etch process has been developed using CCl_2F_2 as the process gas. The investigations have shown that a low pressure, low flow rate and low power regime is favoured for achieving a smooth surface and an anisotropic etch profile. Fig. 16 shows a SEM of a 20 um deep scribe line etch using a resist mask. Average etch rates of 0.25um/min were obtained for a 2" GaAs wafer. Yield enhancement by up to 20% has been obtained in the chip separation stage by using scribe-line etching.

FIG 16 Micrograph of a 20um scribe-line etch using CCl_2F_2 RIE

DISCUSSION

A glow discharge of even a single gas is a highly complex phenomenon. Therefore, rather than adding further complications as in the case of complex gaseous molecules, consider a single diatomic molecular etchant. The etching of GaAs by Cl_2 for example, must inevitably proceed by the following steps:

(i)   Molacular or atomic chlorine diffusion/transport to GaAs surface

$$Cl_{(g)} \longrightarrow Cl_{(surf)} \qquad\qquad (1)$$

(ii)   Surface adsorption of the chlorine species

$$Cl_{(surf)} \longrightarrow Cl_{(ads)} \qquad\qquad (2)$$

(iii) Etch reaction between $Cl_{(ads)}$ and GaAs to form etch products

$$yCl_{(ads)} + GaAs_{(surf)} \longrightarrow GaCl_{x(surf)} + AsCl_{x(surf)} \qquad (3)$$

(iv)   Desorption of etch products

$$GaCl_{x(surf)} \longrightarrow GaCl_{x(des)} \qquad\qquad (4)$$

(v)   Removal of gas phase products from GaAs surface.

Any of these steps may be rate limiting during the etch process.

Enhancement of the etching process by the plasma can only occur by two means. Firstly, by increased reactive species generation following collisional phenomena and secondly, by the influence of ion bombardment on the surface reaction and desorption processes. Ion bombardment of the surface during etching can result in:

(a)   Surface heating, which may lead to breakdown of lattice structure, out diffussion of relatively low volatility compounds [18] and possibly surface roughness.

(b)   Sputtering by collisional energy transfer [7], resulting in lattice damage.

(c)   Enhancement of surface reaction kinetics.

(d)   Lattice damage by penetration of porous surface [19].

Each of these processes will enhance the etch rate either directly as for (a), (b) and(c), or indirectly as in (d) and possibly (a) and (b).

During the substrate thinning investigations with Cl_2 RIE, the surface roughness increased with r.f. power and decreased with increasing pressure, while the etch rate increased with both r.f. power and pressure (see Fig. 10). Simplistically, an enhancement in the generation of radicals, atomic and generally reactive species, together with an increase in the ion bombardment energy, can be attributed to increasing power. However increasing pressure will result in a decrease in the ion bombardment energy whilst increasing the generation of radicals etc. and their residence time [16]. Thus it can be conjectured that the surface roughness is a first order function of the ion bombardment energy, which agrees with ion bombardment effect (a) above. The increase in surface roughness may well be caused by surface heating and possibly the associated phenomena described above.

The addition of Ar to Cl_2 during the sloped wall mesa etch is likely to alter the relative molecular, atomic and radical species concentrations in the discharge [20]. Pure Ar sputtering of GaAs provides low etch rates, typically 400Å /min [21]. The dramatic increase in etch rate, even when a relatively low percentage of Cl_2 is added to Ar (at power levels above 50W), suggests that the sputter mechanism plays a negligable part in the GaAs etch process (see Fig. 5). This is in agreement with the observations made by Klinger and Greene for CCl_2F_2 additions to an Ar plasma [21]. It is interesting to note from Fig.5 that although the surface residues increase above 20W, there is no corresponding decrease in etch rate. This would further suggest that the surface residues are not rate limiting. It is believed that the origin of the polymeric deposits is the resist, caused either by etching of the resist by Cl_2 (being a powerful oxidising agent) or by Ar sputtering of the resist.

Crystallographic etching of GaAs in Cl_2/CCl_2F_2 RIE has been observed during the mesa etching. Such etching has previously been reported in pure Cl_2 and Br_2 plasmas by Ibbotson et al [22]. It is essentially a manifestation of differing etch rates for the various crystallographic GaAs planes. Depending on the density of a particular plane and whether it is As or Ga rich, a certain activation energy is required before the onset of etching. Thus various crystallographic features may be etched depending on the etch time, r.f. power and frequency [22].

The anisotropic etch processes using $SiCl_4$ (mesa isolation etching) and CCl_2F_2 (scribe line etching) rely on the formation of a side wall passivation layer and on the directionality of the ion bombardment. For example, in the case of CCl_2F_2, the formation of C_xF_y polymeric films (particularly at high pressures, p> 30mTorr) and other non volatile products, such as fluorogallium compounds, has been reported [21, 23]. On the GaAs surface, such deposits may be continually removed by ion bombardment sputtering processes. However such deposits on the sidewall would not be affected by ion bombardment and result in the formation of a passivation layer, thereby giving rise to the anisotropic profile. Furthermore, lattice damage caused by the ion bombardment will further increase the etch rate on the exposed GaAs surface. Such processes are also believed to occur during the via hole etch process using CCl_2F_2 [16]. Also, if the ion bombardment enhancement of etch rate was due to the sputter desorption of $GaCl_x$, a weak temperature dependence would be observed. This is contrary to the observation of etch rate dependence on temperature (see Fig. 13).

The etch rate dependence on both the via aperture dimensions (Figs. 12 and 14) and the etch depth (Fig. 12) that the rate limiting step, which is likely to dominate in the later stages of the via hole etch, is the diffusion of reactant and product species into and out of the the via hole. Generally however, the rate limiting step in GaAs etching with CCl_2F_2 is the removal of the non-volatile $GaF_{x(surf)}$ species from the surface. This has been confirmed using optical emission and atomic absorbtion spectroscopy by Klinger and Greene [21] and also using AES and ESCA by Chaplart et al [24].

The degree of damage to the etched GaAs surface during gate recessing using CH_4/H_2 RIE has been reported by Cheung et al [12]. They measured the ideality factor of Schottky diodes (made on the etched surface) and the relative intensity of bandgap transitions using photoluminesence. An ideality factor of 1.05 up to r.f. powers of 150W was reported, compared to a control factor of 1.04. Table 1 compares this ideality factor with others measured on etched GaAs surface using various etch chemistries. From the table, the CH_4/H_2 RIE process yields the lowest variation from the control, thereby suggesting that it provides the lowest surface damage. The photoluminescence studies (at λ = 632.8nm and T = 15K) [12], also suggest a lower substrate damage occurs using CH4/H2 compared to $SiCl_4$ RIE and Ar sputtering; giving a normalised intensity of 0.95 compared to 0.6 and 0.3 respectively.

TABLE 1. Schottky diode ideality factor measurements following RIE

RIE Process Gas	Ideality Factor, n		Reference
	Measured	Control	
CH_4/H_2	1.05	1.04	[12]
CCl_2F_2	1.24		[24]
$Cl_2,SiCl_4,CF_4,CCl_2F_2$	1.07		[25]
O_2	1.20		[25]
H_2	1.26		[25]
Cl_2	>1.08	1.04	[26]
$SiCl_4$	1.17		[27]
Ar (Sputtering)	2.00*		[28]
CCl_2F_2+50% Ar	1.40*		[28]
CCl_2F_2	1.40*		[28]
CF_4	1.30*		[28]

*Values of n taken prior to thermal annealing.

CONCLUSIONS

Reproducible dry etch processes have been developed for the etch steps in GaAs MMIC fabrication. The variety of requirements imposed by the different etch steps have been satisfied using reactive ion etching based on the formation of volatile gallium chlorides or trimetlyl/hydride complexes. In addition to good uniformity across the wafer (+ 5%), the processes offer enhanced performance, etch profile control, yield improvements during chip seperation and potentially higher packing densities.

Some of these processes have been used in discrete MESFET, IC and MMIC fabrication.

REFERENCES

[1]   Pengelly,R.S., "Gallium Arsenide Monolithic Microwave Integrated
       Circuits"Gallium Arsenide for Devices and Integrated Circuits,
       Eds.Thomas,H., Morgan,D.V., Thomas,B., Aubrey,J.E., and Morgan,
       G.B., Peter Peregrinus Ltd., London, 1986.
[2]   Andrade,T., "Manufacturing Technology for GaAs Monolithic
       Microwave Integrated Circuits",Solid State Technology,Vol. 28,2,
       199, Feb.1985.
[3]   Pengelly,R.S., "Hybrid vs. Monolithic Microwave Circuits - A
       Matter of Cost",Microwave Systems News,Jan.1983.
[4]   Woodward,J., "Wet and Dry Processing of GaAs",Gallium Arsenide
       for Devices and Integrated Circuits,Eds. Thomas,H., Morgan,
       D.V., Thomas,B., Aubrey,J.E. and Morgan,G.B, Peter Peregrinus
       Ltd., London, 1986.
[5]   Proceedings of the 3rd International IEEE VLSI Multilevel
       Interconnection Conference, June 9-10, Santa Clara, 1986.
[6]   CRC Handbook of Chemistry and Physics,65th Edition, Ed. Weast
       R.C., CRC Press Ltd., Florida, 1984.
[7]   Yamasaki,K. et al., "Sputter Etching Effects on GaAs Schottky
       Junctions",Journal Electrochemical Society,Solid-State Science
       and Technology, Vol. 129, 12, 2760, Dec 1982.
[8]   Donnelly,V.M., Flamm,D.L., Ibbotson,D.E, "Plasma Etching of III-
       V compound semiconductors",Journal Vacuum Science and Technology
       A1 (2), 626, Apr.-June 1983.
[9]   Smolinsky,G., Gottscho,R.A., Abys,S.M. " Time-dependant etching
       of GaAs and InP with CCl_4 or HCl plasma: Electrode material and
       oxidant addition effects",Journal Applied Physics, 54(6), 3518,
       June 1983.
[10]   Hu,E.L., Howard,R.E., "Reactive-ion etching of GaAs and InP
       using $CCl_2F_2/Ar/O_2$",Applied Physics Letters, 37(11),
       1022, Dec.1980.
[11]   Li,J.Z., Adesida,I., Wolf,E.D., "Evidence of crystallographic
       etching in (100) GaAs using $SiCl_4$ reactive ion etching",
       Journal Vacuum Science and Technology, B3(1), 406, Jan./Feb. 1985.
[12]   Cheung,R.,Thoms,S., Beamont,S.P., Doughty,G., Law,V., Wilkinson,
       C.D.W., "Reactive ion etching of GaAs using a mixture of methane
       and hydrogen", Dept. of Electronics, University of Glasgow,
       Scotland, 1987.
[13]   Electrotech Special Research Systems Ltd., Reactive Ion Etch
       System, Model Plasmafab 340-1.
[14]   Chambers,A.A., Kiermasz,A., Stephens,M., "Substrate Doping Level
       and Process Gas Dependencies in Anisotropic Dry Etching of
       GaAs", Electrotech Special Research Systems, Bristol, U.K.,
       1986.
[15]   D'Asaro,L.A., Butherus,A.D., DiLorenzo,J.V. Iglesias,D.E.,
       Wemple,S.H., "Plasma-Etched Via Connections to GaAs FETs",
       Institute Physics Conference, SN. 56, Thinn, H.W. (Ed),
       Chapter 5, 267, 1981.
[16]   Bhardwaj,J., Chambers,A., Kiermasz,A., Stephens,M., McQuarrie,
       A., "Through Substrate Via-Holes in GaAs Using CCl_2F_2 Reactive
       Ion Etching",Proceedings of the C1P1G Etch and Deposition
       Conference, Societe Francaise Du Vide, Antibes, June 1987.
[17]   Vanner,K.C., McAllister,B.J., "Development of an RIE Process for
       GaAs Through-Substrate Via Hole Etching",Proceeding of the C1P1G
       Etch and Deposition Conference Societe Francaise Du Vide, Antibes,
       June 1987.

[18]   Burton,R.H., Smolinsky,G., "CCl_4 and Cl_2 Plasma Etching of III-V
       Semiconductors and the Role of Added O_2",Journal Electrochemical
       Society, Solid-State Technology, 129(7), 1599, 1982.
[19]   Donnelly,V.M., Flamm,D.L., Tu,C.W., Ibbotson,D.E.,"Temperature
       Dependence of InP and GaAs Etching in a Chlorine Plasma",
       Journal Electrochemical Society, Solid-State Technology,129(11),
       1533, Nov. 1982
[20]   Hu,E.L., Howard,R.E., "Reactive ion etching of GaAs in a
       chlorine plasma",Journal Vacuum Science and Technology, B2,(1),
       85, Jan-Mar. 1984.
[21]   Klinger,R.E., Greene,J.E.,"Reactive ion etching of GaAs in
       CCl_2F_2"Applied Physics Letters,38(8), 620, Apr.1981.
[22]   Ibbotson,D.E., Flamm,D.L. Donnelly,V.M., "Crystallographic
       etching of GaAs with bromine and chlorine plasmas",Journal of
       Applied Physics, 54(10), 5974, 1983.
[23]   Webb,A.P., "Reactive Ion Etching In Chlorinated Plasma",
       Proceedings of Semiconductor International '84,Birmingham,
       25-27 Sept. 1984.
[24]   Chaplart,J., Fay,B., Linh,N.T., "Reactive ion etching of GaAs
       using CCl_2F_2 and the effect of Ar addition",Journal Vacuum
       Science and Technology, B1(4). 1050, Oct-Dec. 1983.
[25]   Pang,S.W. "Surface Damage Induced On GaAs By Reactive Ion
       Etching and Sputter Etching",Journal Electrochemical Society,133,
       784, 1986.
[26]   Al-Assadi,K.F., Chatterton,P.A., Marsland,C.J., Rees,J.A.,
       "Surface Damage Produced During Dry Processing of GaAs",
       Proceedings of the 6th Ion and Plasma Assisted Techniques
       Conference, Brighton, 296, Sept, 1987.
[27]   Doughty,G.F., Thoms,S., Cheung,R., Wilkinson,C.D.W., "Dry
       etching damage to gallium arsenide and indium phosphide",
       Proceedings of the 6th Ion and Plasma Assisted Techniques
       Conference, Brighton, 284, Sept. 1987.
[28]   Chaplart,J., Vatus,J., Chevrier,J., Linh,N.T., "Control of the
       Gate Recess in GaAs FET's and AlGaAs/GaAs TEGFET's Process using
       Reactive Ion Etching",5th Symposium on Plasma Processing, Oct.
       7-12, New Orleans, 1984.

James M. Heddleson, Mark W. Horn, and Stephen J. Fonash

DRY ETCHING OF ION IMPLANTED SILICON: ELECTRICAL EFFECTS

REFERENCE: Heddleson, J. M., Horn, M. W., and Fonash, S. J., "Dry Etching of Ion Implanted Silicon: Electrical Effects", Semiconductor Fabrication: Technology and Metrology, ASTM STP 990, Dinesh C. Gupta, editor, American Society for Testing and Materials, 1989.

ABSTRACT: In this paper we examine the effect of dry etching on p-type and n-type material implanted with $^{11}B^+$ at 100 keV to doses of 1E12, 1E13, 1E14, 1E15, and 1E16 cm^{-2}. Hydrogen-containing etch chemistries and typical etch parameters are simulated by Ion Beam Etching with 100% deuterium. We show that for deuteration of 1E12 and 1E13 cm^{-2} $^{11}B^+$ implants into p-type material, deep deactivation, as is observed for unimplanted material, is suppressed but still observed. Deuteration of the same low dose $^{11}B^+$ implants into n-type material expose two important results. The first is that hydrogen preferentially " pairs " with boron in a compensated n-type environment. The second is that hydrogen deactivates boron acceptors not only in the absence of free holes but even when the Fermi level is near the conduction band edge.

KEYWORDS: dry etching, boron deactivation, ion beam etching, hydrogen/deuterium, implantation, reactive ion etching, plasma etching

INTRODUCTION

Dry etching and ion implantation are key processing steps in the VLSI/ULSI era. The high anisotropy inherent in these processes is imperative in the submicron regime, as is the good selectivity which can be achieved in modern dry etching. However, it is well known that that the very characteristics which make dry etching effective, i.e. energetic ion bombardment and reactive chemical species created in the plasma, cause both physical damage and impurity permeation at and below the etched surface. Recently we have examined these effects when hydrogen is present in the etching chemistry and have reported extensive dopant deactivation in bulk and epitaxial p-type silicon which has been subjected to reactive ion etching (RIE) or plasma etching (PE) [1]. We have also used ion beam etching (IBE) with 100% hydrogen as a highly controllable simulation of the ion bombardment of the industrial dry etching processes of RIE and PE and have seen the same effect on bulk electrical properties; viz, extensive doping deactivation[2]. More recently we have substituted deuterium for hydrogen in the IBE simulations of the etching of bulk and epitaxial

Mr. Heddleson and Mr. Horn are graduate students and Dr. S. J. Fonash is an Alumni Professor in the Engineering Science Program and the Center for Electronic Materials and Devices at The Pennsylvania State University, 132 Hammond Bldg., University Park, PA 16802.

material [3-4]. We have done this in order to trace, using secondary ion mass spectroscopy (SIMS), the permeation of hydrogen during dry etching by exploiting the higher SIMS sensitivity afforded by deuterium.

In this study we examine dopant deactivation and species permeation in ion implanted silicon subjected to dry etching. The samples utilized have been ion implanted and given an activation anneal prior to dry etching. These samples were subsequently monitored using spreading resistance and SIMS to determine the impact of dry etching on the electrical properties of ion implanted silicon. In this report we specifically focus on spreading resistance data to trace the impact of dry etching exposures on the electrical properties of ion implanted silicon; we leave the SIMS characterization to another discussion.

EXPERIMENTAL PROCEDURE

Boron doped p-type epitaxial wafers with an epi layer thickness of 13 microns and resistivity of 10 - 14 Ω-cm and phosphorous doped n-type epitaxial wafers with an epi layer thickness of 5 microns and resistivity of 0.41 - 0.51 Ω-cm were used for this study. These 4 " silicon wafers were cleaned and then implanted with $^{11}B^+$ at 100 keV to doses of 1E12, 1E13, 1E14, 1E15, and 1E16 cm^{-2} in a Varian 350D ion implanter equipped with dual research end stations. The sample chamber base pressure was 6.7x10^{-5} Pa (5 x 10^{-7} torr), while the pressure during the implants was approximately 1.3x10^{-4}Pa (1 x 10^{-6} torr). These implants resulted in a boron profile with a peak concentration at $\approx$ 3100 Å. The implanted wafers were cut into

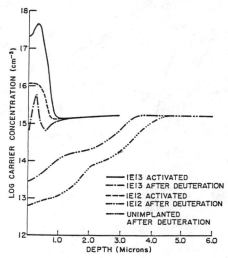

Fig. 1 -- Carrier concentration profiles for p-type epitaxial silicon implanted with $^{11}B^+$ at 100 keV to doses of 1E12 and 1E13 cm^{-2} after activation and subsequent deuteration. Also shown is the carrier concentration profile for unimplanted p-type epitaxial silicon after deuteration.

quarters, given an RCA clean, and the samples were then activated by conventional furnace anneal . The furnace anneal was done in flowing argon and ramped up from 780 °C to 925 °C in 25 minutes, held constant at 925 °C for 25 minutes and ramped down from 925 °C to 780 °C in 40 minutes. After the samples were activated, they were loaded into a Commonwealth Scientific system for IBE. The base pressure of this system was $\approx 1.3 \times 10^{-4}$ Pa (1×10^{-6} torr), while the pressure during etching was $\approx 1.1 \times 10^{-2}$ Pa (8×10^{-5} torr). A residual gas analyzer was used to monitor the background gas levels at base pressure and during etching. The IBE exposure was for 10 minutes with a 0.5 keV deuterium beam which had a current density of 0.3 mA/cm^2. The energies and exposure times used were intended to simulate RIE and PE. Deuterium was utilized to facilitate the SIMS analysis reported elsewhere, as previously noted. The samples were mounted on a rotating, water cooled stainless steel stage; yet, because of ion beam heating and poor thermal heat sinking, their temperature at the end of the etch was 155 °C. This temperature was measured by a Luxtron Model 750 fluoroptic temperature probe equipped with remote sensor capability. This Luxtron unit enabled the actual surface temperature of the sample to be measured during the ion bombardment incurred in this simulation of RIE and PE processing.

RESULTS AND DISCUSSION

Spreading resistance profiling (SRP) was used to monitor the activated implant profile and the deactivation of the activated dopant that results from deuteration. Figure 1 plots the carrier concentration deduced from the spreading resistance vs. depth for the activated 1E12 and 1E13 cm^{-2} ^{11}B$^+$ implantations into p-type epitaxial material and their corresponding profiles after deuteration under the aforementioned

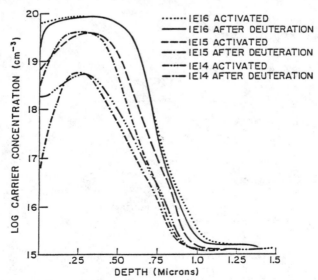

Fig. 2 -- Carrier concentration profiles for p-type epitaxial silicon implanted with ^{11}B$^+$ at 100 keV to doses of 1E14, 1E15, and 1E16 cm^{-2} after activation and subsequent deuteration.

conditions. The deactivation of boron due to deuterium permeation in unimplanted material (which served as a control) is also shown in Figure 1 and is seen to extend to a depth of 4.5 µm exhibiting a distinctive two region behavior, as has been reported previously [2]. The surface carrier concentration is reduced from the bulk value of $1.3E15$ cm^{-3} to only $6E12$ cm^{-3} in this unimplanted but deuterated control sample. For the $1E12$ implantation, the peak carrier concentration is $1E16$ cm^{-2} before deuteration. As can be seen from the figure, the overall deactivation after deuteration is suppressed both in magnitude and depth of penetration but retains the characteristic two apparent diffusion regions observed in the unimplanted case. There are two observations for the $1E13$ cm^{-2} case of Figure 1. First, some deactivation is still observed beyond the implantation depth. Second, there is extensive deactivation within the implanted region and enough deuterium has entered the sample such that in part of the profile the carrier concentration is decreased below the background carrier concentration of $1.3E15$ cm^{-2}.

Figure 2 shows the carrier concentration depth profiles for the $1E14$, $1E15$, and $1E16$ cm^{-2} $^{11}B^+$ implantations and their subsequent deuterations. For these high implant doses of Figure 2, all the dopant deactivation occurs entirely within the implanted region and the carrier concentration is observed to remain above the background carrier concentration. The $1E14$ and $1E15$ cm^{-2} implants are deactivated in the near surface region and a slight amount of neutralization is observed in the tail region of the implant. For the $1E16$ cm^{-2} implant, all the deactivation takes place within the first 1000 Å. We note that the deactivation observed in Figure 2 for ion beam deuteration of the 100 keV $1E15$ cm^{-2} implant is much less than the deactivation observed by Mikkelsen [5] for a 150 keV $1E15$ cm^{-2} implant which was heated to 300 °C and placed downstream from a deuterium microwave discharge for 30 minutes. This is probably due to the shorter exposure time and lower temperature used in this study.

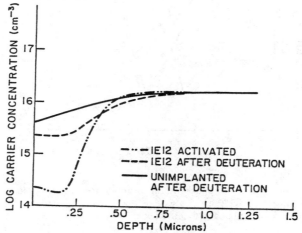

Fig. 3 -- Carrier concentration profile for n-type epitaxial silicon implanted with $^{11}B^+$ at 100 keV to a dose of $1E12$ cm^{-2} after activation and subsequent deuteration. Also shown is the carrier concentration profile for unimplanted n-type epitaxial silicon after deuteration.

In the n-type epi material, Figure 3 shows that very little deactivation is seen in the unimplanted control material as is typical for all n-type silicon. Figure 3 also plots the carrier concentration profile for the 1E12 cm^{-2} ^{11}B$^+$ implant into n-epi material and the corresponding profile after deuteration.   The 1E12 cm^{-2} implant causes the n-type material to be simply compensated before deuteration as evidenced by the decrease in free carrier concentration throughout the implanted region. After deuteration, the carrier concentration increases in the compensated region from a surface carrier concentration of 2E14 cm^{-3} to 2E15 cm^{-3}. This indicates that in compensated material, the hydrogen related species is active and is preferentially "pairing" with the substitutional (active) boron.   An increase in carrier concentration has also been seen in previous work [3] for slightly compensated As doped n-type epitaxial material on a p-type substrate.

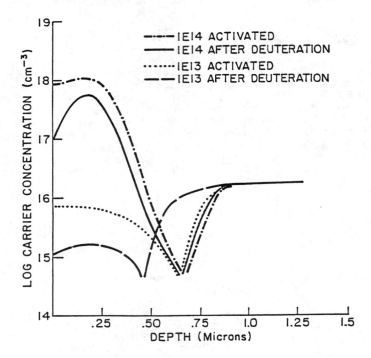

Fig. 4 -- Carrier concentration profiles for n-type epitaxial silicon implanted with ^{11}B$^+$ at 100 keV to doses of 1E13 and 1E14 cm^{-2} after activation and subsequent deuteration.

Figure 4 shows that an activated ^{11}B+ implant dose of 1E13 cm^{-2} forms a p$^-$/n$^-$ diode structure with a junction depth of 0.63 microns. After deuteration, the activity of hydrogen and the preferential deactivation of the p-type dopant is evidenced again by the severe shift in junction depth from 0.63 to 0.45 microns.   More specifically, a 2000 Å region in the p-type implant near the metallurgical junction reverts back to being n-type due to deactivation of the boron in this region. In the case of the 1E14 cm^{-2} implant, also shown in Figure 4, there is no noticeable shift in the junction depth after deuteration, within experimental error, but there is a noticeable decrease in the carrier concentration throughout the implanted region. Comparing the 1E14 cm^{-2} implant of Figure 2 with the 1E14 cm^{-2} implant of Figure 4, one can see distinctly more deactivation in the compensated material with the introduction of hydrogen (deuterium). In fact, much more can be seen than can be attributed to the greater amount of boron present in the p-type material due to the background boron concentration . The 1E15 and 1E16 cm^{-2} dose implants into the n-epi material form p/n junctions like the 1E14 cm^{-2} implant. However, after deuteration, deactivation occurs only in the first 2000 Å and the carrier concentration profiles are almost identical to those shown in Figure 2 for the 1E15 and 1E16 cm^{-2} implants into p-type material.

The deep permeation of deuterium into silicon as seen in Figures 1 through 3 is not due to low energy ion implantation as the implant range for deuterium at the 0.5 keV energies typifying dry etching is approximately 125 Å. The penetration of the deuterium is, therefore, due to temperature dependent ion bombardment assisted diffusion. This method of introducing deuterium is quite different than the deuteration method used by others [5-9] where the monatomic deuterium is introduced by an rf or microwave discharge and substrates are placed downstream on a heated stage. The method used here better simulates hydrogen injection as it would occur in dry etching. In examining the results of the ^{11}B^{+} implants into the epitaxial p-type material to form p^{+}/p structures, clearly the trend is that as the amount of boron is increased, the depth of deactivation by the deuterium is diminished and the two different diffusion regimes observed in the unimplanted material become indistinguishable. We also note that for the implants of Fig.1, the total number of D*B complexes is greater for the 1E13 cm^{-2} implant than for the 1E12 cm^{-2} implant and in turn greater for the 1E12 cm^{-2} implant than for the unimplanted sample. These observations are in agreement with results observed in SIMS data for bulk doped Si [5] in spite of the shorter times, lower temperature, and different deuteration method employed in this simulation of RIE and PE processing. More recently, Tavendale [10] has observed the amount of injected deuterium giving rise to deactivation to vary as the square root of acceptor concentration for samples exposed to wet chemical etching. Our results also show this trend that the amount of deactivating hydrogen (deuterium) increases with acceptor concentration. We see it for p-type substrates, as noted above, and also for n-type substrates as may be seen in Figure 3 and Figure 4.

The deactivation seen in the high .dose implants into both p-type and n-type material suggests either the boron concentrations for the high dose implants are great enough that, for the exposure time and temperature used in this study, all the injected deuterium is tied up in the implanted region or that the high dopant-implant doses alone, regardless of the amount of available deuterium, impede the diffusion necessary for deep deactivation. The 1E12 and 1E13 cm^{-2} implants into the n-type substrates both show a phenomenon not observed in any previous work, namely that in compensated, high resistivity n-type silicon, i.e. silicon with nearly equal amounts of donor and acceptor impurities, the hydrogen species links with actively compensating acceptors. The acceptor deactivation increases the number of free electrons thereby decreasing the resistivity. Early work by Johnson [6,7] and Pankove [8] reported the necessity of free holes for acceptor neutralization and acceptor-hydrogen pairing. However, in a later paper, Tavendale [11] showed that deactivation can occur in the p-type depletion region of a diode in the absence of any free holes. This study shows conclusively that acceptor deactivation can occur amidst the " sea of electrons " present in n-type material. One ramification of the preferential pairing of boron with hydrogen in n-type silicon would be a junction shift in n/p junctions when hydrogen enters due to dry processing. Such a shift is seen in Figure 3 for the 1E13 ^{11}B+ implant into the n-epitaxial material.

As we have done previously for unimplanted material, we tested the recovery of the deactivation observed in Figures 1 and 2 in the ^{11}B+ implanted p-type epitaxial material by subjecting separate pieces of the deuterated 1E13 and 1E16 implants to isochronal anneals. The samples were annealed at 140, 180, and 220 °C for 10 minutes in an Argon ambient. Spreading resistance depth profiles were performed on each annealed sample to monitor recovery of the dopant deactivation and possible deeper deuterium permeation and deactivation. No deactivation was observed beyond the implant depth for any anneal of the deuterated 1E13 or 1E16 implants and full reactivation was observed for both cases after the 220 °C anneal. This former result is important because it shows that the large amount of deuterium paired with boron in the implanted region did not move into pairing sites below the implant region, i.e. the trapped deuterium did not become electrically active upon annealing and thus deactivate dopant deeper in the material. The latter result is also important. It shows that the doping deactivation and p/n junction position shift caused by hydrogen permeation during dry etching disappears provided processing using temperatures above 220 °C follows any hydrogen injection.

CONCLUSIONS

In conclusion, we have shown, using spreading resistance profiles, that hydrogen, as may be present in dry etching plasmas, reacts with boron implanted in silicon in a manner which can be correlated to the hydrogen permeation behavior that has been observed in bulk, boron doped silicon. We have also shown that hydrogen reacts with boron regardless of whether the material is p-type or n-type. For ^{11}B+ implants into p-type silicon, the deactivation effects vary with the concentration of the implanted dose: 1E12 and 1E13 cm^{-2} implants suppress the deep deactivation observed in unimplanted material but do not eliminate it entirely. For higher dose implants into p-type or n-type material, deactivation is confined to the first 0.25 microns and no deep deactivation is observed. This is characteristic of source limited deactivation, i.e. there is not enough D available to passivate all the ^{11}B+ present and diffusion is retarded. In n-type material that has been compensated , such as in the 1E12 and 1E13 cm^{-2} ^{11}B+ implants of our study, deuterium increases the carrier concentration in the compensated region due to what appears to be preferential pairing of deuterium with boron even in the absence of free holes. For low dose p/n junctions, as in the case of a 1E13 cm^{-2} ^{11}B+ implant into n-type material, the deuterium doses used in this study were seen to shift the junction depth significantly. Post deuteration anneals reveal that no deactivation beyond the implant depth is observed upon annealing and that full reactivation of the dopant is observed for temperatures ≥ 220 °C.

ACKNOWLEDGEMENTS

The authors would like to gratefully acknowledge Mr. Robert Hillard and Mr. Robert Mazur of Solid State Measurements for assistance with the spreading resistance measurements. This work was partially supported by the IBM corporation.

REFERENCES

[1] J. M. Heddleson, M. W. Horn and S. J. Fonash, "Effects of Dry Etching on the Electrical Properties of Silicon", Proceedings of the 31st International Symposium on Electron, Ion and Photon Beams, 1987. Journal of Vacuum Science and Technology B 6(1), Jan/Feb 1988 pp. 280-283.

[2] M. W. Horn, J. M. Heddleson, and S. J. Fonash, "Permeation of Hydrogen into Silicon During Low-Energy Hydrogen Ion Beam Bombardment", Applied Physics Letters, Vol. 51, No. 7, 17 August 1987, pp. 490-492.

[3] M. W. Horn, J. M. Heddleson, and S. J. Fonash, "Dopant Deactivation and Diffusion in Low Energy Ion Beam Deuterated Silicon", Presented at the Material Research Society Meeting in Boston, Mass., Fall 1987.

[4] M. W. Horn, J. M. Heddleson, S. J. Fonash, and D. N. Nguyen, "Dopant Deactivation in N-Type Silicon During Ion Etching with Hydrogen Present", Presented at the AVS 34th National Vacuum Symposium and Topical Conference, November 2-5, 1987, Anaheim, CA.

[5] J. C. Mikkelsen, "Atomic deuterium passivation of boron acceptor levels in silicon crystals", Applied Physics Letters, Vol. 46, No. 9, 1985, p. 882.

[6] N. M. Johnson, "Mechanism for hydrogen compensation of shallow-acceptor impurities in single-crystal silicon", Physical Review B, Vol. 31, No. 8, 1985, p. 5525.

[7] N. M. Johnson, "Electric field dependence of hydrogen neutralization of shallow-acceptor impurities in single-crystal silicon", Applied Physics Letters, Vol. 47, No.8, 1985, p. 874 .

[8] J. I. Pankove, C. W. Magee, and R. O. Wance, "Hole-mediated chemisorption of atomic hydrogen in silicon", Applied Physics Letters, Vol.47, No. 7, 1985, p. 748.

[9] A. J. Tavendale, D. Alexiev, and A. A. Williams, "Field drift of the hydrogen-related, acceptor-neutralizing defect in diodes from hydrogenated silicon", Applied Physics Letters, Vol. 47, No.3, 1985, p. 316.

[10] A. J. Tavendale, A.A. Williams, S.J. Pearton, Material Research Society Symposium Proceedings, Vol. 104, l987, p.285.

[11] A. J. Tavendale, A. A. Williams, D. Alexiev, S. J. Pearton, Material Research Society Symposium Proceedings, Vol. 59, 1986, p. 469.

L. Davis Clements, James E. Busse and Jitesh Mehta

REACTION MECHANISMS AND RATE LIMITATIONS IN DRY ETCHING OF
SILICON DIOXIDE WITH ANHYDROUS HYDROGEN FLUORIDE

REFERENCE: Clements, L.D., Busse, J. E., and Mehta, J.,
"Reaction Mechanisms and Rate Limitations in Dry Etching
of Silicon Dioxide with Anhydrous Hydrogen Fluoride,"
Semiconductor Fabrication: Technology and Metrology,
ASTM STP 990, Dinesh C. Gupta, editor, American Society
for Testing and Materials, 1989.

ABSTRACT: A novel dry etching process for silicon dioxide has
been developed. This process, carried out at ambient
temperature and pressure, uses anhydrous hydrogen fluoride,
water vapor in a nitrogen carrier, and a unique processing
sequence to achieve etch rates of about 200A/second, with 5
percent or better uniformity.
   The overall reaction is a complicated sequence of surface
hydration and surface fluorination by adsorption, reaction, and
product desorption. This paper presents two proposed
reaction mechanisms and describes how experimental data from a
laminar flow reactor were used to evaluate the mechanisms.

KEYWORDS: Silicon Dioxide Chemical Etching, Anhydrous Hydrogen
          Fluoride, Reaction Mechanisms

Introduction

   Chemical etching takes place when products which are soluble
(wet) or volatile (dry) are produced by reaction of the surface
material with an etchant. Chemical etching occurs spontaneously with
xenon difluoride and silicon [1]. Beyer and Kastl [2] have described
a process for etching SiO_2 using HF/H_2O vapor. This work focuses on
a new process for chemical etching using anhydrous hydrogen fluoride
with silicon dioxide [3, 4]. This paper describes two proposed
mechanisms for anhydrous hydrogen fluoride dry etching and evaluation
of the apparent kinetics associated with each mechanism.

Dr. Clements is Professor and Chair and Mr. Busse is a Graduate
Research Assistant at the Department of Chemical Engineering,
University of Nebraska - Lincoln, Lincoln, NE 68588-0126. Mr Mehta
is the Japan Process Engineering Manager, FSI International, 322 Lake
Hazeltine Drive, Chaska, MN 55318-1096.

Surface Preparation and SiO$_2$ Etching

The way in which the surface is prepared plays an important role in determining how the reaction of silicon dioxide with anhydrous hydrogen fluoride proceeds.   The surface of silicon resembles a diamond lattice.   The chemical and physical properties of an oxide grown on the silicon surface are dependent on its growing conditions. A SiO$_2$ surface can be grown with either oxygen (dry-oxidation) or steam (wet-oxidation) [5, 6].   The surface grown in oxygen is basically pure SiO$_2$.

The surface grown with steam will have many water and hydroxyl groups remaining absorbed on the SiO$_2$ surface once the oxidation is complete.   The hydroxyl group forms a silanol (Si-OH) group when absorbed on the surface.   The excess water and hydroxyls can be removed by heating the surface [7].   A pure SiO$_2$ surface remains after the removal.   The oxidation with steam is faster, so it is typically used to grow thick oxides [6].

Tyapkina and Guseva [8] found that a wet-oxide surface etches at a much faster rate than a dry-oxide surface.   A wet-oxide strip required 40 percent of the time of a dry-oxide strip, even though the wet-oxide was 10 times thicker.   They also found that pretreatment of the two surfaces with fluorine resulted in a marked increase in the etch rate of the wet-oxide surface.   The pretreatment did not effect the etch rate of the dry-oxide surface.

Arslambekov, et. al. [9] found that HF reacts with pure silicon, but at a much slower rate than with SiO$_2$.   An induction period that was dependent on the temperature was observed.   The activation energy for etching silicon was 13 to 17 kcal/mol. According to the authors, this rather low activation energy indicates that an adsorption process occurs before the reaction actually begins.

White [10] found that the rate-limiting step for the reaction of anhydrous HF with chemically vapor-deposited (CVD) SiO$_2$ involves species other than just HF and that proton transfer plays a minor role in this step.   CVD SiO$_2$ resembles a dry-oxide surface.

Adsorption Mechanisms and Effects on SiO$_2$

The adsorption of both water and anhydrous hydrogen fluoride on the silicon dioxide surface is an important part of the overall anhydrous HF etching reaction mechanism.   Several groups have studied the adsorption process and how it alters the structure of the surface.

The adsorptive properties of silica and SiO$_2$ surfaces are very different.   The water and hydroxyl groups adsorbed on the silica surface promote the adsorption of hydrogen fluoride.   Voronin [7] found that the number of strongly adsorbed hydrogen fluoride molecules is equal to the number of silicon atoms present at the surface.   Since the oxide produced by dry-oxidation has no water or hydroxyls present, its ability to adsorb HF is limited.

Bersin [11] found that after a silicon dioxide surface was exposed to a CF$_4$-O$_2$ plasma, the surface was invulnerable to the hydrogen fluoride reaction.   He postulated that the silanol (Si-OH) groups had been turned into siloxane (Si-O-Si) bridges.   The siloxane bridges do not hydrogen bond with hydrogen fluoride.   The adsorption and reaction of HF onto this surface proceeds at a much slower rate than on the silica surface.

The HF is apparently attracted to the dipole produced by the surface hydroxyls.   The HF molecule is polarized to form H^+ and F^-. Voronin [7] found that the greater the degree of hydration, the more that the hydrogen fluoride becomes like hydrofluoric acid.   The fluorine ion reacts with the silanol to form a Si-F group and H_2O. The fluorine ion can also cleave the siloxane (Si-O-Si) bridges of the SiO_2 lattice [7, 12].

Once Si-F groups form, the structure of the surface changes.   The fluorine is highly electronegative and imparts a large positive charge to the silicon atom.   This positive charge decreases the 3d orbital energy.   The silicon and neighboring oxygen undergo a p-d bond formation.   This results in an increase in the bond angle and a change in the hybridization.   Chukin [12] states that the fluorination of the surface leads to a transition of hybridization of an oxygen atom from sp^3 and sp^2 to sp.   Consequently, the oxygen atom has been passivated.   If the entire surface is fluorinated, the surface becomes very hydrophobic.   This is due to the lack of active sites for adsorption.

Voronin [7] found that extended contact of SiO_2 with HF gave rise to an infrared band at 935 cm^{-1}.   This band indicates the presence of Si-F, showing that fluorination had taken place.   He also found that when silica surfaces are pretreated by vacuum-conditioning at different temperatures, varying degrees of hydration at the surface resulted.   For example, specimens that had been pretreated at 920, 720, and 570 K had an induction period of 30, 20, and 10 minutes respectively, before the surface reaction began. Voronin discovered that the degree of fluorination increased with the degree of surface hydration and with the time during which the adsorbed HF molecules were present on the surface.   Prolonged exposure of the surface to hydrogen fluoride, 10 to 12 hours, resulted in almost complete replacement of the silanol groups.   Five to seven percent of the groups could not be removed chemically.   The silanol groups were only removed through vacuum-baking at 570-670 K.

Proposed Mechanism for Dry Etching of SiO_2 Using Anhydrous HF

The overall dry etching mechanism involves a number of steps. First, the reactants must diffuse to the SiO_2 surface.   The reactants then adsorb onto the surface.   Once the reactants are on the surface, the etching reaction occurs.   This is the point where the proposed kinetic mechanisms are required.   Once the reaction is complete, the products desorb from the surface and diffuse into the bulk gas phase.

The diffusion of the reactants to and the products away from the surface has been described by Clements, et al [13] and Busse [14]. The adsorption, reaction, and desorption steps are all parts of the overall surface mechanism and will be described further here.   The desorption of the products is assumed to be fast and is neglected in the surface mechanism.

Equation 1 describes a proposed etching mechanism consisting of three reactions.

$$SiO_2 + 4HF \xrightarrow{k_1} 2H_2O + SiF_4 \qquad \text{(1A)}$$

$$SiO_2 + 2H_2O + HF \xrightarrow{k_2} Si(OH)_4 + HF \qquad \text{(1B)}$$

$$Si(OH)_4 + 4HF \xrightarrow{k_3} 4H_2O + SiF_4 \qquad \text{(1C)}$$

This mechanism has two distinct reaction paths. The first reaction is water-free. This reaction will occur if only hydrogen fluoride is used as a reacting species and no appreciable amount of water accumulates on the surface as a product of the reaction. The second and third reactions are coupled by the intermediate, $Si(OH)_4$. The formation of the $Si(OH)_4$ intermediate relies on the presence of water. Hydrogen fluoride is used as a catalyst in the hydrating reaction. Once $Si(OH)_4$ is formed, the reaction proceeds much like the first reaction.

A simplification of the three reaction mechanism was also tested. This mechanism involves the assumption that the intermediate in the three-reaction mechanism exists as an activated complex and, therefore, is short lived and does not accumulate. This assumption results in the overall number of reactions being reduced by one. The simplified mechanism is called the two-reaction mechanism shown in Equation 2.

$$SiO_2 + 4HF \xrightarrow{k_1} 2H_2O + SiF_4 \qquad \text{(2A)}$$

$$SiO_2 + 4HF + 2H_2O \xrightarrow{k_2} 4H_2O + SiF_4 \qquad \text{(2B)}$$

The reaction pathway

$$2\ SiF_2\ (ads) \longrightarrow Si\ (s) + SiF_4\ (ads) \qquad \text{(3)}$$

suggested by Chukin's work [12] was disregarded here. This mechanism may represent the steps involved in reaction 2-A, but based upon the data reported by Tyapkina and Guseva [8], this overall reaction is very slow at ambient conditions.

Experimental Results

A laminar flow reactor, shown schematically in Figure 1 and described in detail in reference [3], was constructed to take advantage

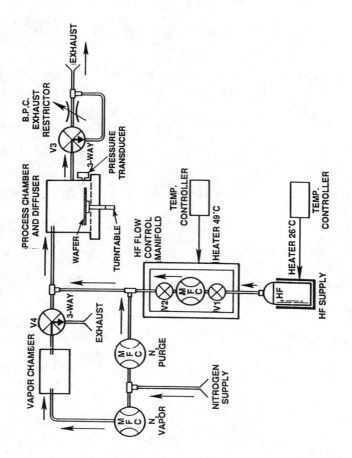

Figure 1. Schematic diagram of the laminar flow reactor

of the increased etch rate when using anhydrous hydrogen fluoride. The reactor allows the wafer to be etched in a continuous flow process. The reactor is vented to the atmosphere to maintain near atmospheric pressure inside the vessel. The reactant gas is a mixture of anhydrous hydrogen fluoride, dry nitrogen, and moist nitrogen. The amount of water and anhydrous hydrogen fluoride is kept low in comparison to the nitrogen. The reaction is terminated by purging the vessel with pure, dry nitrogen. Because of the very rapid sequence of processing steps, high-speed pneumatic valves and an automatic controller were used to operate the reactor system. Novak [4] and Cleavelin and Duranko [15] have described the operational performance of the commercial system.

Table 1 gives the concentrations of reactants and products for the nominal reaction case. Table 2 shows the number of moles of hydrogen fluoride at any given time in any unit volume (cm^3) of space at the entrance of the reactor in relation to the hydrogen fluoride flow rate.

Table 1.   Mole Fractions of Typical
           Entrance and Exit Streams

Component	Entrance	Exit
Nitrogen	0.9690	0.9694
Water	0.0020	0.0028
Hydrogen Fluoride	0.0290	0.0276
Silicon Tetrafluoride	0.0000	0.0002

Table 2.   Relationship Between the HF Concentration
           At The Inlet And The HF Flow Rate

HF Conc. ($gmol/cm^3$)	HF Flow Rate (1it/min)
0.00022	0.3
0.00037	0.5
0.00045	0.6
0.00052	0.7
0.00060	0.8

The thickness of SiO_2 removed as a function of etch time is shown in Figure 2. The amounts removed are linear with etch time and exhibit a definite time lag before reaction begins. A similar lag time before etching was reported by Voronin [7].

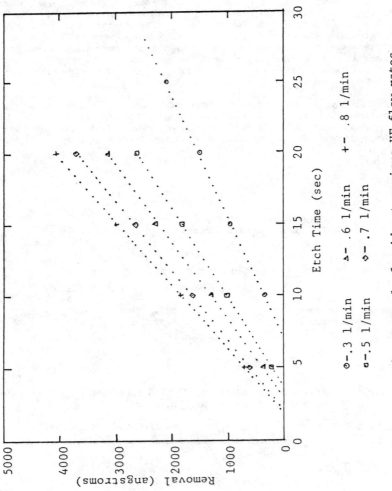

Figure 2. Removal of oxide at various HF flow rates in the laminar flow reactor

Voronin [7] found that there are 2.5 x 10^{-6} moles of silicon atoms for every square meter of surface area of a silicon dioxide surface. A 4.0 inch (10.16 cm) wafer that has been oxidized has 2 x 10^{-8} moles of silicon atoms at the surface. Since there are five active sites for the adsorption of water for each silicon atom, there are about 10^{-7} sites available for water to adsorb.

The lag time observed in etching a hydrated surface is accounted for by the time required for the adsorption of the hydrogen fluoride on the surface of the silicon dioxide. This phenomenon is called loading in the description to follow. The rate of adsorption of the hydrogen fluoride is related to the HF concentration over the surface, as illustrated by the data in Figure 2. The lag time appears to decrease as the amount of hydrogen fluoride increases.

The rate of loading of hydrogen fluoride on the surface can be estimated based upon a gas-phase model in the following manner. The gas phase acts as a high concentration source for hydrogen fluoride, while the reactions at the surface act as a sink for the adsorbed HF. The rate of transport of the HF to the surface can be assumed to be controlled by the diffusion rate of the HF from the gas bulk to the surface.

A certain fraction of the HF molecules that strike the surface actually bond to the surface. The diffusion expression, when multiplied by a coefficient that represents the fraction of molecules that stick, represents the rate of adsorption. If the coefficient is less than one, adsorption is the rate controlling mechanism, or if the coefficient is equal to one, then diffusion is the rate controlling mechanism for HF loading. The rate of accumulation of hydrogen fluoride on the surface can then be estimated using the diffusion equation shown in Equation 4.

$$Vr|_{Accum} = A(1-\theta)\beta D_{HF,M}\frac{\partial n_{HF}}{\partial y}|_{\bullet} \qquad (4)$$

Here V and A are the characteristic volume and area, θ is the fraction of available sites for hydrogen fluoride adsorption, β is the sticking coefficient, and $D_{HF,M}$ is the rate of diffusion of hydrogen fluoride. The partial differential is the molar flux of HF evaluated at the surface, and θ is defined in Equation 5 as the number of sites where adsorption has occurred, n, divided by the total number of adsorption sites, n^*.

$$\theta = n_{NH_\bullet}/n^* \qquad (5)$$

Determination of β

An estimate of the sticking coefficient, β, is needed for a description of the lag phenomenon. This estimate is determined from data shown in Figure 2. For each of the five different flow rates of hydrogen fluoride, a least-squares curve fit was used to determine at what time the reaction began, based on the time axis intercept.

Table 3 shows that as the surface is subjected to a higher concentration of hydrogen fluoride, the time before the reaction commences decreases. This decrease is not linear with respect to the concentration because it is dependent upon the diffusion rate, which, in turn, depends upon the HF concentration gradient at the surface.

Table 3.   Observed Time Lag As A
            Function Of Concentration.

HF Conc. ($gmol/cm^3$)	Time Lag (sec)	r^2
0.00022	6.76	0.9952
0.00037	3.68	0.9973
0.00045	2.88	0.9991
0.00052	2.08	0.9990
0.00060	1.81	0.9967

Voronin [7] found that 90 to 95 percent of the sites available for hydrogen fluoride adsorption must be filled before the reaction begins. For the purpose of determining β , the percentage of sites filled before the reaction begins is assumed to be 94 percent. This assumption will be justified later.

Equation 5 is substituted into Equation 4 with the resulting expression, Equation 6, used to determine β .

$$V \frac{dn_{HF}|_s}{dt} = A \left[1 - \frac{n_{HF}|_s}{n^*} \right] \beta D_{HF,M} \frac{\partial n_{HF}}{\partial y}\Big|_s \quad (6)$$

Here, V represents the volume where the reaction occurs. Since the reaction occurs at a surface, an assumption must be made to give the same basis to A and V. The volume chosen is an incremental volume above the surface represented by $A(\Delta y)$. Then the diffusive flux is discretized using a forward difference. This results in the transformation of Δy into the step width, h. The accumulation of hydrogen fluoride at the surface due to adsorption is given by

$$\frac{dn_{HF}|_s}{dt} = \left[1 - \frac{n_{HF}|_s}{n^*} \right] \beta D_{HF,M} \frac{n_{HF}|_h - n_{HF}|_s}{h^2} \quad (7)$$

where $n/_s$ is the number of moles at the surface and $n/_h$ is the number of moles at a height h above the surface. This derivation results in the assumption that the region of the reaction from the surface to one step width above the surface is identical to a continuous stirred tank reactor (CSTR). The properties in this region are considered constant, with no convective or diffusive fluxes.

With the information in Table 3, β can be found for each concentration. The resulting values for the sticking coefficient are shown in Table 4.

Based on the   results shown in Table 4, the value of β
selected for the simulation is 6.3 x 10^{-6}. When β has this value
and the appropriate lag time is assigned at the various flow rates,
the percentage of surface covered by hydrogen fluoride as a function
of the concentration is within the range of 92 to 95 percent.   This
is listed in Table 5.   The result   is in agreement with what was
observed by Voronin [7].   The assumption that the reaction begins
when 94 percent of the surface sites are filled at any flow rate
appears valid and is used in the simulation, since the largest error
in this determination is 2 percent.

Table 4.   Sticking Coefficient At
             Varying HF Concentrations

HF Conc. (gmol/cm^3)

0.00022	6.0 x 10^{-7}
0.00037	6.0 x 10^{-7}
0.00045	6.2 x 10^{-7}
0.00052	7.0 x 10^{-7}
0.00060	6.9 x 10^{-7}

Table 5.   Percentage Of Sites Filled At The
             Reaction Onset With β = 6.3 x 10^{-6}
             At Various HF Concentrations

HF Conc. (gmol/cm^3)	Percent of Sites	Percent Error
0.00022	94.5	+0.5
0.00037	95.0	+1.0
0.00045	94.5	+0.5
0.00052	92.0	-2.0
0.00060	92.5	-1.5

Two-Reaction Mechanism

The rate expressions for the two-reaction mechanism, Equation 8,
are determined from Equation 1.   The rate expressions describe the
rate of change of the apparent number of moles of each component at
the surface.

$$\frac{dn_{HF}|_s}{dt} = -4k_1 n_{HF}|_s - 4k_2 n_{HF}|_s n_{H_2O}|_s^2 \qquad (8A)$$

$$\frac{dn_{H_2O}|_s}{dt} = 2k_1 n_{HF}|_s + 2k_2 n_{HF}|_s n_{H_2O}|_s^2 \qquad (3B)$$

$$\frac{dn_{SiF_4}|_s}{dt} = k_1 n_{HF}|_s + k_2 n_{HF}|_s h_{H_2O}|_s^2 \qquad (8C)$$

The rate of accumulation at the surface is equal to the rate of adsorption plus the rate of reaction. The overall mechanism of reaction is different than the overall mechanism for adsorption. For the reaction mechanism, the rate of accumulation of any species in the flow regime is zero. Setting the rate of accumulation equal to zero in Equation 4 results in an expression that can be used to solve for the apparent number of moles of hydrogen fluoride at the surface. Similar expressions apply to the other components. Combining the assumption of no accumulation at the surface with the requirement that the rate of adsorption and reaction is matched by the rate of diffusion to the surface results in Equation 9. As before, the modelling is based on the gas phase, with the reactions at the surface entering as boundary conditions.

$$O = \chi D_M \frac{\partial n}{\partial y}\Big|_s + r|_{React} \qquad (9)$$

Here χ is the sticking coefficient for the kinetic mechanism. The rate of adsorption during reaction is just the rate of diffusion multiplied by the constant, χ. If χ is less than 1.0, then the rate of adsorption controls this mechanism. However, if the coefficient is equal to 1.0, then the rate of diffusion is the controlling rate. The reaction sticking coefficient will only affect the rate expression of hydrogen fluoride, as was the case in the overall adsorption mechanism. χ is 1.0 for all other flow components.

Initially, only the rate constant for the first reaction is known. This value was determined from data taken by Tyapkina and Guseva [8]. A reaction on a wafer that was prepared by dry-oxidation showed an etch rate about 0.5 angstroms/sec. The value of the rate constant was backed out using the simulation described by Clements et al. [13]. The rate constant for the dry reaction, k_1, was varied until the etch rate matched the rate observed by Tyapkina and Guseva. The rate constant at this etch rate is approximately 2.5×10^{-4} sec^{-1}.

With k_1 known, the value for k_2 can be determined through a search technique. An approximate rate constant must be determined to find the time dependence of the reaction system. The value of   is initially set equal to 1.0. The results with the adsorption coefficient at this value will show how the kinetics depend on the diffusion controlled system of equations and whether adsorption is important.

To find the rate constant, a reaction with known surface removal characteristics is chosen. For the results given here, the stream consists of 15 lit/min of nitrogen, 2 lit/min of water-saturated nitrogen, and 0.5 lit/min of hydrogen fluoride. This base case is used throughout as a basis for initial comparison of the simulation to the actual data. The simulation is run with this base case as the input with an etch time of 10 seconds. k_2 is varied to determine the sensitivity of the reaction system to the rate constant. The rate constant that provides the greatest removal is chosen as a candidate for the rate constant, since it corresponds to the diffusion controlled system.

The sensitivity of the results for the mechanism as a function of k_2 is shown in Figure 3. At values of $k_2 < 10^5$, the mechanism seems to be dominated by the first reaction. The amount of surface removed is around 3.0 angstroms. As k_2 is increased, the second reaction begins to compete. When k_2 exceeds 10^7, the second reaction dominates the kinetic mechanism. As k_2 is increased further, the amount of surface removed dramatically increases. When k_2 reaches 7 x 10^{11}, a maximum removal of 6860 angstroms in 10 seconds occurs. As k_2 is increased further, the amount of surface removal approaches zero at values greater than 10^{14}.

The decrease in the amount of surface removal to zero is a result of limits on the rate of adsorption. There exists a minimum surface concentration of HF necessary for the reaction to be maintained. If the reaction is very fast, a large portion of the adsorbed HF will react. This results in a surface concentration well below the minimum. The reaction cannot proceed until at least the minimum amount is readsorbed. This requires a prolonged period of no reaction, resulting in very little or no surface removal.

The value for k_2 used in the two-reaction kinetic mechanism is 7 x 10^{11}. This rate constant predicts that 6860 angstroms of surface is removed in ten seconds. The actual amount removed was 1030 angstroms. Dividing these two numbers gives a value for X of 0.150. Since this is less than 1.0, the rate of adsorption is assumed to be the controlling rate in the kinetic mechanism.

The two-reaction simulation is run with the set of parameters shown in Table 6. The results of the two-reaction mechanism are shown in Figure 4.

Table 6. Parameters Used in the Two-Reaction Simulation

Parameter	Numerical Value
k_1	2.5×10^{-3}
k_2	7×10^{11}
F	2.0
β	6.3×10^{-6}
X	0.150

The results in Figure 4 indicate that the two-reaction kinetic mechanism provides an acceptable correlation for the observed data for all HF flow rates except the flow rate at 0.6 l/min at etch times between 5 and 20 seconds. The predicted removals at 0.6 l/min are in excess of the observed removals by more than 100 angstroms.

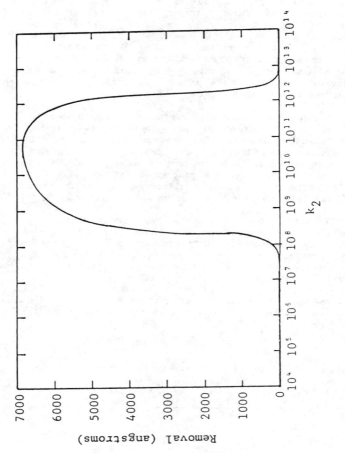

Figure 3.   Sensitivity of the two-reaction mechanism to k_2

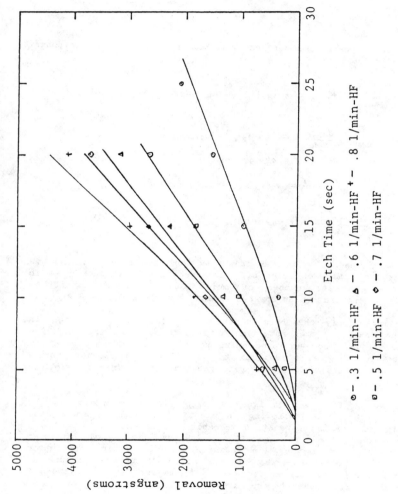

Figure 4.   Comparison of removal data with the two-reaction
mechanism

The error seems to increase at etch times around 20 seconds for large HF flow rates. There is also an error at low etch times. However, even though the percent error is large for the 5 second runs, the difference in the values is no greater than 145 angstroms.

Three-Reaction Mechanism

The rate expressions, derived from Equation 1, for each component are shown in Equation 10.

$$\frac{dn_{HF}|s}{dt} = -4k_1 n_{HF}|_{\bullet} - 4k_3 n_{HF}|_{\bullet} n_{Si(OH)_4}|_{\bullet} \qquad (10A)$$

$$\frac{dn_{H_2O}|_{\bullet}}{dt} = 2k_1 n_{HF}|_{\bullet} - 2k_2 n_{HF}|_{\bullet} n_{H_2O}|_{\bullet}^2 \qquad (10B)$$
$$+ 4k_3 n_{HF}|_{\bullet} n_{Si(OH)_4}|_{\bullet}$$

$$\frac{dn_{SiF_4}|_{\bullet}}{dt} = k_1 n_{HF}|_{\bullet} + k_3 n_{HF}|_{\bullet} n_{Si(OH)_4}|_{\bullet} \qquad (10C)$$

$$\frac{dn_{Si(OH)_4}|_{\bullet}}{dt} = k_2 n_{HF}|_{\bullet} n_{H_2O}|_{\bullet}^2 - k_3 n_{HF}|_{\bullet} n_{Si(OH)_4}|_{\bullet} \qquad (10D)$$

where k_1, k_2, and k_3 are rate constants for each reaction, and n/s represents the number of moles of a component at the surface. As in the previous case the number of moles at a surface cannot be physically determined, so an apparent quantity must be found.

As before, only the rate constant for the first reaction is known. The remaining two rate constants must be determined using a search technique. However, the value of the third rate constant is dependent upon the value assigned to the first and second. As a result, there exists a family of rate constants that will satisfy the problem.

A value of 10^{12} was assigned a priori to k_2. This can be substantiated by the following argument. Figure 5 shows the sensitivity of the three-reaction mechanism to changes in k_3 at two different values of k_2, 10^{12} and 10^{15}. The curves for both values of k_2 are so close that they are indistinguishable at the resolution that Figure 5 provides. The maximum value of removal occurs at slightly different k_3 values for each k_2. However, the magnitude of the removal for both cases is the same.

With two of the rate constants known, k_3 can be found in the same manner as the second rate constant was determined for the two-reaction mechanism. The value of X is set equal to 1.0 to determine the sensitivity of the diffusion controlled system and to determine if the rate of adsorption is important.

The sensitivity of the mechanism to changes in the rate constant is shown in Figure 5. When k_3 is below 1.0, the mechanism is solely

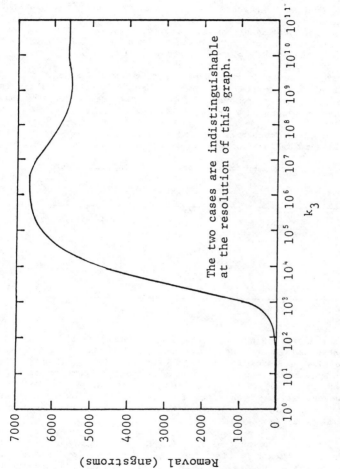

Figure 5. Sensitivity of the three-reaction mechanism with k_2 held constant at 10^{12} and 10^{15}

dependent on the first reaction. The amount of surface etched is about 3 angstroms. As k_3 exceeds 10^1, the overall mechanism becomes solely dependent on the water inclusive reaction. As the rate constant increases, the amount of surface removed increases dramatically. When k_3 approaches 10^5, the removal reaches a plateau. The greatest amount of surface removal occurs when k_3 attains a value of 3×10^6, where 6660 angstroms is removed. As the rate constant increases further, the amount of surface removed drops off to another plateau, with a value of 5670 angstroms removed.

The value for k_3 used in the three-reaction mechanism is 3×10^6. 6660 angstroms of the surface are removed when this rate constant is used. The actual amount removed is 1030 angstroms. Dividing the above two numbers provides a value for X of 0.155.

The three-reaction mechanism is implemented with the use of the parameters listed in Table 7. The results are seen in Figure 6.

Table 7. Parameters Used in the Three-Reaction Simulation

Parameter	Numerical Value
k_1	2.5×10^{-4}
k_2	10^{12}
k_3	3×10^6
F	2.0
β	6.3×10^{-6}
X	0.155

The three-reaction kinetic mechanism compares well with the actual data obtained at all HF flow rates. The mechanism is most accurate generally at medium (10 to 15 second) etch times. The three-reaction mechanism seems to be somewhat more inaccurate at high etch times for large HF flow rates, with errors as large as 17.5 percent. However, at low etch times for all of the flow rates, the match appears to be very good. Even though the percentage error is large, the absolute difference is not great.

The description of the surface reaction has two separate paths, a dry path and a wet path. The dry path involves only hydrogen fluoride as a reacting species. The hydrogen fluoride diffuses down to the surface and reacts on contact with the silicon atoms at the surface. The wet path involves the formation of an intermediate. The intermediate is formed when the water diffuses to the surface. The hydrogen fluoride is used as a catalyst. Hydrogen fluoride may prepare the surface in some way for the hydration to proceed or it may alter the characteristics of the water which leads to the hydration. Once the intermediate is formed, the hydrogen fluoride replaces the hydroxyl groups to form silicon tetrafluoride. It is apparent that the hydration reaction is many times faster than the dry reaction.

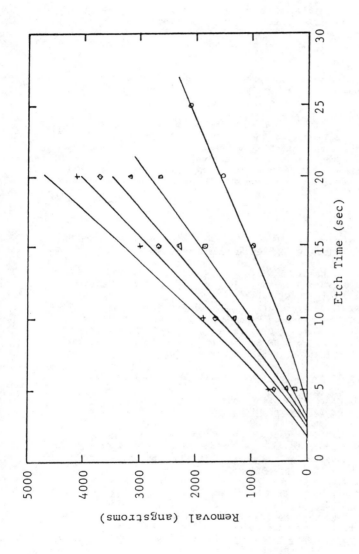

Figure 6.   Comparison of removal data with the three-reaction mechanism.

Summary

The results for both kinetic mechanisms appear to give reasonable correlations of the data. Considering both mechanisms together, 50 percent of the predictions were within 100 angstroms of the experimental result and 75 percent of the predictions were within 150 angstroms.

After etch times of 5 to 10 seconds, the etch rates for the simulated runs increase only slightly. However, the experimental data show a constant rate once the reaction starts.

The fact that the two mechanisms give essentially identical results could be explained on the basis that the $Si(OH)_4$ intermediate proposed for the three reaction mechanism appears to have a high reaction rate and may serve as an activated complex. It would be necessary to follow the surface reactions using an analytical tool such as FTIR to verify the presence of the silicon tetrahydroxide.

REFERENCES

(1) Winters, H. F. and Coburn, J. W., "The Etching of Silicon with XeF₂ Vapor," Applied Physics Letters, Vol. 34, No. 1, 1979, pp. 70-73.

(2) Beyer, K. D. and Kastl, R. H., "Impact of Deionized Water Rinses on Silicon Surface Clenaing," J. Electrochem Soc., Vol. 129, No. 5, 1982, pp. 1027-1029.

(3) Blackwood, R. S., Biggerstaff, R. L., Clements, L. D., and Cleavelin C. R., "Gaseous Process and Apparatus for Removing Films from Substrates," U.S. Patent 4,749,440, June 7, 1988.

(4) Novak, R. E., "Anhydrous HF Etching of Native SiO_2: Applications to Device Fabrication," Solid State Technology, Vol. 31, No. 3, 1988, pp. 39-41.

(5) Sze, S. M., VLSI Technology, McGraw-Hill Book Company, New York, 1983.

(6) Ruska, W. S., Microelectonic Processing, An Introduction to the Manufacture of Integrated Circuits, McGraw-Hill Book Company, New York, 1987.

(7) Voronin, E. F., "Spectroscopic Investigation of Hydrogen Fluoride Chemisorption on the Surface of Aerosils with Various Degrees of Dehydration," Zhurnal Prikladnoi Spektroscopii, Vol.42, No. 6, 1985, pp. 954-959.

(8) Tyapkina, V. V. and Guseva, N. S., "Interaction of a Silicon Surface with Fluorine and Hydrogen Fluoride," Russian Journal of Physical Chemistry, Vol. 40, No. 5, 1966, pp. 573-576.

(9) Arslambekov, V. A., Corbunova, K. M., and Guseva, N. S., "Reaction of Si with Gaseous HF," Izvestiya Akademii Nauk SSSR, Neorganicheskie Materialy, Vol. 12, 1976, pp. 2124-2126.

(10) White, L. K., "Etch Rates of SiO_2 Films in Deuterated Acidic Fluorides," Thin Solid Films, Vol. 79, 1981, pp. L73-L76.

(11) Bersin, R. L. and Reichelfelder, R. F.," The DryOx Process For Etching Silicon Dioxide," Solid State Technology, Vol. 20, No. 4, 1977, pp. 78-80.

(12) Chukin, G. D., "An IR Spectroscopic Study of the Surface Properties of Fluorinated Silica Gel," Zhurnal Prikladnoi Spektroskopii, Vol. 81, No.5, 1974, pp. 879-884.

(13) Clements, L. D., Busse, J. E., Smith, G. W., and Mehta, J.,
     "Hydrogen Fluoride Dry Etching of Silicon Dioxide: Process
     Modelling for a Laminar Flow Reactor," presented at 172nd
     Meeting of The Electrochemical Society, October 18-23, 1987,
     Honolulu, Hawaii.
(14) Busse, J. E., "The Reaction Modelling of a Vapor-Phase Semi-
     conductor Etching Process," M.S. Thesis, University of
     Nebraska-Lincoln, 1987.
(15) Cleavelin, C. R. and Duranko, G. T., "Silicon Dioxide Removal
     in Anhydrous HF Gas," Semiconductor International, Vol. 10,
     No. 12, 1987, pp 94-98.

Ching-Hwa Chen, Steve DeOrnellas, and Bill Burke

PLASMA ETCHING OF ALUMINUM ALLOYS IN BCL_3/CL_2 PLASMAS

REFERENCE: Chen, C.H., DeOrnellas, S., and Burke, B., "Plasma Etching of Aluminum Alloys in BCl_3/Cl_2 Plasmas," Semiconductor Fabrication: Technology and Metrology ASTM STP 990, Dinesh C. Gupta, editor, American Society for Testing and Materials, 1989.

ABSTRACT: Aluminum etching in BCl_3/CL_2 plasmas is characterized by studying the etch rate of aluminum and native aluminum oxide films as functions of reactant flow rates and rf power in a parallel plate plasma etcher. Results indicate that the etch rate is primarily dependent upon the Cl_2 concentration and is only slightly dependent upon the rf power used to sustain the discharge. Several additives are used to achieve the high resolution and anisotropic pattern required for aluminum alloys. Parametric studies support the roles of the additives have been made.

KEYWORDS: Aluminum etching, anisotropic profile, nitrogen mixing, spectral analysis, sheath voltage.

Plasma etching of aluminum alloys has been studied in both single wafer and batch type reactors with chlorine chemistries. (1-12) The aluminum etch rate limiting factor has been found to be the gas phase generation of active chlorine species (5). The greater the chlorine species are present, the higher the aluminum etch rate is obtained, until the reaction is limited by the desorption of product. In a single wafer reactor, a high etch rate is required for throughput considerations. A high concentration of chlorine species is therefore required to achieve the desired etch rate. This paper discusses the reactions observed in the $BCl_3/Cl_2/CHCl_3/N_2$ plasma in a single wafer reactor. BCl_3 was used to facilitate the removal of the aluminum oxide layer. $CHCl_3$ and N_2 were added to maintain the sidewall anisotropy under high chlorine concentration environments.

EXPERIMENTAL PROCEDURES:

The study was conducted on a Lam Research 4600 Metal System, which is a parallel plate, single wafer diode reactor (see Figure 1). The 4600 applies power to the top or bottom electrode. The unit is equipped with entry and exit vacuum loadlocks which permit the process chamber to remain at low pressure, free from contamination from the environment. The system applies power at 13.56 MHz. An adjustable electrode gap allows flexibility in plasma confinement and also provides optimum uniformity across a wafer. Process recipes, gas flows, wafer transport, gap setting, and end-point monitoring are micro-processor controlled for multi-step etching process. The wafers used in this study were 5 inch Al 1% Si wafers patterned with Shipley 1400 photoresist. The resist was deep UV treated and baked at $200^{\circ}C$ prior to etch to improve the resist stability in the chlorinated plasmas. Optical emission of spectrums of the etch processes were taken with a Tracor TN 6500 to analyze the etch rate mechanisms.

Mr. Chen is a manager and Mr. Burke a process engineer in the R&D department at Lam Research Corp., 4650 Cushing Parkway, Fremont, CA 94538; Mr. DeOrnellas is Vice President of Marketing at Lam Research Corp.

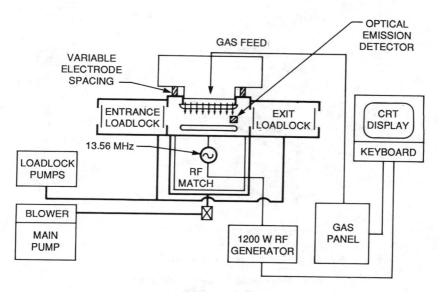

Figure 1 - LAM Research Rainbow 4600.

Results:

The following experiments were performed with 5.5 cm electrode spacing and the wafers were placed on the bottom powered electrode, unless specified otherwise.

Native Aluminum Oxide Etching: The initiation process of etching through the native aluminum oxide was found sensitive to rf power density and partial pressures of BCl_3, N_2, Cl_2 and $CHCl_3$. The initiation time was shorter under higher power density conditions (see Figure 2.) The lower powered configuration gave a shorter punch through time of the native oxide than the upper configuration. Figures 3, 4, and 5 show the trend curves of initiation time and DC bias in the Cl_2 plasmas with the addition of BCl_3, $CHCl_3$ or N_2. DC bias was found to increase with the BCl_3 and N_2 partial pressures and to decrease with the $CHCl_3$ partial pressure. These curves reveal that a higher DC bias does not necessarily shorten the native oxide punch through process. The initiation process is basically controlled by the partial pressure of the BCl and CCl reducing species.

Spectral analysis of the optical emission was performed during the initiation steps of various plasma chemistries in etching aluminum wafers. These wafers had no photoresist patterns so as to minimize the reducing carbon species that are available from the photoresist. The spectrums generated by the BCl_3/Cl_2 and BCl_3/Cl_2 $CHCl_3$ plasmas are shown in Figure 6. There are larger amounts of free Cl_2 species available in the BCl_3/Cl_2 plasma. More free Cl_2 species mean more chlorine to recombine with the CCl (259 nm) or the BCl (266 nm) reducing species, and hence lengthen the initiation time. The addition of nitrogen slows the native aluminum oxide punch through process. Spectral analysis indicates that N_2 will react with both $CHCl_3$ and BCl_3 gases. Both BCl and CCl reducing species are significantly reduced with the addition of the N_2 into the plasma.

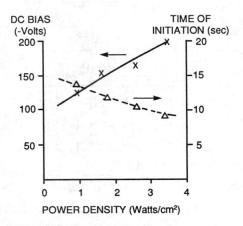

Figure 2 - Power density versus initiation process.
Other parameters include: 250 mTorr,
50 BCl_3, and 50 Cl_2.

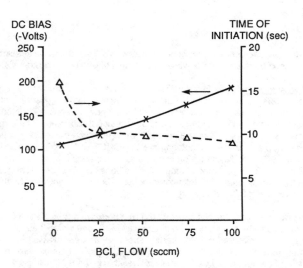

Figure 3 - BCl_3 partial pressures versus the initiation
process. The total pressure was 250 mTorr,
with 2.5 Watts/cm² power density. The total
gas flow was 100 sccm.

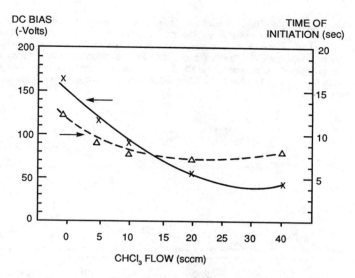

Figure 4 - Effects of $CHCl_3$ addition to BCl_3/Cl_2 plasmas during the initiation process. Other parameters include: 250 mTorr, 2.50 Watts/cm², 50 Cl_2, and 50 BCl_3.

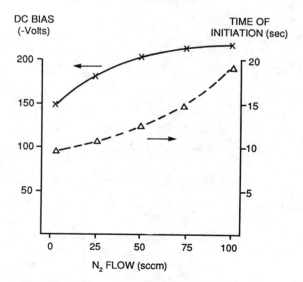

Figure 5 - Effects of N_2 addition to BCl_3/Cl_2 plasmas during the initiation process. Other parameters include: 250 mTorr, 2.50 Watts/cm², and 50 Cl_2, 50 BCl_3.

Aluminum Etching: The aluminum etch rates were measured as a function of Cl_2 flow, BCl_3 flow, $CHCl_3$ flow and the power level. The etch rate was found to be proportional to the partial pressure of the chlorine flow. The aluminum etch rate limiting factor is the gas phase generation of active Cl_2 species. The influence of the $CHCl_3$ addition to the aluminum etch rate is shown in Figure 7. Small amounts of $CHCl_3$ did not affect the etch rate, while large amounts of $CHCl_3$ might reduce the active Cl_2 species or passivate the aluminum surface and slowed the reaction.

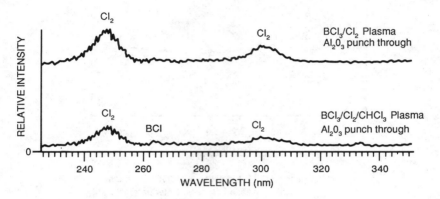

Figure 6 - Spectrums of aluminum products with either $BCl_3/Cl_2/CHCl_3$ or BCl_3/Cl_2 plasmas during the initiation process step and main etch step.

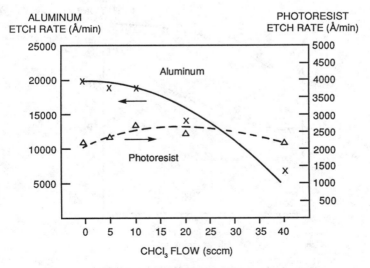

Figure 7 - $CHCl_3$ flow rates versus aluminum and photoresist etch rates. Other parameters include: 250 mTorr, 2.5 Watts/cm², 50 Cl_2, and 50 BCl_3.

It is well known that aluminum etching is purely chemical.[4] No power is required to etch aluminum after the aluminum oxide punch through process. In $BCl_3/Cl_2/CHCl_3/N_2$ plasmas, blocking species were used for the anisotropic sidewall protection. The aluminum etch rate increased slightly with the power density as shown in Figure 8. More power density perhaps promotes a better removal of the inhibitor layer on the etching surface. This inhibitor layer could be a polymerized film with CH or CCL compositions.

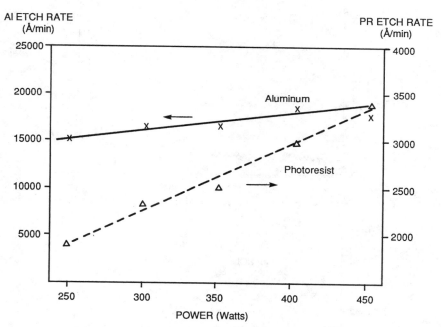

Figure 8 - Effects of power density to aluminum and photoresist etch rates. Process parameters include 250 mTorr, 50 BCl_3, 50 Cl_2, and 20 $CHCl_3$.

Many changes were observed with the addition of nitrogen into the $BCl_3/Cl_2/CHCl_3$ plasmas during the aluminum etch step. The plasma color was changed from a whitish to a pinkish color. Analysis to the spectrum (see Figure 9) confirmed that the pink color was due to the peaks (295, 315, 337, 358 nm) of the nitrogen emissions. DC bias also increased with the partial pressures of the nitrogen gas. The increase in DC bias might be oriented from a less confined plasma with the increase of the N_2 flow. The less confined plasma will give higher area ratio and higher DC bias. Higher DC bias tend to give a better anisotropic etch under similar plasma conditions. Figure 10 shows the comparison of the aluminum anisotropy in $BCl_3/Cl_2/CHCl_3$ plasmas with and without the additions of nitrogen. To illustrate the role of nitrogen, an isotropic recipe was used to see the difference on the sidewall anisotropy. Process anisotropy was significantly improved with the nitrogen addition into the plasma, as shown in Figure 10. However, the presence of nitrogen into the plasma complicates many reactions, and additional experimentation is needed to fully understand its role.

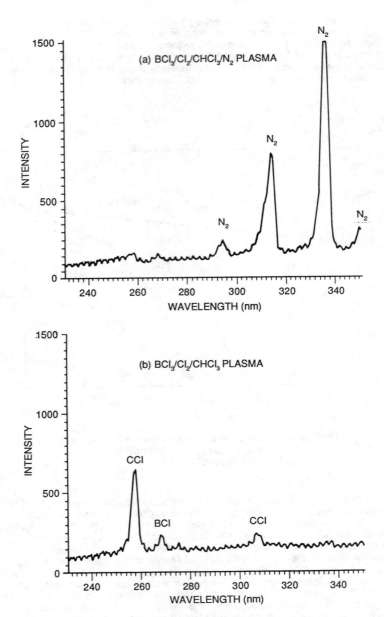

Figure 9 - Spectrums during aluminum etch processes
(a) $BCl_3/Cl_2/CHCl_3/N_2$, (b) $BCl_3/Cl_2/CHCl_3$.

(a) Cl$_2$/BCl$_3$/CHCl$_3$/N$_2$ PLASMA

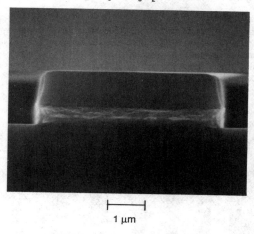

1 μm

(b) Cl$_2$/BCl$_3$/CHCl$_3$ PLASMA

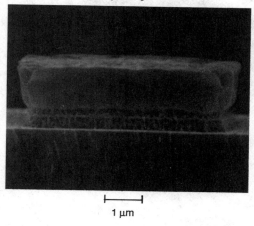

1 μm

Figure 10 - Effects of N$_2$ to the aluminum sidewall anisotropy,
(a) Cl$_2$/BCl$_3$/CHCl$_3$/N$_2$ plasma, (b) Cl$_2$/BCl$_3$/CHCl$_3$ plasma.

Almost no CCl (259 nm) species were observed in the plasma with nitrogen addition. CCl species might be consumed through the reaction with N_2 specie. We were unable to trace the CN (387 nm) band in both plasmas due to the broad band products obtained around 387 nm.

A scanning electron micrograph of a 1.5 um minimum feature is shown in Figure 11. The wafer was etched into a 1.0 μm Al-1% Si film using a Cl_2, BCl_3, $CHCl_3$, N_2 gas mixture. The etching was completed in a 65 second cycle after a 12 second initiation period. However, after etching, the wafer was left in the reactive discharge for an additional 30 second overetch to accentuate the absence of undercutting. This is reflected in a vertical sidewalls.

Al-Si

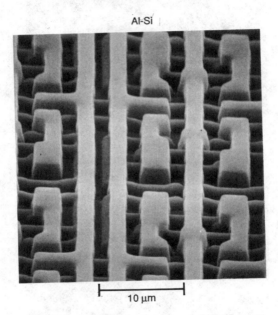

|← 10 μm →|

Figure 11 - Aluminum features 1.5 μm wide etched with
a mixture of Cl_2, BCl_3, $CHCl_3$, N_2.
The total pressure was 200 mTorr,
with 2.5 Watts/cm², and 13.56 MHz rf power.

Summary

A $BCl_3/Cl_2/CHCl_3/N_2$ plasma process is discussed to etch aluminum alloys in a single wafer diode reactor. The breakdown of the native aluminum oxide was found to be controlled mainly through the reduction process. Process anisotropy is enhanced with the addition nitrogen. One micron per minute aluminum etch rates are achieved in the single wafer diode reactor.

ACKNOWLEDGEMENTS

The authors acknowledge with appreciation the help of H. Nguyen, L. Adkins, M.Chang and D. McGowan in the preparation of this paper.

REFERENCES

1)   Danner, D.A. and Hess, D.W., Journal of Electrochemical
     Society, Vol. 133, January 1986, page 151.

2)   Sinha, A.K., "Interconnect Materials Technology for
     VLSI," Proceedings of the First International Symposiumon
     VLSI Science and Technology, The Electrochemical
     Society, 1982.

3)   Schaible, P.M., Metzger, W.C., and Anderson, J.,
     Journal of Vacuum Science Technology Vol. 15, 334,
     1978.

4)   Choe, D. and Knapp, C., "Selective Aluminum Alloy
     Etching," Solid State Technology, page 165, March 1985.

5)   Hess, D.W., "Plasma Etching of Aluminum," Solid State
     Technology, page 189, April 1981.

6)   Mizutani, T., Komatsu, H. and Harada, S., "A New Al
     Plasma Etching Technology for Fine Metallization of
     Highly Packed LSI," 582, IEDM 81.

7)   Blech, I., 10th AIME 1982 Electrochemical Symposium,
     Santa Clara, 1982.

8)   Evans, S.A., Morris, S.A., Arledge, L.A., Englade, J.O.
     and Fuller, C.R., IEEE Trans. Electron Devices, ED 27,
     1373 (1980).

9)   Schaible, P.M., Metzger, W.C. and Anderson, J.P.,
     Journal of Vacuum Science Technology, 16, 377 (1979).

10) Morgab, C.J. and Levinstein, H.J., Journal of Vacuum
     Science Technology, 17, 72 (1980).

11) Purdes, A.J., Journal of Vacuum Science Technology,
     Vol. A, 1.712 (1953).

12) Winters, H.F. Journal of Vacuum Science Technology,
     Vol. B, 3.9 (1985).

13) Chapman, B., "Glow Discharge Process", page 158 (1980).

Microcontamination

Thomas R. Lettieri

NBS SUBMICRON PARTICLE STANDARDS FOR MICROCONTAMINATION MEASUREMENT

REFERENCE: Lettieri, T. R., "NBS Submicron Particle Standards for Microcontamination Measurement," Semiconductor Fabrication: Technology and Metrology, ASTM STP 990, Dinesh C. Gupta, Ed., American Society for Testing and Materials, Philadelphia, 1989.

ABSTRACT: There is a recognized need for standard artifacts with which to calibrate the laser-scanning instruments which detect and monitor microcontamination on semiconductor wafers. Although commercial calibration wafers are available for this purpose, the present paper proposes the use of National Bureau of Standards (NBS) particle-sizing standard microspheres, deposited on polished silicon substrates, as an alternative working standard until such time as a true national calibration artifact is developed. To this end, several techniques for depositing the microspheres on semiconductor surfaces are presented in the paper. In addition, the techniques used to certify the NBS particle standards and the measurement results from each technique are summarized.

KEYWORDS: contamination, laser scanning, microspheres, particulates, semiconductor wafers, standards

The contamination of semiconductor wafers by microparticulates has been recognized as one of the major problem areas in the fabrication of VLSI circuits and other semiconductor devices. Contaminant particles (as well as scratches and pits) can decrease the yield rate by causing short circuits, photolithographic errors, and other problems which degrade device performance [1]. Contaminant particles can occur at any step in the processing of a wafer, and a great deal of effort has been expended in controlling them. These include: class 10 or better clean rooms, ultra-filtration of processing liquids, clean garments on production workers, and laminar-flow air circulators. Yet the problem of unwanted particle contamination remains today and, indeed, is expected to get worse as IC features approach 0.1 um in size [1].

LASER-SCANNING INSTRUMENTS FOR DETECTION OF MICROCONTAMINATION

To detect and monitor the presence of unwanted contaminants during the wafer-processing cycle, several instruments based on laser scanning

Dr. Lettieri is a physicist at the National Bureau of Standards, Met-A117, Gaithersburg, MD 20899.

have been developed and are now commercially available (Figure 1).
These instruments can measure the locations, amounts, and sizes of
particulate contaminants, pits, and scratches. Up to now, however,
these measurements have been rather qualitative, making it difficult to
make meaningful intercomparisons between contamination measurements made
with instruments from different manufacturers.

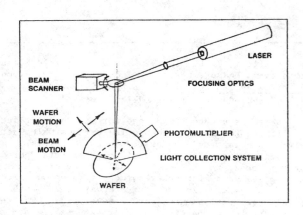

FIG. 1 -- Schematic diagram of laser-scanning instrument for microcontamination detection [from Ref. 2].

     In order to make more quantitative measurements with laser-scanning
instruments, they must be calibrated in some manner for absolute
particle size and concentration. This can be done in at least two ways:
(i) by comparison with a standard artifact or (ii) by comparison with
a theoretical model for laser scattering from a particle on a surface.
One quantity of special interest, the lower size limit for detection of
a microparticle (i.e., the sensitivity), has been difficult to determine
since it depends strongly on the physical and chemical characteristics
of the particle, in particular its shape and composition. In addition,
there is evidence that the size of a contaminant particle, as measured
by laser-scanning instruments, depends on the substrate material [3].

     Clearly, there is need for either a standard artifact or a
theoretical model with which to calibrate laser-scanning instruments.

STANDARD WAFERS FOR INSTRUMENT CALIBRATION

     In response to the need for a standard artifact, several vendors
now fabricate and sell calibrated wafers for routine monitoring of
contamination-detection instruments; an example is shown in Figure 2.
These commercial standards contain both fabricated features with
controlled geometry and microspheres deposited in a controlled manner
[3,4]. The former simulate the effects of contaminant particles, and

are fabricated at a variety of spacings in order to correspond to a
range of particle sizes.

    Although   these   commercial products are useful for   routine
application on the production line, what is actually needed is a
national standard artifact to which all semiconductor manufacturers can
reference their measurements;   there are no such standards currently
being developed at the national level.

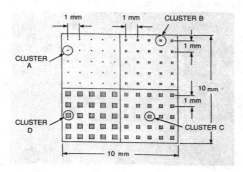

FIG. 2 -- Example of a commercial standard for surface contamination
measurement [from Ref. 3].

    As an interim standard, the National Bureau of Standards (NBS) is
now selling a series of monosized polystyrene microspheres calibrated
for mean diameter; these can be deposited on a silicon wafer for use as
a working standard in laser-scanning instruments.   [The advantage of
this type of particle-on-wafer calibration artifact is that it would
more closely resemble a real world situation than would a silicon wafer
with fabricated features.] As a working standard, a silicon wafer
containing the NBS microspheres could be used for daily calibration and
performance-monitoring of contamination-detection instruments.   However,
it would still not be valid as an absolute standard for intercomparing
measurements made on different instruments.

    As noted by Berger [3], a silicon wafer with polystyrene
microspheres deposited on it is a logical choice for a calibration
artifact for contamination-detection instruments for several reasons:
(i)   polystyrene microspheres have a well-defined shape   (nearly
spherical); (ii) they are available in a wide range of diameters (from
about 0.05 um up to several hundred micrometres); (iii) their size
distribution is narrow; and (iv) their optical properties are well-
known.   For most applications in the semiconductor industry, the
polystyrene microspheres available from commercial suppliers   are
calibrated accurately enough.   However, if a high-accuracy standard is
desired, then the NBS series of particle-sizing Standard Reference

Materials (SRMs) can be used.

The remainder of this paper outlines the techniques by which the NBS particle-sizing SRMs were certified, the results and accuracies of the techniques, and the potential use of the SRMs in the development of calibration artifacts for surface-contamination instruments.

NBS STANDARD REFERENCE MATERIALS FOR PARTICLE SIZING

The NBS particle-sizing SRM microspheres, developed in a cooperative program with ASTM, will ultimately range in diameter from 0.1 um to 100 um; the 0.3, 0.9, 10, and 30 um SRMs are currently available and the 0.1, 3, and 100 um SRMs will be available soon. All of the NBS microspheres are made of polystyrene and each SRM sample has a very narrow size distribution. Of the seven particle-sizing SRMs to be certified by NBS, three have dimensions less than 1 um, making them of special interest to producers of ICs and microcontamination-detection equipment.

SRM 1691:   Nominal 0.3-um-Diameter Spheres

The smallest particle-sizing SRM now available from NBS is the nominal 0.3-um-diameter polystyrene spheres, SRM 1691 (Figure 3). They are sold in 5 ml vials at a weight concentration of particles of about 0.5%. For these microspheres, two methods were used to determine a mean diameter: transmission electron microscopy (TEM) and quasi-elastic light scattering (QELS). In the TEM measurements, the nominal 1-um-diameter spheres (SRM 1690) were used to set the dimensional scale (Figure 3). The results from each technique are given in Table 1.

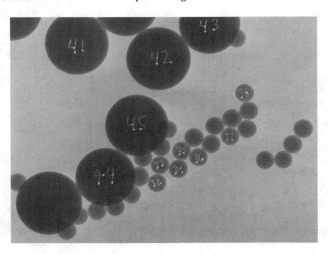

FIG. 3 -- TEM photomicrograph of 0.269 and 0.895 um SRM spheres.

Neither technique was able to detect a size distribution for this
material.

TABLE 1 -- Results for SRM 1691.

Technique	Diam., um	Uncertainty, um
TEM	•0.269	± 0.007
QELS	0.276	± 0.007

SRM 1690: Nominal 1.0-um-Diameter Spheres

    Three methods were used in the certification of the nominal 1-um-
diameter polystyrene spheres, SRM 1690 (Figure 3): Mie light scattering
from particles in liquid, Mie light scattering from single particles,
and optical array sizing [5].   The mean-diameter measurements from all
three agreed to within their stated uncertainties and are presented in
Table 2.   This SRM is also sold in 5 ml vials at a volume concentration
of about 0.5%.

    The first result in Table 2, that from light scattering from
particles in liquid suspension, was taken to be the certified mean
diameter.   The size distribution of this material was determined to be
very narrow (standard deviation about 0.009 um), and there were
relatively few outliers (less than 0.6% oversized and undersized
outliers not on the main distribution peak).

TABLE 2 -- Results for SRM 1690.

Technique	Diam., um	Uncertainty, um
LS from suspension	0.895	± 0.008
LS from single spheres	0.900	± 0.011
Array sizing	0.900	± 0.015

Future Submicron SRM: Nominal 0.1-um-Diameter Spheres

    As IC feature size approaches 0.1 um, the need becomes greater for
a particle standard in this size range.   Several techniques may be used
at NBS for certifying this future submicron SRM including QELS, small-
angle X-ray scattering, and array sizing using an electron microscope.
Pending receipt of suitable material, current plans call for completing
the certification of this SRM by early- to mid-1988.

NBS PARTICLE-SIZING SRM APPLICATIONS IN MICROCONTAMINATION MEASUREMENT

    Because of their accurate mean diameters, narrow size distributions, and high sphericities, NBS particle-sizing SRMs can be used in their present form as a working standard for monitoring the size distribution of contaminant particles on semiconductor wafers. [Note, however, that they are not useful for concentration measurements since particle concentration was not accurately determined for the bottled SRM.] To be useful for contamination-monitoring and sizing purposes, the SRM particles must first be deposited on an appropriate substrate, such as a polished silicon wafer. There are several ways this can be done: (a) applying a drop to a wafer straight from the SRM bottle; (b) dipping a wafer into a diluted suspension of the microspheres; and (c) nebulizing a diluted SRM sample and letting the particles fall onto a wafer. Once the particles are deposited, they will adhere tightly to the substrate due to the strong van der Waals and other forces present [6].

Although (a) is the easiest deposition technique, the problem is that the dried patch of particles will be covered with a layer of surfactant and biocide, which are added to the bottled samples of SRM material. In addition, the microspheres will in general form close-packed structures which are too concentrated for measurement by a laser-scanning instrument. The second method (b) gives a much better result if the SRM is diluted by three to five orders of magnitude (that is, to about 5 to 0.05 ppm of particles by weight). This dilutes the surfactant and biocide, and also reduces the average density of microspheres on the substrate. However, it is difficult to control this particle-deposition process, and there will still be localized regions of high particle concentration, as well as contacting strings of particles. These can cause problems in laser-scanning instruments.

The final method (c), allows the greatest control of particle deposition. Here, the SRM sample is first diluted by 3 to 5 orders of magnitude, and then repeatedly washed by centrifuging the diluted sample and pouring off the supernatant liquid. About 3 or 4 washings is sufficient. Next, the diluted sample is atomized, and the wafer left in the falling spray of particles for a preset amount of time in order to get the desired density of particles per unit area. Using this procedure, the concentration should be fairly uniform across the wafer.

Once the working standard wafer has been made, it should be kept in a clean environment (class 10 or better) and should be checked periodically for particle count and size by at least one other independent technique (for example, optical microscopy).

CONCLUSIONS

As discussed in this paper, there is a definite need in the semiconductor industry for standard artifacts with which to calibrate laser-scanning instruments for microcontamination detection. Such artifacts would promote accuracy and uniformity in measurements throughout the industry, and would allow quantitative intercomparison of instrument specifications. One possibility for an interim, working standard for use in a semiconductor facility is the NBS/ASTM series of submicron polystyrene SRM particles deposited on polished silicon wafers. The NBS particles are well-characterized for mean diameter and are very monosized, although the local particle concentrations on the wafer would have to be accurately determined by some independent means.

When the time comes to develop national calibration artifacts for microcontamination measurement, the work could be carried out at NBS under the aegis of an appropriate ASTM committee; this would permit direct traceability to NBS. Note, however, that it will still be necessary to correlate measurements made on these artifacts with measurements made on actual contaminated semiconductor wafers. To address this and related problems, an ASTM subcommittee could be formed for the purpose of developing standard procedures for using the artifact to measure semiconductor contaminants and standard procedures for interpreting and presenting the data. A logical choice for this group is the ASTM F-1.04 subcommittee on Semiconductor Physical Properties.

REFERENCES

[1] Fisher, W. G., "Particle Monitoring in Clean Room Air with the TSI 3020 Condensation Nucleus Counter," TSI Journal of Particle Instrumentation, Vol. 2, No. 1, Jan.-June 1987, pp. 3-19.
[2] Gise, P., "Measuring and Specifying Particle Contamination by Process Equipment: Part III, Calibration," Microcontamination, January 1986, pp. 51-55.
[3] Berger, J. and Tullis, B. J., "Calibration of Surface-Particle Detectors," Microcontamination, July 1987, pp. 24-29.
[4] Monteverde, R., Ervin, R., and Berger, J., "Uniform Latex Spheres Standardize Surface Particle Detection," Research and Development, June, 1986, pp. 90-93.
[5] Mulholland, G. W., Hartman, A. W., Hembree, G. G., Marx, E., and Lettieri, T. R., "Development of a One-Micrometer-Diameter Particle Size Standard Reference Material," Journal of Research of the National Bureau of Standards, Vol. 90, No. 1, Jan.-Feb. 1985, pp. 3-26.
[6] Khilnani, A. and Matsuhiro, D., "Adhesion Forces in Particle Removal from Wafer Surfaces," Microcontamination, April 1986, pp. 28-30.

Susan H. Goldsmith and George P. Grundelman

PARTICULATE CLEANLINESS TESTING OF FILTERS AND EQUIPMENT IN PROCESS FLUIDS

REFERENCE: Goldsmith, S.H. and Grundelman, G.P., "Particulate Cleanliness Testing of Filters and Equipment in Process Fluids," Semiconductor Fabrication: Technology and Metrology, ASTM STP 990, Dinesh C. Gupta, editor, American Society for Testing and Materials, 1989.

ABSTRACT: Filters and equipment components used in critical semiconductor process lines must be accurately evaluated for particulate cleanliness. This requires accurate test methods, particle counting instruments, testing apparati, and careful analysis of data. This paper describes these criteria and how they can be applied.

KEYWORDS: Particulate cleanliness, cleanliness testing, particle counting, and filter cleanliness.

Susan H. Goldsmith is Director of Engineering, and George P. Grundelman is President of Inter Basic Resources, Inc. 727 W. Ellsworth Rd. Ann Arbor, MI 48108.

222

INTRODUCTION

Particulate cleanliness evaluations have been performed in both liquids and gases on a wide variety of filters and components, including piping fittings, valves, flow controllers, and filters [1,2]. In general, evaluations are done to compare relative cleanliness of the test samples. For instance, comparisons of different cleaning methods, materials of construction, and manufacturers can be made.

The very low particulate levels of many filters and components require that rigorous attention be given to four areas. These are test method, particle counting instrumentation, test apparatus, and analysis of data.

TEST METHOD GOALS

Meaningful particulate cleanliness tests must be capable of evaluating three distinct phases of shedding. The first is the initial particulate level. This shedding is typically caused by manufacturing debris. The second is particulate level as a function of time or flush volume. This shedding is typically caused not only by manufacturing debris, but also by loose particles from the filter or component itself. The test for this phase indicates how long a filter or component should be precleaned before installation on a critical line. The third phase of shedding is due to instability of the filter or component under stress or use. This may be from mechanical shock, vibration, or simply extended use (e.g. valves actuated over 10,000 cycles). Samples which show shedding and instability under these test conditions should not be specified for process lines which experience these conditions.

Meaningful test methods must also reflect actual use conditions. These include flow rates, pressures, temperatures (including gradients), and component operation.

Accurate test methods must provide a uniform basis for comparison of results from different facilities or labs. Specifically, this means that any test method must:

- Use commercially available and calibrated instrumentation
- Specify test conditions which can be reproduced by commercially available test equipment.

DESCRIPTION OF CURRENT METHODS

Methods are similar for filters or components. Methods for liquid and gas-line filters are being reviewed by ASTM F01.10 committe for process contamination. These methods consist of challenging the test sample with ultracleaned water or air which has been prefiltered. Effluent counts from the test sample are continuously monitored throughout the test. Apparati for gas and liquid tests are shown in Figures 1 and 2.

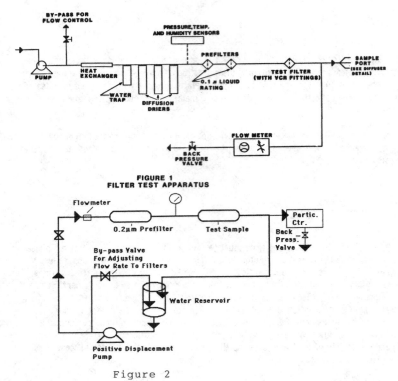

FIGURE 1
FILTER TEST APPARATUS

Figure 2

Particulate Cleanliness
Test Apparatus for Liquids

Before the test sample is installed, both the system and particle counter(s) are evaluated for background counts. System background is determined by installing a precleaned filter or component into the test loop. This system background is monitored for a time at least equal to the anticipated test time. System backgrounds for liquid tests should be less than 10 counts per liter greater than 0.5μm. System backgrounds for air tests should be less than 2 counts per ft^3 greater than 0.014μm. Particle counter background is determined by installing a precleaned filter at the inlet of the sensor, and then monitoring counts until a counter background mean and standard deviation is determined with a variance of under 0.05.

After backgrounds have been determined, the test sample is installed into the test stand. To minimize extraneous contamination, this should be done under Class 100 conditions, and the technician should wear talc-free gloves.

The initial portion of the test is conducted under steady conditions. This portion of the test evaluates both the initial cleanliness level and cleanliness as a function of time. After this, specific stress testing for specialized applications is performed. This may include mechanical shock, pressure shock, flow or temperature ramping, or extensive operation or wear of the test sample.

CLEANLINESS DATA REPORTS

Cleanliness test data must be reported with full descriptions of the following items:

- Test sample description
- Test system instrumentation description (including sampling methods and volumes).
- System background ,as counts per unit of volume and sample volume
- Particle counter background, as mean counts per unit of volume and variance
- Test sample effluent counts vs. time and conditions
- Operating conditions

Data should be presented and analyzed both graphically and in summary form by Poisson statistics.

Liquid Sampling Techniques and Considerations:

Liquids should be sampled by the particle counter under pressure. Numerous papers[3] have shown that pressure is required to prevent bubble formation in the particle counter sensor. Bubbles will cause false counts, and can significantly affect data. On-line sampling is the simplest way of introducing pressurized samples to the counter sensor. Figure 3 shows a well designed liquid on-line sampler. The sample probe is inserted into an elbow, with the probe's inlet facing directly into the flow stream. Sample tubing must be sized to prevent particle loss due to settling. In addition, sampling lines must be configured to prevent particle loss by impaction or entrapment. All flow controls and meters should be downstream of the sensor.

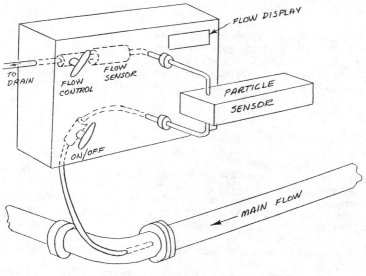

LIQUID ON-LINE SAMPLER
Figure 3

On-line sampling is not possible when system pressures are not high enough to prevent bubble formation. In these cases, samples are drawn into ultracleaned bottles, and the bottles are sampled using a pressure sampler. See Figure 4.

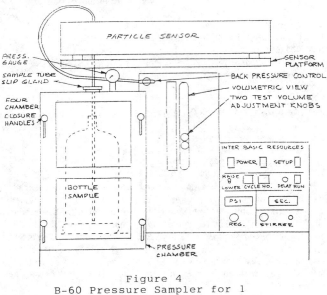

Figure 4
B-60 Pressure Sampler for 1
Gallon Bottles

Liquid particle sensor calibrations are strongly affected by flow rate and the relative refractive index of the test liquid and particles. Any sampling technique must provide accurate, pulse-free flow through the sensor. In addition, the sensor should, if possible, be calibrated in the test fluid. As an example, it has been reported [4] that a 1μm particle in sulfuric acid will scatter the same amount of light (and thus be detected by the sensor as the same) as a 0.5μm particle in water.

GAS SAMPLING TECHNIQUES AND CONSIDERATIONS

Sampling of gas streams is also best done on-line at system pressure. This reduces possible contamination and/or particle loss from pressure reduction valves or orifices. Unfortunately, only a few particle counters are capable of this. When line pressure sampling is not possible, a carefully designed pressure diffuser can provide minimal error. Figure 5 shows a properly designed diffuser. The most important features of a good diffuser are:

- Conical expansion section, to prevent particle loss and surface erosion which result from standard right-angle orifices.
- Outer envelope with circuitous air exit to help prevent contamination from ambient air.
- Smooth, static free surfaces

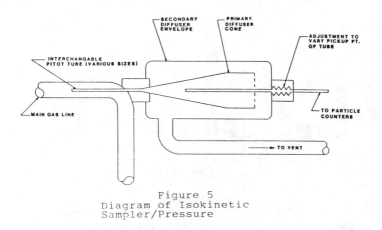

Figure 5
Diagram of Isokinetic
Sampler/Pressure

TEST APPARATUS AND DESIGN

Test apparati must be designed and constructed using techniques similar to any clean system or process. Specifically, this means avoidance of threaded fittings, static areas, valves, or gages between the final system prefilter and the particle sensor. The apparati must also allow for clean installation of test samples and simple disassembly for thorough cleaning.

Liquid test stands must be specifically designed to minimize erroneous counts due to air bubbles. This means not only maintaining adequate pressures to prevent degassing, but also providing vents to remove air.

ANALYSIS OF DATA

Cleanliness data is presented both graphically and in summary form by Poisson analysis. The most common graphical representation is particle counts as a function of time. Careful selection of the amount of time per reported count is required for accurate representation of the data. Too short a time will cause the graph to be too crowded, with less visually obvious trends in the data. Too long a time will cause data spikes and and short-term events to be hidden. See Figure 6 for a comparison of graphs from the same valve data with different time groupings.

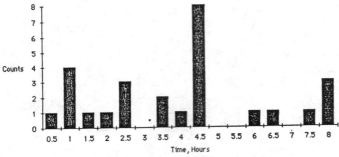

Figure 6A - Half Hour Increments

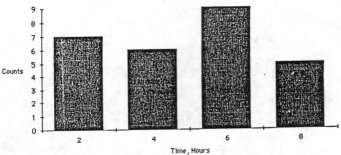

Figure 6B - Two Hour Increments

In addition to graphical representation, summary analysis of data is important for determining conclusions from data. These analyses are needed to determine if different data groups are significantly different from one another - graphical representations can be misleading. Poison distribution of counts is generally assumed when calculating means and variances of cleanliness data[5]. Comparisons of data from two different tests (e.g. components cleaned by two different methods) are done by comparing the difference of the means of the two tests with a critical value. This critical value is based on the difference of the two tests' variances, as well as the required level of confidence.

For example, a gas-line valve was first tested for initial cleanliness, and then again in a second test after 10,000 actuations. See Figure 7 for a graphical representation of these data. The initial mean count was 5 counts/ft^3, with a sample volume of 0.5 ft^3. After 10,000 actuations, the mean count was 15 counts/ ft^3, with a sample volume of 0.5 ft^3. Analysis by assuming a Poisson distribution for these two tests then will show that there is no significant difference in particulate level between these two tests. In this case, even though the graphical representation shows a significant difference in particulate level (the initial particulate level was only one third of the final level), in reality they are not statistically significantly different. For this reason, summary statistical analysis must be used in conjunction with graphical reporting.

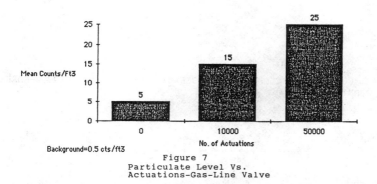

Figure 7
Particulate Level Vs.
Actuations-Gas-Line Valve

SUMMARY

Particulate cleanliness testing of critical filters and components can be very useful in the evaluation of cleaning methods, manufacturers, and determination of filter or component resistance to operation under stressful conditions. This testing must, however, be done by applying accurate testing methods, particle counting instrumentation, apparati, and data analysis.

References:

[1]   Jensen, D., and Goldsmith, S. "Evaluation of Critical Gas-Line Filters," in Journal of Environmental Sciences, Nov/Dec 1987, pp. 39-43.
[2]   Thorogood, R., and Schwartz, A., " Performance Measurement of Gas Ultrafiltration Cartridges", in IES 1986 Proceedings, pp. 459-467.
[3]   Dillenbeck, K., "Advances in Particle Counting Techniques for Semiconductor Process Chemicals," in Microcontamination, Feb 1987
[4]   Knollenberg, R., " The Importance of Media Refractive Index in Evaluating Liquid and Surface Microcontamination Measurements", in IES 1986 Proceedings, pp. 501-511.
[5]   Van Slooten, "Statistical Treatment of Particle Counts in Clean Gases", in Microcontamination, Feb 1986.

Alvin Lieberman

PARAMETERS CONTROLLING COUNTING EFFICIENCY FOR OPTICAL LIQUID-BORNE
PARTICLE COUNTERS

REFERENCE: Lieberman, A. "Parameters Controlling Counting
Efficiency for Optical Liquid-Borne Particle Counters",
Semiconductor Fabrication: Technology and Metrology, ASTM
STP 990, Dinesh C. Gupta, editor, American Society for
Testing and Materials, 1989.

ABSTRACT: Present-day optical liquid-borne particle counters (OPCs) present data in digital format, frequently
accepted as absolute by many users. However, counting
efficiency of these devices is affected by instrument
design, performance and operation. This discussion summarizes some of the pertinent parameters affecting OPC
accuracy, explains effects on data and indicates means of
maximizing OPC efficiency. Operation of OPCs using light
extinction or scattering is described, including discussion of the pertinent optical parameters. Effects on OPC
response are summarized, considering the relationships
between the optical properties of the calibration material
and typical contaminants with those of the liquid. It is
shown that as OPC response varies with differential refractive index, then particle counts for polydisperse
materials will also change.

KEYWORDS: optical particle counters, counting errors, particle properties, sampling, coincidence

Optical particle counters (OPCs) are widely used for determining particulate cleanliness in process liquids used in semiconductor
manufacturing. These instruments produce data that define both particle size and concentration in these liquids. The OPC data are
normally accepted as being valid in all cases. However, there are a
number of error sources that reduce the counting efficiency and accuracy of the OPC. A better understanding of OPC operating principles,
objectives for its use and its procedures will aid in reducing errors.

The OPC is frequently accepted as being a primary measuring

Mr. Lieberman is Technical Specialist at Particle Measuring Systems,
Inc., 46729 Fremont Blvd., Fremont, CA 94538

instrument that produces data derived solely from the pertinent parameter of particle size that is being measured.   However, the device
responds to particle size as well as other parameters of the particle-
liquid system.   Differences in OPC design and operation will also
affect the data.   This discussion will point out some parameters which
affect counting efficiency, the errors that can occur and will indicate where remedial measures can aid in improving data reproducibility.

OPC DESIGN AND CONSTRUCTION EFFECTS

Optical Effects

        The operating principle for OPCs used to characterize particu-
late content of semiconductor liquids is measurement of the scattered
light flux from individual particles in the liquid passing through a
viewing volume.   Some OPCs operate on the basis of measuring light
extinction resulting from particles in the viewing volume, but these
OPCs are never used for measurement of particles much smaller than 2
μm or so in size.   In operation, the OPC observes the difference in
light level with and without a particle in the viewing zone.   The OPC
does not detect the image of each particle in the zone; it observes
the total light level difference resulting from a change within the
viewing zone.   This change can result from passage of a single particle, an assembly of particles, a gas bubble, a filament of liquid
other than the base liquid or a change in the illumination level.

        The capability of an OPC to detect particles requires that the
illumination flux produce an adequate scattered light level from a
particle while the background optical and electrical noise is low
enough so that interference with the signal is not significant.   For
this reason, OPCs with submicrometer capability use lasers for illumination.   Either HeNe or diode lasers are used.   The direct beam from
the laser is blocked from the photodetector after passing through the
viewing zone, while scattered light is collected by a suitable optical
system.   Figures 1 and 2 each show the optical layout of a commercially available submicrometer OPC.   Note that the collection optics of
the two systems are different.

        Figure 3 shows how a particle scatters light by a combination
of refraction, diffraction and reflection.   The quantity of light
which is scattered from the particle depends on the particle size, the
index of refraction for the particle in the liquid in which it is
suspended, the wavelength of the illumination and the angles over
which the scattered light is observed.   Not shown in this sketch is
the absorption of light within the particle.   This factor will reduce
the light level after interaction with the particle.   Considering the
different optical systems of Figures 1 and 2, it is seen that the same
particle-liquid system will probably not produce the same information
from the two OPCs unless both OPCs have been calibrated with the same
material.

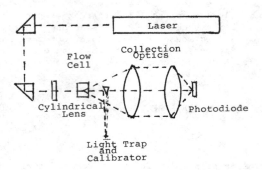

FIG. 1 -- Submicrometer Forward-Angle Optics/Flow System

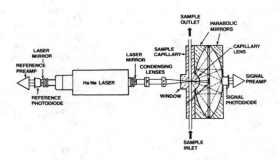

FIG. 2 -- Submicrometer Wide Angle Optics/Flow System

1. Diffraction
2. Refraction
3. Reflection

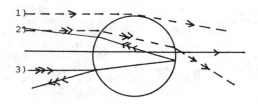

FIG. 3 -- Geometric Light Scattering

OPC sensor resolution can be defined as the ability to differentiate between two particles that are nearly the same size. If the
illumination level in the viewing volume is not uniform, then the
signal from identical particles passing through different parts of the
viewing volume will vary. Resolution can also be defined as the range
of particle sizes that may be attributed to a group of monosized,
identical particles.   It is normally stated as the relative standard
deviation of the indicated particle size over and above the relative
standard deviation of the true particle size[*]1].   The effects of
poor sensor resolution are related to the shape of typical contaminant
size distributions.   Sensors with poor resolution will undersize to
the same extent that they will oversize.   Most contaminant suspensions
are much richer in small particles than they are in large ones; therefore, many more small particles are reported than are large ones for
sensors with poor resolution.   These will tend to overcount more than
will sensors with better resolution.

    Calibration: Since OPCs respond to several particle-liquid
parameters, an empirical calibration is usually carried out before
use.   The calibration material for a light scattering OPC is normally
a water dispersion of spherical latex particles with refractive index
1.6 - 0i.   (The last term of the refractive index is related to the
absorptive power of the material.)   These spheres are available in a
wide range of sizes with relative standard deviations of 1-2%.   In
calibration, a suspension of this material is passed through the OPC
sensing zone and a pulse height distribution and relative standard
deviation determined for each specific batch of spheres.   The mean
pulse height from this material is then used as the signal level to
identify particles as having the same "equivalent optical diameter" as
that latex sphere.   Figure 4 shows monosize latex spheres.   Needless
to say, few real world particles have the same refractive index or
shape as a transparent isotropic latex sphere.

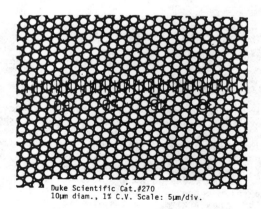

Duke Scientific Cat.#270
10μm diam., 1% C.V. Scale: 5μm/div.

FIG. 4 -- Monodisperse Latex Calibration Spheres

    As the liquid to be observed changes, then the relative refrac-
tive index of the particles in that liquid will also change.   Common

semiconductor process liquids have refractive indexes that vary from 1.29 (hydrofluoric acid) to 1.50 (xylene). Most particulate contaminants have refractive indexes close to 1.55 - 0.01i. The effect of changing liquid on relative refractive index is apparent. The same particle will appear smaller as the relative refractive index decreases. As shown by Knollenberg[a], a 1 μm latex sphere in trichloroethane would scatter the same as a 0.63 μm sphere in water. The relative refractive index problem might be handled by using equivalent optical size data on a relative basis for the same liquid, correcting mathematically for known refractive indices or by diluting <u>carefully</u> with very clean low index solvent. Figure 5 shows how dilution of sulfuric acid (refractive index 1.45) with water to a refractive index of 1.33 moves number data upwards for particles with refractive index of 1.55. Note that this procedure requires availability of clean diluent and that the original suspension have sufficient particle concentration so that the diluted material data will have statistical validity.

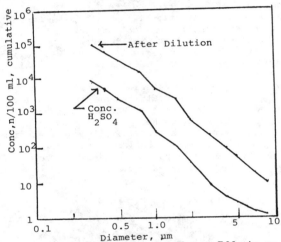

FIG. 5 -- Refractive Index Change Effects on Count

Particle Concentration Effects

Particles in a liquid are usually distributed randomly in the liquid, not uniformly. In any small batch of liquid, the particle concentration can vary widely around the average concentration. If the overall concentration becomes too high, then two effects occur that can cause problems. These are coincidence and saturation. Coincidence is defined as the simultaneous presence of more than one particle at a time in the sensing zone. Saturation is the inability of the electronic pulse-processing system to detect and size individual electrical pulses that arrive too fast for the system to respond. These problems occur only with high particle concentrations.

<u>High Concentration Effects:</u> If high concentrations of particles are present in the liquid, then both the concentration and the par-

ticle size reported can be in error. The indicated concentration will be lower than the true value and the particle size distribution will shift towards larger sizes since pulses from two or more small particles is indicated as a single particle of larger size. The true particle concentration can be calculated from an equation derived from probability theory[³]. This equation states that the ratio of indicated to true concentration is equal to one minus half the product of true concentration and viewing volume. This version of the exponential equation is valid to the point where that product is less than 0.1. This value also reflects the average view volume population.

If the concentration of particles in the liquid increases above the 10% view volume population level, then indicated concentration levels become much smaller; eventually, the OPC indicates zero count. This occurs when one or more particles is present within the view volume at all times and the scattered light level never decreases so that the electronic system can reset. Another situation can occur with very high concentrations. If the liquid contains a very high concentration of very small particles that are below the detection level of the OPC, randomly varying concentrations of these small particles will pass through the viewing volume. The sum of their scattering may result in detectable light levels above the background noise so that particle counts in the small size ranges of the OPC will be seen[⁴].

Low Concentration Effects: If particle concentration is very low, then the data quantity obtained in any measurement may be so low that statistical validity of the data is questionable. Any samples where less than 20 or so counts are obtained are difficult to define with acceptable confidence limits. This problem is handled by measuring larger sample volumes to obtain more data. However, the OPC noise level should be adequately low so that the quantity of noise counts during the sample period is insignificant compared to the particle count. Otherwise the true particle count data will be difficult to separate from the total noise plus particle data. A suggested maximum noise count rate of less than five pulses per ten minute period is suggested.

Electronic System Effects: Pulse-processing systems characterize discrete pulses. Each pulse must rise above a low level baseline so that a definite pulse amplitude can be established. The baseline level is set sufficiently above the background noise so that only signals from particles are registered. That baseline level must be present long enough so that the electronic system can differentiate between consecutive particle pulses. If the pulses are too closely spaced, then the electronics will record only one pulse. As a general rule of thumb, a counter that can record randomly spaced pulses with an amplitude range of 10,000 must be capable of counting at a uniform rate about ten times the long term average rate for randomly spaced events[⁵]. Eventually the indicated counting rate decreases to zero, as the baseline duration or dead time decreases below minimum required time for the particular electronics system. This problem is aggravated if a broad particle size distribution exists. Since many OPC viewing volume dimensions are a fraction of a cubic millimeter, a large particle will produce a large amplitude pulse that may require excessive time for the signal level to decrease to baseline level. During this time period, other particle pulses may not be registered.

If liquid flow rate is varied, then particle residence time in the viewing zone will also vary. This produces pulses of varying duration and rise times. If the electronic system has inadequate band width, the recorded pulse amplitudes will be incorrect. At high flow rates, pulses are clipped and indicated particle size is smaller than it should be for the measured particle. Unfortunately, increasing bandwidth increases electronic noise, degrading OPC particle sensitivity. Therefore, OPC makers must compromise between sensitivity and ability to accept flow variation. The operator should set liquid flow rate where the OPC was calibrated and maintain a uniform flow rate.

OPC recalibration is recommended at six months intervals. This procedure is suggested since OPC drift can occur in the electronic, optical or liquid handling systems. Electronic system drift is a minor problem with OPCs that have been in operation long enough so that unstable components will have been found and replaced. However, some value change will occur over long time periods with almost any electrical components. Optical system drift is more of a problem with incandescent illumination sources than with laser sources, since the former source is maintained at a constant light level by changes in power as a light path transmission may change with time. This can result in changes in emitted wavelength distribution, while the laser sources do not change wavelength as power to the laser is changed. If illumination wavelength changes, then the scattering function will also change slightly. This will result in sizing differences as the particles in the sample change in nature.

SAMPLE HANDLING EFFECTS

There are two methods of sample feeding used for OPCs. In one, the liquid is aspirated into the OPC sensing cell; in the other the liquid is forced through the cell under pressure. Figure 6 illustrates a typical aspiration feeder; operation of a pressure feeder is shown in Figure 7. Note that the aspiration feeder evacuates the space above the OPC cell in order to draw the liquid through the OPC sensor, while the pressure feeder forces the liquid through the sensor by pressurizing the liquid.

OPC manufacturers build sample feeders of both types. There are advantages and problems with both types. The user should select the one that is best fitted to his needs. In some situations, only one type can be used. For example, if a sample is to be removed from a large vessel, then aspiration may be the only available sample acquisition method even though it may cause some problems with the liquid being handled, as discussed below.

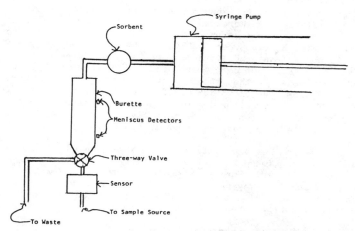

FIG. 6 -- Aspiration Sample Feeder

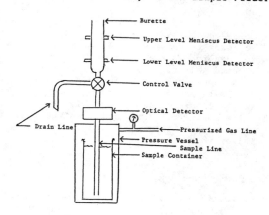

Fig. 7 -- Batch Sample Pressure Feeder

Liquid Property Effects

Differential pressure required to pass the liquid through the OPC cell will change as liquid viscosity changes. If an aspiration feeder is being used, then the one atmosphere or less of suction may be inadequate to draw the liquid through the OPC at the correct flow rate. In addition, the pressure in the OPC may be so low that the liquid may boil or cavitate in going through the OPC cell. Bubbles will form and be reported as particles. Reducing viscosity by increasing the measurement temperature should not be tried, since the liquid vapor pressure will also be increased. Mixing with a lower viscosity miscible solvent is not recommended, since the solvent may also dissolve particles. The best approach is to transfer the sample vessel to a clean container so that the liquid can be fed under pressure. If the liquid is not viscous but does have high vapor pressure, one may lower the OPC and feeder so that the line to the feeder will be under a head resulting from the elevation difference between the sample point and the OPC; the aspiration feeder is used only as a flow controller. Samples in containers smaller than five liters or so can be fed with a pressure feeder system, as shown in Figure 7.

These devices can be used with pressure well above that available from an aspiration feeder. High vapor pressure liquids will not boil in this type of feeder. Some samples can not be transferred to a container from which they may be fed under pressure. When using a pressure feed system, careful selection and safe operation is needed. This is especially important when glass containers are used.

If a liquid sample may contain dense particles, it will be necessary to keep the particles suspended in the liquid by stirring. Otherwise the particles will stratify in the container. A magnetic stirrer or a propellor can be used if the stirring element is clean. If the particles may be magnetic, then avoid the use of a magnetic stirrer. It is also necessary to make sure that the stirring speed is below that where a vortex can form. Air drawn into a vortex will form bubbles that will be counted as particles. When stirring, it is best to use a container with a spherical base. Stirring in a cylindrical container tends to concentrate heavier particles along the periphery of the container since the liquid motion is mainly radial. As the liquid level drops in the container, then radial stratification increases. For this reason, sample removal is not recommended from the last 20-30% of the container volume.

Sample Acquisition and Handling

The need for representative sampling is accepted widely, but good sampling practice is seldom followed. Isokinetic sample inlets are recommended with minimum line tortuosity. This keeps sampler inlet efficiency maximum. Even though inlet efficiency is not affected significantly for liquid-borne particles smaller than 5-10 μm, isokinetic sampling is always recommended so that any large particles that may be present will be collected and the exact sample point can be defined better. Figure 8 illustrates recommended sample line layouts to minimize particle losses. Sampling points should be located where the flow is turbulent, rather than laminar, to minimize gravitational effects. This point applies for in situ sample observation and for sample removal for subsequent measurement.

In situ sample measurement involves an optical system to observe liquid flowing through a line. The sample observation point should be chosen so to be representative of the entire line. The in situ observation volume should be large enough so that a statistically valid sample can be obtained in a reasonable time period, no more than one hour for very clean liquids. A viewing volume that will handle liquid flows of 0.1 to 10 ml/min should be acceptable, with the smallest flow rates usable for higher contamination levels. A particle count of 1000 or more is desired per sample.

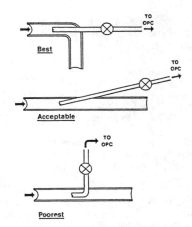

Fig. 8 -- Sidestream Sample Acquisition

When varying liquid samples are to be counted, there are some potential problems. The operator must make sure that sequential samples do not react to form hazardous mixtures, which may form toxic or corrosive substances, or will generate heat of mixing. Mixing of inert immiscible liquids can form colloidal droplets that will be counted. When changing liquids, the system should be flushed with mutually miscible, clean, non-reactive solvent between measurements. If liquids contain dissolved non-volatiles that may form crystals or films that deposit on critical optical elements, the OPC system should be flushed with clean solvent before shutdown as well as between samples. Once crystals form as the solvent liquid evaporates, they may take a long time to dissolve in the next batch of added liquid.

CONCLUSIONS

This discussion has covered some of the error sources that exist with optical single particle counters for liquid-borne particles. The source areas include OPC design and construction, OPC operation and sample characteristics and processing. Where possible, remedial measures are suggested. These can aid even where complete solutions are not possible.

REFERENCES

[1].   ASTM F 658-87, "Standard Practice for Defining Size Calibrat-
ion, Resolution, and Counting Accuracy of a Liquid-Borne Particle
COunter Using Near-Monodisperse Spherical Particulate Material,"
Annual Book of ASTM Standards, Vol. 10.05, 1987.

[2] Knollenberg, R. G., "The Importance of Media Refractive Index in
Estimating Liquid and Surface Microcontamination Measurements," Journal of Environmental Sciences, Vol 30, No. 2, March/April 1987, pp.
50-58.

[3] Bader, H., Gordon, M.R., and Brown, O.B., "Theory of Coincidence
Counts and Simple Practical Methods of Coincidence Count Correction
for Optical and Resistive Pulse Particle Counters," Review of Scientific Instruments, Vol. 43, 1972, pp.1407-1412.

[4] Whitby, K. T. and Liu, B. Y. H., "Generation of Countable Pulses
by High Concentrations of Subcountable Sized Particles in the Sensing
Volume of Optical Counters," Journal of Colloid and Interface Science,
Vol. 25, 1967, pp. 537-546.

[5] Lieberman, A., "Flow Rate and COncentration Effects in Automatic
Particle Counters," presented at National Conference on Fluid Power,
Chicago, IL, October, 1975.

Metallization and Interconnects

Francois M. Dumesnil, Mike Bruner, and Mike Berman

A CORRELATION STUDY OF ALUMINUM FILM WET ETCH
UNIFORMITY WITH THE SPUTTER ETCH OF OXIDE FILMS

REFERENCE: Dumesnil, F. M., Bruner, M., and Berman, M.,
"A Correlation Study of Aluminum Film Wet Etch Uniformity with The
Sputter Etch of Oxide Films," Semiconductor Fabrication: Technology
and Metrology, ASTM STP 990, Dinesh C. Gupta, editor, American
Society for Testing and Materials, 1989.

ABSTRACT: Recent research in the fabrication process of sputtered
aluminum (30 ppm silicon) films for device interconnection shows a
correlation between the ability to wet metal etch the film in a uniform
manner, and the surface reflectance of the film. Aluminum grain notching
of patterned metal lines causing subsequent open device circuits is
shown to be related to the amount of residual gas incorporated into the
metal film. Reflectance measurements of the deposited aluminum films
exhibit lower values of reflectance for films that incorporate residual
gases. Low reflectance films show a greater degree of metal grain
notching than those of higher surface reflectance when wet metal etched.
Removal of the sputter etched by-products from the aluminum deposition
is necessary to avoid residual gas incorporation. Two methods are
successful in increasing the aluminum reflectance as well as minimizing
metal line width grain notching. These two methods are described and
compared in their ability to optimize the uniformity of metal wet etching.

KEYWORDS: sputtered aluminum, metal grain notching, sputter etch,
reflectivity, residual gases

INTRODUCTION

The degree of residual gas incorporated during the deposition of
aluminum films is directly dependent on the deposition method and the
process conditions. Aluminum is difficult to sputter deposit free of
impurity gases because of its high affinity to oxidation as the metal is

F. M. Dumesnil is a Project Engineer at Therma-Wave Inc., 47320
Mission Falls Court, Fremont, CA 94539; M. Bruner and M. Berman are
Process Engineering Supervisors at American Micro Devices,
2175 Mission College Boulevard, Santa Clara, CA 95051

243

being deposited. The incorporation of these gases into the metal film, if not minimized, will increase the films bulk resistivity, increase the film susceptibility to hillock formation, and decrease the film's ability to be uniformly wet chemical etched.

PECVD (Plasma Enhanced Chemical Vapor Deposition) undoped and doped silicon dioxide is commonly used as a dielectric layer in a two level metalization scheme. Contact openings must be made through the PECVD oxide layer to allow electrical contact between the first and second aluminum layers at specific points. These contact openings, known as vias, must be completely free of residual oxide to maintain good ohmic contact between the two aluminum layers.

To ensure that all residual oxide has been removed in the via contacts, a plasma of argon gas in the sputtering system bombards the substrate causing the oxide layer on the substrate to be physically sputter etched. The etch rate, and etch uniformity can be carefully controlled by the manipulation of bias voltage, rf power level, and gas pressure.

As the sputter etch station resides in the same vacuum chamber as the aluminum deposition stations, the incorporation of residual gas into the aluminum film during its deposition from the sputter etch process is very possible. By measuring the reflectivity of the deposited aluminum film, the extent of residual gas incorporation into the film can be characterized.

The ability to wet metal etch the patterned aluminum lines in a uniform manner becomes more important as the metal line widths shrink further and further. The susceptibility to metal grain notching of the patterned lines increases rapidly with reduced line width. This becomes fatal if the metal grain notching is more than fifty percent of the patterned line width. During the production and test of devices, wafers that exhibit a high degree of metal notching commonly exhibit lower than normal reflectivity.

In an effort to understand the correlation between metal notching and aluminum film reflectivity, one hundred 100 mm (4 inch) diameter wafers, with 3000 Angstroms of thermal oxide were processed on a Varian 3190 sputtering system. The wafers were processed with a sputter etch, and then an aluminum deposition within one processing cycle in an identical fashion as performed upon product wafers. Reflectivity measurements of the one hundred wafers after aluminum deposition exhibited a normal distribution with a mean value of 86.1 % and a standard deviation of 6.7 % Fig. 1.   These measurements were taken with a Dynoptics Reflectometer Model 520D with an optical 400 nanometer wavelength filter.

FIGURE 1

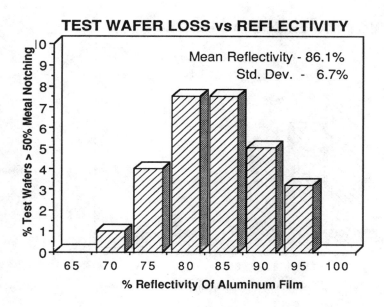

A thermal oxide wafer was then placed with every five product wafers as they were processed through the Varian 3190. Each product wafer had a layer of undoped PECVD oxide which needed to be sputter etched to clean the contact areas before aluminum deposition. A total of one hundred monitor wafer were processed and evaluated using the Reflectometer. As can be seen on Fig. 2, most of the wafers had measured reflectivities below the mean value of 79.2 %.

FIGURE 2

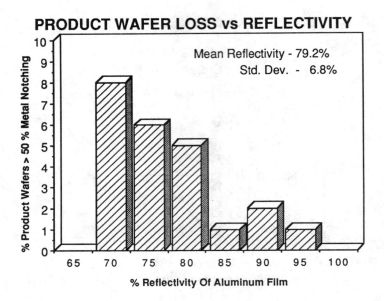

PRODUCT WAFER LOSS vs REFLECTIVITY

This led to the following experiment whose purpose was to optimize the metal film reflectivity and reduce the metal grain notching of product wafers during subsequent wet metal chemical etch.

EXPERIMENTAL METHOD

Test Procedures

Silicon substrates, 100 mm (4 inch) in diameter, with 1 micron of either Low Temperature deposited undoped Oxide (LTO), Plasma Enhanced Chemical Vapor Deposited (PECVD) undoped oxide, or thermally grown undoped oxide, were processed with a sputter etch and an aluminum deposition on Varian 3190 systems.

Fifty wafers from each group of wafers were processed identically using a process recipe which called for the sputter etch to take place separately at the same time as the metal deposition (Parallel Deposition Process). Two separate Varian 3190 systems were used, one system ("A") had no special attachments to the system. The second system ("B") had a Varian VIPS ™ module (Vacuum Isolated Process System) attached directly to the RF sputter etch station of the system.

The other fifty wafers of each group, were processed in the same manner, but the process recipe on both sputtering systems was altered to delay the sputter deposition until after the sputter etch process was completed (Serial Deposition Process).

Deposition Systems

Varian 3190 sputtering system configuration:

Station 1	Station 2	Station 3	Station 4
RF Etch	Pre-Heat	Aluminum Dep.	Aluminum Dep.

System A	System B
No VIPS ™ Module Attached	VIPS ™ Module Attached

VIPS ™ is a registered trademark of Varian Associates Inc

Measurements

Film reflectivity was measured using a Dynoptics Model 520
Reflectometer System filtered to 400 nanometers .

RESULTS

With the Parallel Deposition Process the average measured reflectivity
for the thermal oxide group was consistently higher compared to the
other oxide groups. The PECVD Group by contrast was consistently
lower than that of the other groups as Fig.3 shows. The wafers were than
patterned, wet metal etched, and inspected with an optical microscope.
As had been the case earlier with product wafers exhibiting lower than
average reflectivity, the PECVD Group of wafers on system A were found
to have a much higher degree of metal grain notching than those
deposited upon thermal oxide. This was not the case for wafers
processed on system B.

FIGURE 3

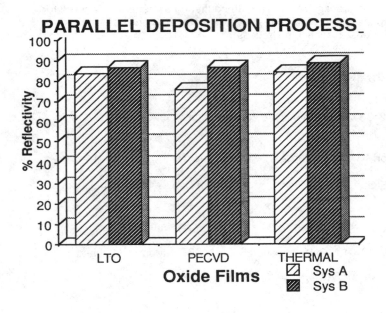

TABLE #1   PARALLEL DEPOSITION RESULTS

PERCENTAGE REFLECTANCE

	SYSTEM #A		SYSTEM #B	
	Average	Range	Average	Range
PECVD OX.	75.9	72.9-83.9	86.7	85.8-87.2
LTO	83.7	82.7-85.9	86.8	85.1-92.2
THERMAL OX.	84.4	83.9-84.8	88.6	87.5-93.1

Wafers from the Serial Deposition Process exhibited an over all increase in film reflectivity as shown in Figure #4 compared to those wafers processed using the Parallel Deposition Process. Again the Thermal Oxide group had the higher average reflectivity values where the PECVD group had the lowest average values. The wafers were than patterned and wet metal etched. As expected, the PECVD Group showed signs of some metal grain notching, but to a much smaller degree than those processed using the Parallel Deposition Process.

TABLE #2   SERIAL DEPOSITION RESULTS

PERCENTAGE REFLECTANCE

	SYSTEM #A		SYSTEM #B	
	Average	Range	Average	Range
PECVD OX.	80.4	77.7-80.4	89.1	87.2-90.7
LTO	86.4	85.3-88.1	89.3	88.1-90.9
THERMAL OX.	86.8	85.4-87.9	91.2	90.2-92.3

FIGURE 4

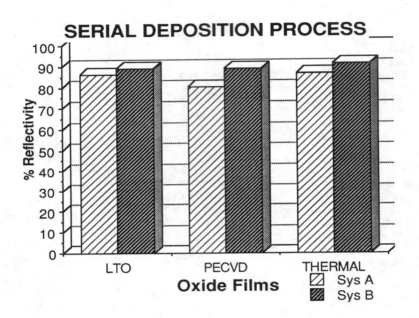

CONCLUSIONS

The VIPS module is effective at removing the contaminates generated during the sputter etch process. Average measured reflectivity increased by nine to eleven percent for the PECVD Group, three percent for the LTO Group, and four to five percent for the Thermal Oxide Group. Also effective was the use of the Serial Deposition Process, though the average reflectivity increases and extent of reduced metal grain notching were not found to be as improved by the sole addition of the VIPS module. The greatest increases in reflectivity were obtained with the combination of the Serial Deposition Process and the VIPS module.

ACKNOWLEDGEMENTS

The authors acknowledge with appreciation the help and experience of Forest Kreiss in helping to modify the Varian 3190 Sputtering Systems.

REFERENCES

[1] Casalnuovo, S.A., Renschler C.L., Stiefield, R.E., Draper B.L., Mahoney, A.R., "Effect of Diffuse Reflectivity on Photoresist Linewidth Control," Sandia National Laboratories, #77120,Albuquerque, New Mexico 87185.

[2] Pauleau, Y.,"Interconnect Materials for VLSI Circuits," Solid State Technology, April 1987, Centre National D'Etudes Des Telecommunications, Meylan, France.

Toshimichi Iwamori, Yasushi Sakata, Hitoshi Kojima, and Yuji Yatsuda

CRACK FREE AND HIGHLY RELIABLE DOUBLE LEVEL METALLIZATION PROCESS
USING PLASMA OXIDE AND SILANOL-TYPE SOG LAYERS

REFERENCE : Iwamori, T., Sakata, Y., Kojima, H. and Yatsuda, Y.,
"Crack Free and Highly Reliable Double Level Metallization
Process Using Plasma Oxide and Silanol-type SOG Layers",
Semiconductor Fabrication: Technology and Metrology, ASTM STP
990, Dinesh C. Gupta, editor, American Society for Testing and
Materials, 1989.

ABSTRACT : A double level metallization process using a sandwich
structure of Plasma CVD(P-CVD) / Spin-On-Glass (SOG) / PSG oxide
for an interlevel dielectric layer has been developed. A very
thin phosphorus-doped silanol-type SOG is coated for
planarization. The plasma-oxide which is deposited beneath
the SOG film suppresses hillock growth in the 1st Al layer and
together with the very thin coat of SOG prevents the SOG layer
from cracking. Furthermore, silanol-type is found to be more
reliable compared with siloxane-type.The surface topography is
found to be planarized very well by cross-sectional SEM. The
failures of 2nd Al open and short and short between 1st Al and
2nd Al are all negligible in our 2.0-1.3µm process proven by
TEG(Test Element Group) evaluation. No problems have appeared in
our reliability test program.

KEYWORDS : LSI, fabrication process, double level metallization,
planarization, Spin-On-Glass (SOG)

INTRODUCTION

With the higher integration of LSIs, multi-level interconnection
technology at finer process conditions is increasingly recognized to
be important to accomplish higher packing density, more design
latitude and operating speed enhancement. Various methods have been
extensively studied, but all of them have distinct disadvantages.

T. Iwamori, Y. Sakata, H. Kojima, and Y. Yatsuda are engineers at
the Electronic Imaging & Devices Research Lab. in Fuji Xerox
Co.,Ltd., 2274 Hongoh, Ebina 243-04, Japan.

Etch back method[1] is difficult to be applied to finer process as the dielectric layer must be deposited so thick that a void appears in the groove between the 1st Al lines. In biased sputter method[2], problems such as the damages to the MOS characteristics and low through put have also been pointed out. Spin-On-Glass(SOG) method[3][4] has been supposed to be difficult to apply to finer process due to the SOG cracking and incomplete filling of narrow grooves. Therefore, there exists a need for a feasible double level interconnection process in VLSI fabrication technology.

This paper presents the new double level metallization process in which an interlevel dielectric is composed of the sandwich structure of Plasma CVD(P-CVD) oxide / SOG / PSG. This process features good producibility using SOG technology and solves the cracking and incomplete filling problems.

EXPERIMENTAL

The main fabrication steps were as follows; 1st Al was deposited in a sputtering system at 250 °C and patterned in halide gas plasma by RIE system. Then P-CVD oxide was deposited at about 300 °C. Next, SOG was coated by a spinning coater. The film was baked on a hot plate at 120 °C to dry and cured at 250 °C. The final cure was performed at 400 °C in N_2 ambient. For the finer patterns, SOG was multi-coated. After that, PSG(Phospho Silicate Glass) was deposited by AP-CVD system. Next, the via holes were etched in CF_4+H_2 plasma by RIE system in an ordinary way. Then 2nd Al was deposited in a sputtering system at 250 °C with RF plasma-cleaning, and patterned by RIE. Finally, the sintering was performed and the passivation film was deposited.

Evaluation Procedures

Planarization properties were evaluated visually by the cross-sectional SEM and electrically using TEG(Test Element Group).A series of test structures specially designed to evaluate this process were prepared with feature sizes at or below our 2.0 μm design rules. The main two types of test structures used were shown in Fig. 1. Type A consisted of 1st Al topography over poly-Si meanders. 1st Al lines were defined at right angles to poly-Si lines with a variable pitch. This structure allowed measurement of open and short of poly-Si, and leakage characteristics between poly-Si and 1st Al. Type B contained underlaid poly-Si lines running parallel to 1st Al lines with variable edge offset distance (0.0 - 2.0μm by 0.5μm step) to simulate severe topographical surface in an actual device. This type allowed open and short testing of 1st Al / 2nd Al, and leakage characteristics between 1st Al and 2nd Al.

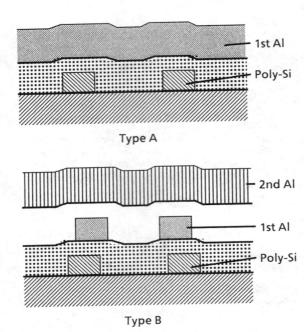

Type A

Type B

FIG. 1 -- Schematic Diagrams of DLM Structure

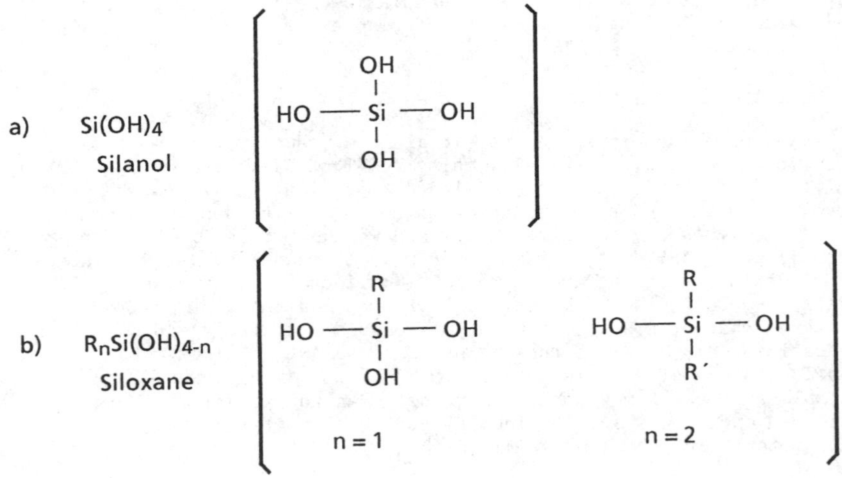

FIG. 2 -- Composition of 2 Types of SOG

MATERIALS

SOG Material Type

Two types of SOG material were used in our evaluation. These were Silanol-type and Siloxane-type whose compositions are represented in Fig. 2. IR absorption spectra of these SOG film are shown in Fig. 3 for wave numbers between 400 and 4000 cm^{-1}. Both SOG materials were coated on a Si wafer and cured at 400 °C in N_2 ambient. As a reference, thermal SiO_2 spectrum is also shown in Fig. 3 c). In the spectrum of the Silanol-type film the main absorption peak of Si-0 bonds was located between 1060 and 1080 cm^{-1}. Also a small absorption peak associated with OH bonds in the film was found at the extended region between 3200 and 3800 cm^{-1}. The broader peak in this extended region was the sum of the absorption peaks associated with OH bonds and with the absorbed water. This spectrum was very similar to the spectrum of thermal SiO_2. On the other hand, there were additional peaks associated with two types of bond in the spectrum of Siloxane-type film. One of them was associated with the benzene ring and peaks were located at 700, 1150, 1450, 1600 cm^{-1}, and the other was associated with the Si-C bonds with peaks at 800, 1270 cm^{-1}. It was found that more carbon bonds remained in the Siloxane-type film. This type film had characteristics similar to an organic film. The carbon bonds caused the concern about induced troubles in the fabrication process. In the via etching process, this SOG exhibited different dry etch characteristic from CVD oxide, which complicated the via process. In addition, there was another problem of crack generation during the ashing process. From these results, the Silanol-type SOG material was chosen for application in planarization schemes in spite of its low crack resistance.

Doping the Material

As Silanol-type SOG material had low crack resistance, its slightly thicker coating on the underlaid structure induced crack generation as shown in Fig. 4. The crack ran along the 1st Al lines and its length reached over approximately 50 μm. To avoid cracking, the appropriate doping (~4 wt%) of phosphorus to the material was very effective as shown in table 1, but excess doping (~8 wt%) made another problem on storing the material ; storing time changed the characteristics of the SOG material. In the case of using excess doped SOG stored for a long time, micro-cracks appeared at the surface of the coated device after curing as shown in Fig. 4 b). Micro-cracks were approximately 0.5 μm in size, far smaller than the 50 μm type cracks. So, SOG material doped ~4 wt% Phosphorus was used in our process.

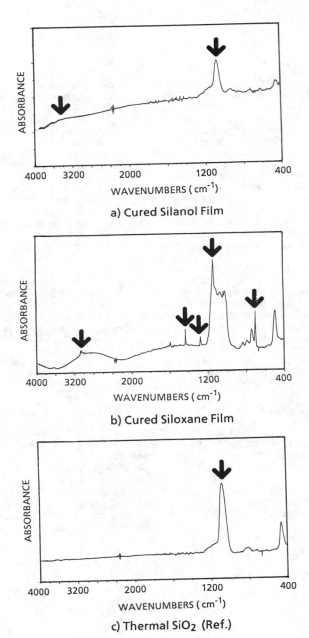

a) Cured Silanol Film

b) Cured Siloxane Film

c) Thermal SiO$_2$ (Ref.)

FIG. 3 -- IR Spectra of Cured SOG Film

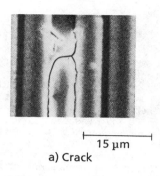

├─── 15 μm ───┤

a) Crack

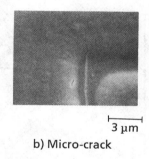

├─ 3 μm ─┤

b) Micro-crack

FIG. 4 -- SEM Micrographs of Crack and Microcrack of SOG

TABLE 1 -- Relationship between Crack Fail and P_2O_5
Doping Concentration

P conc. Fail Mode	No	Low (~4wt%)	High (~8wt%)
Crack	Fair	Good	Good
Micro-crack	Good	Good	Fair

PROCESS

Curing Process

The curing process is the most important part of the fabrication
process to make the SOG film stable without cracking. We investigated
the curing characteristics of SOG by differential thermal analysis
and thermal gravity analysis. From the results shown in Fig. 5, it
was found that the solvent was evaporated at about 120 °C, the SOG
material formed a network of Si-O bonds at the range between 250 °C
and 300 °C and the SOG film was densified over 400 °C. Therefore, the
SOG film should be cured over 400 °C to make it stable. But, if the
SOG film was cured quickly at 400 °C, it would crack easily by the
mismatch in the thermal expansion coefficient. So, we cured the SOG
at three steps ; the first step was drying at 120 °C, the second was
curing at 250 °C, the third was densifying at 400 °C.

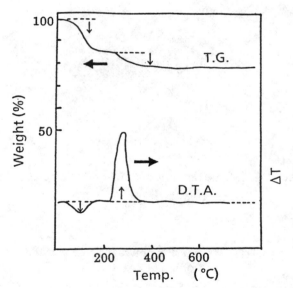

FIG. 5 -- Differential Thermal Analysis & Thermal
Gravity Analysis of SOG

Dielectric Film Constitution

In our process, the interlevel dielectric film was composed of a
triple layered structure as shown in Fig. 6.

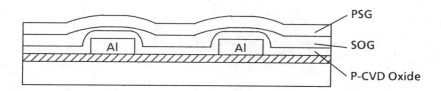

FIG. 6 -- Triple Layered Inter-level Dielectric of
P-CVD Oxide / Spin-On-Glass / PSG

The bottom layer is P-CVD oxide used for two purposes. One is the
suppression of the hillock growth in the 1st Al layer, and the other
is the prevention of cracking of SOG film. P-CVD oxide can be
deposited at about 300 °C lower than the LP-CVD oxide at about 400
°C. Deposition at this temperature was found to be effective to
suppress the hillock growth in the 1st Al layer by the optical check
with a microscope. This was also confirmed by TEG results described
later. The P-CVD oxide was deposited also as a buffer layer to
prevent cracking of SOG film induced by the mismatch in the thermal
expansion coefficient during the SOG film curing.

The middle layer was the appropriately P-doped SOG film to
planarize the surface topography. The thickness of SOG film was
determined by the concentration of SOG material and coating
condition. The concentration was set at ~4 wt% to maintain the SOG
material stability during storage. SOG was coated at 4000 rpm to
control the thickness uniformity of the coated film. At this
condition the thickness on the 1st Al lines was less than 300 Å, and
it was controlled less than about 5000 Å between 1st Al lines.

The top layer was the PSG deposited by the conventional AP-CVD
system. This layer was used to shield the SOG layer from the etchant
gas plasma during the 2nd Al patterning. If the SOG film was exposed
to the etchant gas plasma, the SOG layer would be damaged and film
decomposition would occur. Thereby,the 2nd Al etching uniformity
became so bad that the shorting between 2nd Al lines occurred.

The thickness of top and bottom layers was set as follows. PSG
should be deposited thick enough that the underlaid SOG film was not
exposed during the 2nd Al etching. PSG thickness was set 2000 Å to
avoid exposing SOG film.

Then, the thicker the bottom P-CVD oxide was deposited, the better
the planarized property was as shown in Fig. 7. But, too thick
interlevel dielectric film can lead to the failure of via contact
open because the aspect ratio of vias approaches one. Also voids

occurred in the grooves between 1st Al lines for a finer process. Therefore, the thickness of P-CVD oxide was limited to 1.0 - 1.2 μm for our 2μm process.

For the via opening process, this triple layered dielectric film had no problem to be etched as in the conventional via etching condition. The SEM cross-sectional view of the via hole is shown in Fig. 8. The via hole was very well shaped.

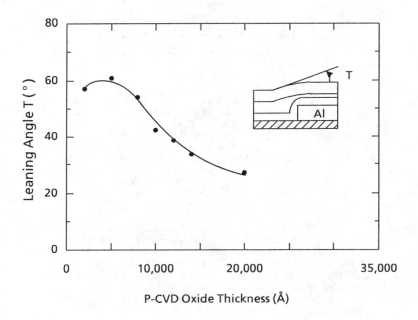

FIG. 7 -- Relationship between Planarization
Property and P-CVD Oxide Thickness

EXPERIMENTAL RESULTS

The SEM micrograph of the sandwich structure of P-CVD oxide / SOG / PSG is depicted in Fig. 9. The SOG film exhibited good planarization properties as shown. No void or cracks appeared. The 1st Al line can be sufficiently planarized down to 2μm-pitch by quadruple coating as shown in Fig. 10. It is found that multiple coating was very effective to achieve planarization.

2 μm

FIG. 8 -- SEM Micrographs of Cross-section of Via Hole

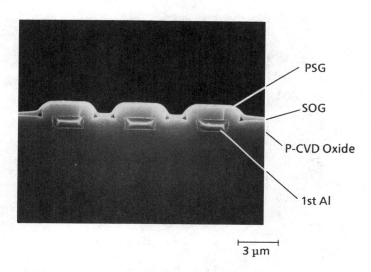

3 μm

FIG. 9 -- SEM Micrographs of Cross-section of Sandwich
Structure of PSG / SOG / P-CVD Oxide

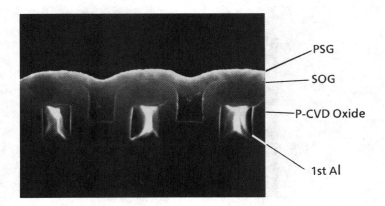

FIG. 10 -- SEM Micrographs of Cross-section of Planarized
Surface of 1st Al with Pitch of 2µm by SOG Quadruple Coating

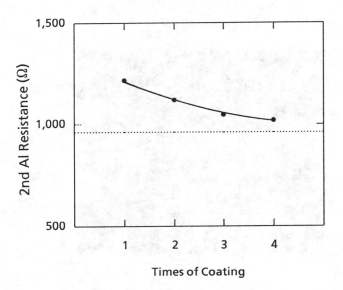

FIG. 11 -- Resistance of 2nd Al Line

The open and short yields of the 2nd Al lines were very good, and
the resistance of the 2nd Al line decreases to 1.0 kΩ at quadruple
coating (from 1.2 kΩ at single coating) as shown in Fig. 11. The
planarization properties were better as the coating thickness was
increased.

Compared with the conventional LP-CVD oxide for bottom oxide, the
short fail yield between 1st and 2nd Al was well improved using P-CVD
oxide as shown in Fig. 12.

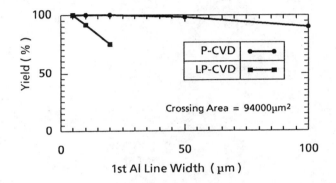

FIG. 12 -- Short Yield between 1st and 2nd Al

For the via holes contact characteristics were good at sizes down
to 1.5μm□ as shown in Fig. 13.

Furthermore, test transistor characteristics such as V_{th} of active
and field Trs., BVds, etc. were evaluated to confirm that this
process did not influence the underlaid devices characteristics. No
change appeared in these transistor characteristics with the double
level metallization process.

Reliability

Four main tests were performed for the reliability validation:
Temperature Cycling Test, High Temperature Operating Life Test,
Temperature Humidity & Bias Test and Pressure Temperature Humidity
Test (Autoclave Test). We used 3.2k-gate gate array device for these
tests. All 40 samples passed the former three tests up to 1000 cycles
or 1000 hours, respectively. 30 samples also passed an Autoclave Test
after 200 hours. Test results are summarized in table 2.

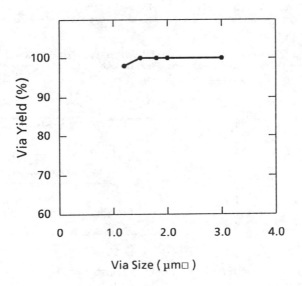

FIG. 13 -- Via Characteristics

TABLE 2 -- Summary of Reliability Test Results

	Test Condition		Failure (samples)
Temperature Cycling	-55°C~150°C	1000cycles	0/40
High Temp. Operation	125°C, Vcc = 5.5V	1000hrs.	0/40
Temperature Humidity & Bias	85°C, 85% RH, Vcc = 5.5V	1000hrs.	0/40
Autoclave	121°C, 2atm, 100% RH	200hrs.	0/30

CONCLUSION

   A double level metallization process using a sandwich structure of
P-CVD oxide / SOG / PSG for an interlevel dielectric layer was
studied. In this process, planarization properties are very good by
cross-sectional SEM, and the failures of 2nd Al open & short and
short between 1st Al and 2nd Al were all negligible in our 2.0-1.3µm
process confirmed by TEG. No problems appeared in our reliability
test program.

ACKNOWLEDGMENT

   The authors would like to acknowledge Mr. S.Tomiyama, manager of
the Electronic Imaging & Devices Research Laboratory for his
continuous encouragement during this work,and Mr. T.Kobayashi for his
heartful discussion. In addition, we would like to thank members of
the Device Process Technology & Fabrication Group in the Electronic
Imaging & Devices Research Laboratory for significant contributions.

REFERENCES

[1]   Honma, Y., Harada, S. and Kaji, T., "LSI Surface Leveling
        by RF Sputter Etching", Journal of the Electrochemical
        Society, Vol. 126, No. 9, Sep. 1979, pp.1531-1533.
[2]   Morimoto, M., Mogami, T., Okabayashi, H. and Nagasawa, E.,
        "SiO2 Planarization by Two Step RF Bias Sputtering", 1983
        Symposium on VLSI Technology, Digest of Technical Papers,
        Sep., 1983, pp. 100-103.
[3]   Chu, J. K., Multani, J. S., Mittal, S. K., Orton, J. T. and
        Jecmen, R., "Spin-On-Glass Dielctric Planarization for
        Double Metal CMOS Technology",1986 Proceedings Third
        International IEEE VLSI Multilevel Interconnection
        Conference, Jun, 1986, pp. 474-483.
[4]   Rey, A., Lafond, D., Mirabel, J. M., Tacussel, M. C. and
        Coster, M. F., "A Double Level Aluminum Interconnection
        Technology with Spin On Glass Based Insulator",1986
        Proceedings Third International IEEE VLSI Multilevel
        Interconnection Conference, Jun, 1986, pp. 491-499.

Harold G. Parks, Clair E. Logan, and Carol A. Fahrenz

VLSI DEFECT DETECTION, CLASSIFICATION, AND REDUCTION FROM
IN-PROCESS AND POST-PROCESS SRAM INSPECTIONS

REFERENCE: Parks, H. G., Logan, C. E., and Fahrenz, C. A.,
"VLSI Defect Detection, Classification, and Reduction from
In-Process and Post Process SRAM Inspections," Semiconductor
Fabrication: Technology and Metrology, ASTM STP 990, Dinesh
C. Gupta, editor, American Society for Testing and Materials,
1989.

ABSTRACT: As device dimensions shrink to the order of one
micron and chip sizes approach 100mm^2, containing more than
10^5 transistors, some of the standard yield enhancement
practices lose effectiveness. In particular, in-process
inspections suffer as it becomes increasingly probable that
defects will not be detected due to the reduced circuit
dimensions and increased pattern complexity. Another area
hard hit is post process probe yield failure analysis. With
the greater number of components and functions per chip
extremely large vector sets (thousands) must be run to
adequately characterize and isolate failures at probe test.
This results in long test times as well as a significant
increase in the time required for data analysis to isolate
circuit failures. Adoption of a static RAM (SRAM) as a yield
vehicle can reinstate the effectiveness of both of these
techniques for VLSI. The repetitiveness and regularity of
the RAM pattern facilitates visual inspection, even at the
micron level, and bit mapping provides easy test isolation of
defects at post process probing. The application of a SRAM in
a VLSI yield enhancement strategy for defect classification
and reduction is discussed in this paper.

KEYWORDS: VLSI, yield, random defects, gross defects, SRAM

Dr. Parks is an electronics engineer, Mr. Logan a chemical engineer
and Mrs. Fahrenz a test technician. They are all members of IC Process
Engineering Branch of the VLSI Technology Laboratory at the General
Electric Company Corporate Research and Development Center, P.O. Box 8,
Schenectady, NY 12301.

INTRODUCTION

The General Electric Company has developed a 1.25μm CMOS process at its Research and Development Center in Schenectady, NY and transferred this process to the Micro Electronics Center in North Carolina. Process highlights include twin tub ion implant tailoring of the n and p wells with retrograde p well and epi substrate for latch up immunity, lightly doped drains with oxide spacers for hot electron reduction, and two level metal with refractory MoTi/W metal 1. A key elemnt of the process development and transfer was a pilot foundry line operation at the Research and Development Center VLSI facility. This included a yield enhancement program based on the concept of a 4K static RAM test monitor.

The yield enhancement strategy is summarized in the flow chart shown in Figure 1. The nature of the yield loss mechanisms were ascertained early in the program with a process sensitivity analysis of parametric yield followed by visual inspection of completed small circuits. These initial efforts confirmed the robustness of the process and showed that the yield loss was primarily due to random and non random mechanisms introduced in the processing. As a result, an in-process inspection procedure, based on a statistical sampling plan, was developed and established on the foundry line. This was accompanied by an in depth "post mortem" analysis of completed yield monitors. The selection of a 4K bit SRAM as a yield monitor enhanced the success of both of these efforts. The SRAM was incorporated with parametric and yield test structures in a test element group (TEG) chip design. The TEG chip can be used as a "drop in" on product wafers or processed on separate wafers within a product lot for process monitoring and yield enhancement.

The in-process inspections performed at patterning and after pattern transfer are extremely effective in locating defect sources. This has provided an immediate process enhancement feedback that in general has prevented catastrophic yield losses. They have also provided an effective monitor that has maintained defect levels below a prescribed limit. Post mortem analysis allows defects to be further classified with respect to their origin at defect levels too low to be reliably found with the in-process inspections. This has provided a longer term more refined process enhancement feedback path for defect characterization and reduction.

DEFECT CLASSIFICATION

Yield loss in integrated circuits is a result of defects which can be defined as any imperfection in the wafer either from the starting material or introduced during the processing through physical steps or through the chip design and layout. Within this definition defects fall into one of the three classifications of point defects, line defects, or area defects. Point defects are oxide pinholes, isolated etch pits, particles or process related effects of particles, etc., that affect an area much smaller than the chip itself. Line defects are scratches, slip lines, etc. that have a high length to width aspect ratio. Area defects consist of misalignment, stains, cleaning problems and most parametric design related failures. In general area defects affect an area as large or larger than the chip area itself. Typically defect density is associated with randomly distributed point defects. Line and area defects are considered a gross yield loss mechanism that would adversely

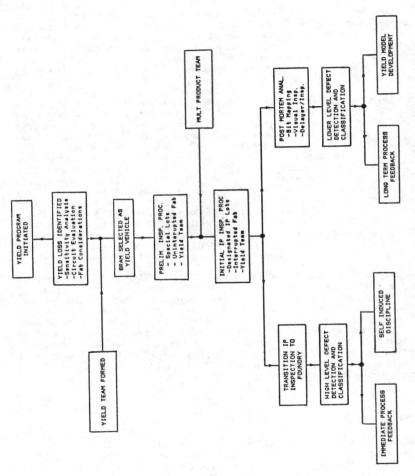

FIGURE 1. CRD SRAM BASED YIELD ENHANCEMENT PROGRAM

affect a die of any practical size. Thus to first order a yield model consists of a chip area independent component as well as a chip area dependent component:

$$Y = Y_G \, Y_R \, (A_C, D) \qquad (1)$$

In this equation Y_G represents the chip area independent term due to gross yield loss mechanisms. The other component represents the portion of yield governed by random defects and is therefore highly dependent on chip area, A_C , and average defect density, D. In general the yield for a multi step or full process is modeled by generalizing Eq 1 to n independent process steps [1] as,

$$Y = Y_G \prod_{i=1}^{n} Y_{Ri} \, (A_{Ci}, D_i) \qquad (2)$$

The formulation of the model with the area independent gross yield is essential for accurate yield modeling and defect classification. In a yield analysis application mental note is usually taken of the sources of gross losses. However, Y_G is usually separated out from level as indicated in Eq 2. The random yield component can be described by virtually any of several models discussed in the open literature [2-5]. For now we will just look at the random yield component in a more global manner. In the most general sense the n components could represent every process step. However, in the context of a modern VLSI CMOS process with 150 or more individual process steps this would be absurd and thus n is taken as some critical number of processing steps. In the early days of LSI and perhaps even into early VLSI n was taken as the number of critical masking steps [6]. However, as dry etching and thin film deposition have taken their rightful roles in VLSI processes the number of critical steps now represents more a combination of masking, etching, and deposition steps. Typically for a modern three or four conductor level CMOS process n would be on the order 10 - 12.

The partitioning of yield into gross and random defect limited components represents a first order classification of yield loss mechanisms. As noted previously, the random yield is characterized by the sensitivity of the product to point defects at each critical level. Of the n critical levels n_1 are associated with visual defects, i.e. defects that can be seen with a conventional light microscope or a scanning electron microscope (SEM). The remaining n_2 defects are nonvisual random defects that are observable only by electrical test or delayering followed by delineation and visual inspection. Gross defects fall in the general classifications of area or line defects and can also be separated into visual or nonvisual components. One difference for the visual classification is that gross defects are always large enough to be identified with a light microscope. As a result of these classifications the general yield formulation can be rewritten with visual (subscript V) and nonvisual (subscript N) components:

$$Y = Y_{GN} \, Y_{GV} \prod_{i=1}^{n_1} Y_{RV} \, (A_{Ci}, D_i) \prod_{j=1}^{n_2} Y_{RN} \, (A_{Cj}, D_j) \qquad (3)$$

Several subclassifications of visual and nonvisual gross defects according to area or line type are summarized in Table 1. Reviewing the types of defects in this table may cause some controversy as to classification among readers. For example, some workers might be tempted to categorize scratches as random defects since they occur randomly on the wafer. Similarly one might be tempted to classify large particles, hair, or threads as random defects due to their airborne particulate nature and/or random occurrence. However, with the fundamental operating premise of adverse yield affect regardless of die size, the classifications of Table 1 are justified.

TABLE 1 -- GROSS DEFECT CLASSIFICATION

AREA DEFECTS:
VISUAL-MISALIGNMENT   NONVISUAL-BLANKET IMPLANT
   -STEP COVERAGE   -SUBSTRATE
   -FOCUS/DEVELOPMENT   -STEP COVERAGE
   -SPOTS/STAINS   -OVER ETCH
   -FEATURE SIZE   -LAYER THICKNESS
   -GROSS PARTICLES   VARIATIONS

LINE DEFECTS:
VISUAL-PARTICLE STREAKS   NONVISUAL-SUBSTRATE
   -SCRATCH   -IMPLANT
   -THREAD
   -HAIR

Random defects belong to the general class of point defects. Visual defects are usually the result of particulates from people, equipment, materials, process, handling, etc., which alter lithographic or pattern transfer operations. They manifest themselves as missing or excess material in the patterned layers of the integrated circuit. Pattern transfer defects are easily distinguished from excess lithography defects because the pattern is seen in relief in the defect in the transfer case. Also the edges of of excess lithography defects are usually more sharply defined than in transfer defects. Nonvisual defects are oxide/insulator defects, perturbations in local implants or etch conditions, or localized substrate defects. Many of these are due to the same particle sources as visual defects but occur in underlying layers and thus are not detectable by visual or SEM inspection without deprocessing and delineation.

IN-PROCESS INSPECTIONS

In the early days of integrated circuit manufacture, in-process yield enhancement efforts were essentially responsible for defect characterization and reduction. This was accomplished primarily by inspections of lithographic patterns. Due to the small dimensions of today's devices and the large number of elements per chip the emphasis of in-process inspection has shifted from one of primary defect characterization to one of catastrophic yield loss prevention. This does not mean that in-process inspections are not important, but merely that their charter has changed as mandated by the evolution of integrated circuit technology. Therefore, in-process inspections are aimed at detecting high level visual random defects and gross yield loss mechanisms. They should be done at all critical patterning and pattern transfer steps as a minimum. The effectiveness of the in-process inspection procedure is significantly enhanced with a repetitive circuit pattern such as the SRAM. This is illustrated in Figure 2 with the comparison of 1.25 μm circuits for a multiplier and an SRAM. In order to be done rapidly these inspections must be effective at low manification. Defects as small as a few microns in size are easily detected at powers as low as 100 - 200X in the repetitive SRAM pattern shown in this figure. Reject/rework criteria for the inspections are set by the product yield requirements. The number of die inspected is determined with a statistically based sampling plan based on the confidence level of defect detection for a given die size. As an example, if the reject criteria were 1 defect per cm^2 , then the number of die would be based on the area needed to insure a 95% confidence level in defect detection at this density. This again suggests the usefulness of the SRAM for in-process inspections. Because of the repetitive nature of the pattern defects are more likely to be found. Furthermore, because the die is always the same size a fixed number of die can be established for the inspections based on realistic defect density requirements for products being run in the facility. Strict procedural guidelines for defect inspections must be developed and adhered to.

POST PROCESS INSPECTIONS

Post process yield enhancement provides failure analysis feedback to process engineering regarding the level and sources of defects so that they may be reduced or eliminated. Rapid detection and classification of defect sources is imperative for an effective yield enhancement activity. These authors have found the TEG chip with a SRAM to be an excellent vehicle for this purpose. Electrical failures in the SRAM can be easily detected by bit mapping and correlated with physical die location as indicated in Figure 3. The bit map superimposed on the TEG chip in this figure shows a column stuck at "1". The tester is configured to show a one to one position correspondence with the physical circuit as indicated by the arrow connecting the bit map and the physical circuit in the figure. Given the physical location of the defect one can visually inspect the wafer in the indicated region. Of course if the defect is non visual it will not be found, however, knowing the type of fault and its location puts bounds on the search preventing a large waste of time. Furthermore, it has been these authors experience that most defects are visual and can be found by inspection of the wafer as indicated in Figure 4. Visual inspection of the failed column has revealed a metal transfer short of submicron dimensions. Based on circuit considerations this defect causes a short between the not bit line and ground as indicated on the schematic shown in Figure 4. This results in the bit line failing high and confirms the bit map error. In this example we have shown the characterization of a relatively simple failure. However, it should be pointed out that knowledge of the layout and operation of the SRAM leads one to search the correct area of the circuit for much more complicated failure maps and detect, classify, and confirm defect sources. Also we stress that the defect classification is not considered complete unless the observed defect can verify the bit map failure through circuit considerations as illustrated in Figure 4.

The most easily detected failures are gross and random visual defects. Visual gross defects such as scratches map such that they

SRAM   MULTIPLIER

   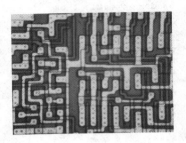

HIGH MAGNIFICATION

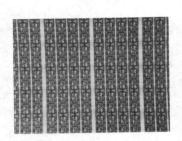   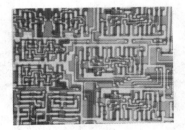

LOW MAGNIFICATION

FIGURE 2.   SRAM AND MULTIPLIER CIRCUIT PATTERNS

FIGURE 3.   BIT MAP/SRAM FAULT IDENTIFICATION

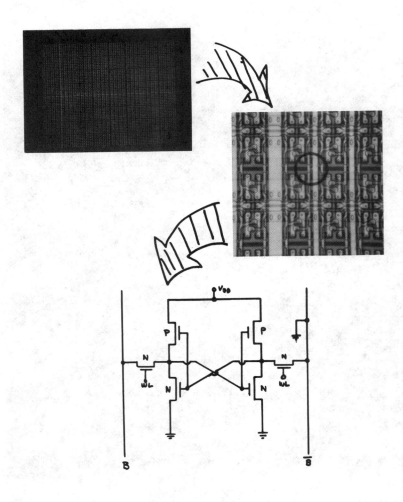

FIGURE 4. POST MORTEM DEFECT CHARACTERIZATION

appear as scratches on the bit map and are thus generally easily confirmed. Sometimes the SRAM gives a failure signature of all bits high or all bits low as a result of gross visual defects. An example of this type of defect is shown in Figure 5. Here massive active area shorts have resulted from a focus/resolution problem at active area patterning which electrically manifest themselves as all bits high on the bit map. These are easily confirmed by visual inspection as can be seen by noting the thick-thin oxide steps in the cell array are obliterated in this figure when compared with SRAM array shown previously in Figure 2. Several examples of visual random defects which illustrate the ease of identifying and classifying them without delayering, even though they can occur at sub levels, are shown in Figures 6 and 7. Note that many of the defects shown in these figures are extremely small (i.e. micron to sub micron). The fact that they can be easily detected is a result of the electrical fingerprinting of failure position through use of the SRAM. Occasionally visual defects cannot be completely characterized by optical inspection alone and require other surface analysis techniques such as SEM and X-ray analysis. As an example, consider the particle defect shown in Figure 8 which can be seen to have caused a lithography problem even at the low power of 200X magnification. From visual inspection alone one has no idea what the particle is and thus it cannot be fully characterized. SEM inspection at 3000X magnification clearly shows the physical nature of the particle to be a metal chip. X-ray analysis with the SEM shows the particle is Ti/W that was spalled from the metal deposition chamber.

Nonvisual defects are more difficult to detect than visual defects. Gross nonvisual defects can often be detected and classified with the aid of parametric test data. As an example of this type of defect classification consider two different cases, each involving a single wafer from two different lots, in which SRAM measurements showed large standby current. In the first case the large standby current was also accompanied by the RAM failing with all bits high. Visual inspection did not reveal any cause for this failure. Inspection of the parametric test data showed high NMOS leakage, low N channel threshold voltage, and low N channel punchthrough voltage. Diagnostic interpretation of the parametric data suggested a missed NMOS threshold implant as the failure mechanism which was subsequently confirmed by simulation. In the second case a large SRAM standby current was also observed but in this case the RAM itself was functional. Examination of the parametric data indicated high PMOS leakage, high PMOS threshold voltage, and low PMOS punchthrough voltage. Diagnostic interpretation of the parametric data suggested that the PMOS punchthrough implant was missed and again this failure mechanism was confirmed by simulation. The fact that the RAM did not work in case 1 and did work in case 2 but exhibited large standby current in both cases can be explained with reference to the electrical schematic of the memory cell shown previously in Figure 4. In case 1 the NMOS transistor leaked which allowed charge to be continually dumped on the bit line giving an all bits high failure. In case 2 the PMOS transistors that were leaky were blocked from the bit lines by the good NMOS transistors and thus the RAM functioned although out of spec due to the large standby current. Random nonvisual defects are the most difficult to classify. Sometimes their cause can be deduced from parametric data (i.e. high oxide defect density, interlevel shorts, more leaky devices than usual) however, definite confirmation of nonvisual SRAM failure is extremely difficult and time consuming. In general this requires meticulous delayering, without disturbing underlayers, followed by optical or SEM inspection after each layer removal. This process of repeated delayering and inspecting is time

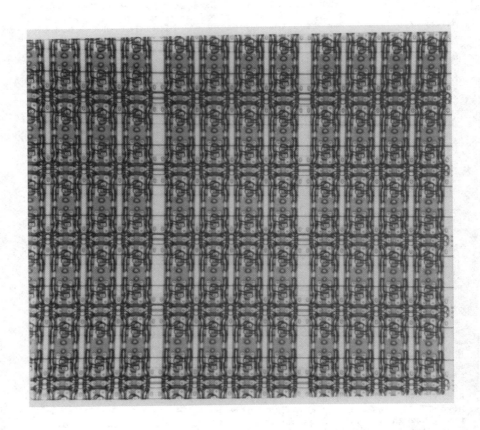

FIGURE 5.   VISUAL GROSS DEFECT

EXCESS ACTIVE AREA

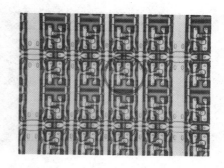

EXCESS POLY TRANSFER

MISSING CONTACT

MISSING POLY

FIGURE 6.   VISUAL RANDOM DEFECTS

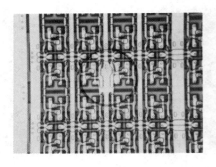

EXCESS METAL LITH

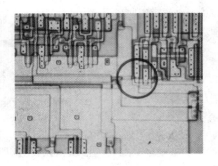

EXCESS METAL TRANSFER

MISSING METAL

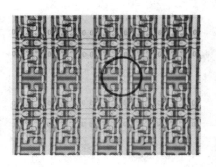

EXCESS METAL TRANSFER

FIGURE 7. VISUAL RANDOM DEFECTS

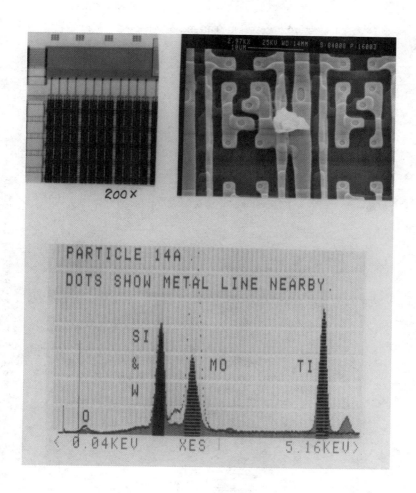

FIGURE 8. SEM/X-RAY DEFECT CLASSIFICATION

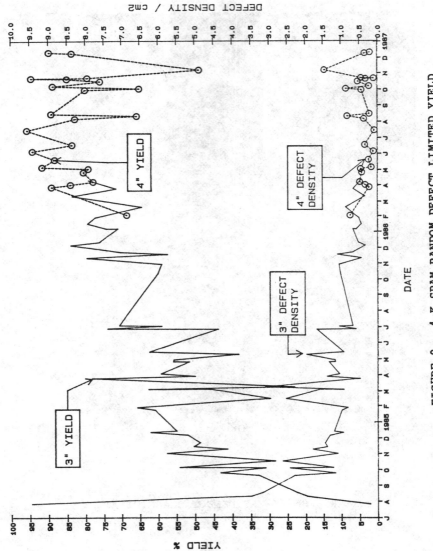

FIGURE 9. 4-K SRAM RANDOM DEFECT LIMITED YIELD

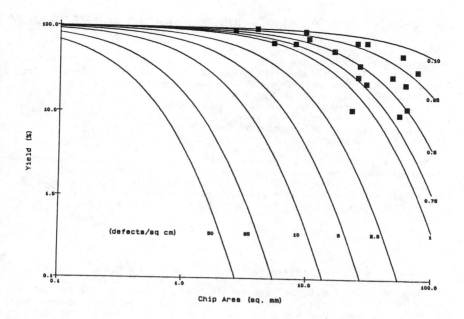

FIGURE 10.   CRD 1.25-μm CUSTOM CIRCUIT YIELD

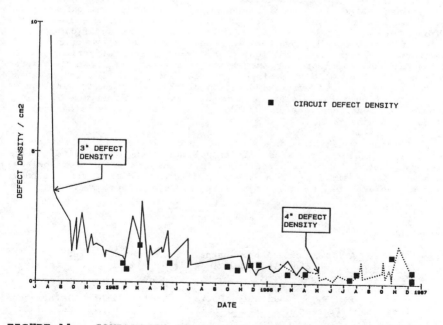

FIGURE 11.   COMPARISON OF CIRCUIT AND SRAM DEFECT DENSITIES

consuming but must be done to fully characterize nonvisual defect sources [7]. The best approach is an intuitive defect interpretation from parametric data that suggests process fixes which are usually not confirmed until the process fix has been instituted. In other words there is no substitute for experience and intuition when it comes to identifying nonvisual random defects. However, the SRAM/TEG does offer advantages here in that it provides localized data for both parametrics and functional circuit operation which aids the intuitive process.

The end result of post process yield enhancement is to identify defects as one of the four basic types i.e. random visual and nonvisual or gross visual and nonvisual. This classification of the defects identifies major yield loss mechanisms so that prioritys can be established in an organized attack to reduce or eliminate them.

RESULTS

Figure 9 shows the process monitor 4K SRAM random yield achieved in the research line that started at zero in early '84, climbed to 60% by year end, achieved 70-80% by year end '85 and increased to the 90% range through a 3" to 4" wafer transition in 1986. This curve also shows the random defect density per critical level which was reduced from $32/cm^2$ initially to $10/cm^2$ with the first yielding lot, to an average approaching $0.3/cm^2$ in 1986. A number of critical yield killers were identified during this time period by in-process inspections and post mortem analysis. The most specific of these were: 1) high particulate levels associated with specific equipment, 2) resist/lithography, 3) scratches and precipitates. Once identified, solutions were instituted through process, facility, and equipment changes or modifications to reduce particulates, improve handling, and improve quality controls and monitoring of materials and equipment. Proof of the effectiveness of using the SRAM for improving and maintaining yields is shown in Figure 10 and 11. Figure 10 summarizes the excellent yields for larger area custom chips achieved over the duration of this program. The influence of the SRAM on these yields is more clearly seen in Figure 11 which shows excellent correlation of defect density between the custom circuits and the 4K SRAM yield monitor.

Obtaining reasonable process yields on complex custom chips having 1.25 micron features requires a continual monitoring of both individual process steps and overall process quality. The use of a test monitor can provide timely corrective feedback information to a VLSI foundry line and an SRAM is an excellent vehicle to use as a test monitor.

REFERENCES

[1] Glaser, A. B., and Subak-Sharpe, G. E., Integrated Circuit Engineering, Chapter 16, Addison Wesley Publishing Co., Reading, MA., 1977, pp. 746-799.

[2] Murphy, B. T., "Cost-Size Optima of Monolithic Integrated Circuits," Proceedings of the IEEE, Vol. 52, No. 12, Dec. 1964, pp. 1537-1545.

[3] Price, J. E., "A New Look at Yield of Integrated Circuits," Proceedings of the IEEE, Vol. 58, No. 8, Aug. 1970, pp. 1290-1291.

[4] Seeds, R. B., "Yield, Economic, and Logistic Models for Complex Digital Arrays," IEEE International Convention Record, Part 6, 1967, pp. 60-61.

[5] Stapper, Jr., C. H., "On a Composite Model to the I.C. Yield Problem," IEEE Journal of Solid State Circuits, SC-10, Dec. 1975, pp. 537-539.

[6] Morgan, W. L., and Burnett, J. R., "Concepts for World Class Manufacturing Plants," Semiconductor International, Vol. 7, No. 6, Jun. 1984, pp. 137-141.

[7] J.D. Reyes; "Deprocessing Locates IC Failure Causes" Semiconductor International, Vol. 10, No. 6, May 1987, pg-108.

Yue Kuo

ADVANCED VLSI ISOLATION TECHNOLOGIES

REFERENCE: Kuo, Y., "Advanced VLSI Isolation Technologies", Semi-conductor Fabrication: Technology and Metrology, ASTM STP 990 , Dinesh C. Gupta, Ed., American Society for Testing and Materials, 1989.

ABSTRACT: Common issues in VLSI isolation technologies have been identified. Based on these issues, a critical review of conventional and novel isolation technologies such as oxide, trench, SEG, SOS, SIMOX, and ZMR is presented in this paper.

KEYWORDS: VLSI, isolation, oxide isolation, trench isolation, SEG, SOI, SOS, SIMOX, ZMR

INTRODUCTION

As integrated circuit technology improved from LSI to VLSI, the device geometry shrank drastically. Yet still the substrate surface has to be fully utilized. When devices come close together, some electrical, material, and structure defects and interference which were not critical before become serious. Since single crystal intrinsic silicon has a large dielectric constant (11.9), a relatively low breakdown voltage (3.0E5 V/cm), a moderate resistivity (1.0E5 Ω.cm), and the dopant diffusion in silicon is isotropic, the conventional junction isolation method can not satisfy the stringent electrical, material, and reliability requirements of VLSIC's(1). New and more efficient isolation technologies have to be introduced. Recently, the oxide isolation and the trench isolation methods were popular because of their effective utilization of the precious substrate surface and their good electrical isolation characteristics. They are still far away from the concept of perfect isolation. New isolation methods such as selective epitaxy growth (SEG) and silicon on insulator (SOI) were proposed and tested recently. Because of process and material drawbacks, these new methods are not as popular as the oxide or trench isolation method. But they are promising technologies which are worth further studies. A critical review and a comparison of the above isolation technologies are presented in this paper.

Dr. Yue Kuo is with IBM T.J. Watson Research Center, P.O. Box 218 Yorktown Heights, N.Y. 10598

MAJOR ISSUES IN AN ISOLATION TECHNOLOGY

In spite of the many different approaches people use for isolation purposes, there are several common issues in each technology. Table 1 lists these issues and some major concerns for each issue. A detailed discussion is as follows:

Structure

An ideal isolation structure is to enclose each device in a totally closed insulating shell with openings for interconnections only. The electrical, radioactive, and environmental interferences can be eliminated. Based on this school of thought, the SOI with five insulating walls is an ideal isolation structure. The success of depositing a single crystal silicon on a dielectric layer has been achieved in recent years (2,3). Before that, the four-sidewall isolation structure-such as the oxide and trench isolations-were the closest structures. For VLSI applications, the four-wall structure should also a) supply a smooth topography for the thin film depositions which occur afterwards, b) occupy the minimum amount of substrate surface area for high packing density, and c) grow deep dielectric sidewalls for minimum latchup or punchthrough between neighboring buried layers. Usually, during the lithography step, the isolation structure can be well defined. But after the process is finished, the topography and the cross-section figure are drastically changed.

Dielectric Materials

Thermal oxide, CVD oxide, nitride, polysilicon, sapphire, and fused silica are dielectrics used in the isolation technologies. An ideal isolation dielectric should have a low dielectric constant, a low stress, a low defect density, a high breakdown voltage, and a thermal expansion coefficient comparable with that of the substrate.

Process Simplicity and Material Reliability

The introduction of the isolation process usually complicates the whole IC process. So, a simple isolation process is essential to the success of the whole process. Many material defects are related to the process conditions. To identify the key process steps it is necessary not only to simplify the process but also to reduce material defects. Very often extra process steps are introduced to fix the defects. However the advanced isolation process should be simple and should be compatible with existing VLSI technologies.

Device Effects

An isolation technology that supplies a good topography and cross-section structure does not always give satisfactory device performance. For instance, the substrate may be damaged by the isolation steps,and an interfacial charge may build up. This directly affects device functions such as current leakages, gate integrity, short channel phenomena, and capacitances (4-11). Recently, CMOS latchup immunity was an important topic both in IC process and design. Radiation hardness is a required property in military and space applications. So, device properties have to be thoroughly examined before a new isolation method is integrated into the whole process.

REVIEW

Oxide Isolation

The oxide isolation technology is carried out by oxidizing the exposed silicon around the device active area to form silicon dioxide insulator structure. Figure 1 shows some of the published structures. Table 2 is a short table for comparing the oxide and trench isolation technologies according to the issues in Table 1.

An oxide isolation process involves two major steps: the masking technique and the oxide growth.

Because of its low oxidation rate and the low diffusion of oxygen through it, silicon nitride is widely used as the masking material (12). A thin oxide layer between the nitride and the substrate can release the stress of the nitride layer. Localized oxidation of silicon (LOCOS) , as shown in Figure 2, is a typical example of the oxide isolation structure. The bird's beak intrusion, the lateral diffusion of the channel stop doping into the device area, white ribbon formation, and defects along the oxide edge are the major material problems (13-15). The following undesired device properties result from material defects: the increase of sidewall capacitance, the narrow channel effect, decrease in breakdown voltage, threshold voltage changes, and hot carrier reliability problems. The available oxide thickness is limited. Various kinds of improved LOCOS methods were proposed to solve these problems.

The recessed oxide isolation (ROI) structure is formed by etching the silicon openings before the oxide growth. The final structure has shorter bird's beaks than the LOCOS structure. However the bird's head formation increases the surface topography (16). Although the bird's head can be planarized with the etchback or the multiple oxidation method, the whole process is more complicated (17-20). Since the bird's beak is formed by the reaction of the silicon substrate and oxygen or water diffused through the pad oxide, the most obvious way of stopping the diffusion is to deposit a thin layer of nitride on the edge of the mask. According to this principle, new methods such as the framed oxide isolation (FOI), the sidewall masked isolation (SWAMI), and the sealed interface local oxide isolation (SILO) were proposed and studied (21-23). The final FOI structure has no bird's beak and small bird's heads (24). But some substrate surface is wasted by the extended nitride strip. The SWAMI process is similar to the concept of the sidewall protection method presented at an earlier time (22,25,26). This process has several complicated steps, and it is free of bird's head. The SILO process is simpler but less coplanar than SWAMI (23,27). A critical comparison of the bird's beak intrusion and the field implantation incursion of LOCOS, ROI, SWAMI, SILO, and other isolation methods was published by Oldham (4). In his calculation the field implantation incursion was expressed as $4 (Dt)^{1/2}$, where D is the oxidation- enhanced dopant diffusivity and t is the field oxidation time. It was concluded that at all practical process

TABLE 1   Common Issues in Isolation Technologies

Issues	Major Concerns
Structure	Topography, Cross-section, Depth
Dielectrics	Dielectric characteristics, Substrate compatibility, Defect density
Process simplicity & Material reliability	Key process steps, Subsequent treatment, Process compatibility, Defects and uniformity
Device Effects	Electrical properties, Charge accumulation, Latchup, Radiation hardness

TABLE 2 Current Popular Isolation Technologies

Issues	Oxide Isolation	Trench Isolation
Structure	Figure 1	Figure 2
Dielectric	Thermal oxide	Oxide/Nitride/Polysilicon
Key Process Issues	Masking technique (nitride, oxide), Recessed Si etch, Sidewall coverage, Oxide growth	Trench etch (depth, round corner, tapered edge, vertical wall), Trench filling, Planarization
Material Issues	Defects from sidewall & corners, Thinning of gate oxide	Excess stress from sharp corners, Interfacial charge
Device Effects	Junction leakage, Sidewall capacitance, Parasitic transistor, Channel stop diffusion, Narrow channel effect, V threshold, V breakdown, Hot carrier, Scaling-down limit, Subthreshold I	V Punchthrough, V breakdown, Base resistance, ECL gate delay, Ic-e leakage, Subthreshold change, Junction $I_{leakage}$, Interfacial charge,
Comments	Min. iso. width several folds litho. limit, Not very deep oxide, Good for LSI	Min. iso. width close to litho. limit, Deep trench, Less latchup N-channel reliability, Cost consideration

temperatures, the field implantation incursion consumes more active area than the bird's beak does (4).

There are two areas where oxide isolation-induced defects were observed: in the crystal and in the gate oxide. Defects in the crystal are most often originated from the oxide-silicon interface, and are responsible for leakages, sidewall capacitance, parasitic field transistor on-off behavior, etc. Defects in the gate oxide such as the white ribbon formation contribute to the narrow channel width effect, the short channel effect, the subthreshold current change, the low gate breakdown, etc.

When the device shrinks, the oxide isolation shows some small geometry effects. Iwai et al. studied the scaling-down limitations of LOCOS and ROI and concluded that there would be some electrical and morphological limitations for future small devices, especially for the LOCOS method (13). The potential and the subthreshold current behaviors proved very different for various kinds of oxide isolation methods (28). In LOCOS, the surface potential decreases toward the oxide. In ROI, the reverse is true. Devices isolated with LOCOS have lower threshold currents than those isolated with ROI. Devices isolated with the SWAMI method have fewer defects than those isolated with LOCOS (25). SWAMI has the inverse narrow channel effect. SILO devices probably have the gate oxide thinning phenomena (23). Generally speaking, oxide isolation is efficient for LSI applications. When device geometry shrinks to small VLSI range, electrical properties such as those device effects listed in Table 2, have to be carefully examined.

Trench Isolation

A trench isolation structure is similar to the ROI structure. Instead of filling the trench with thermal oxide, the trench is filled with CVD dielectric materials. Figure 2 shows some of the important published trench structures. A list of key issues in a trench isolation technology is in Table 2.

A trench isolation process includes three key steps: trench etching, trench filling, and surface planarization.

Silicon oxide or nitride is commonly used as the mask for the device active area during the trench formation (9,10,29-35). Because of its anisotropic and selective characteristics, reactive ion etching (RIE) is exclusively used in the trench etch. Plasma etch and reactive sputtering etch could also be used to etch the trench structure (36,37). To minimize the substrate surface occupancy, the trench wall is usually vertical and the depth is several microns. This kind of structure may save a field implant step and can reduce the latchup susceptibility.

The common trench filling dielectrics are CVD silicon dioxide, silicon nitride, polysilicon, and various combinations of these (9,10,29,38-45). The trench wall is oxidized before the filling. The excess stress from the corner of the thermal oxide generates defects in the substrate (46). By reducing the oxide thickness to less than 1500 Å, or by raising the oxidation temperature to higher than 1050 °C, these defects can be eliminated. Probably the simplest trench

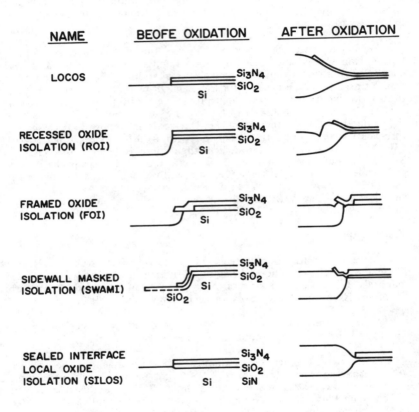

FIGURE 1

OXIDE ISOLATION PROCESSES

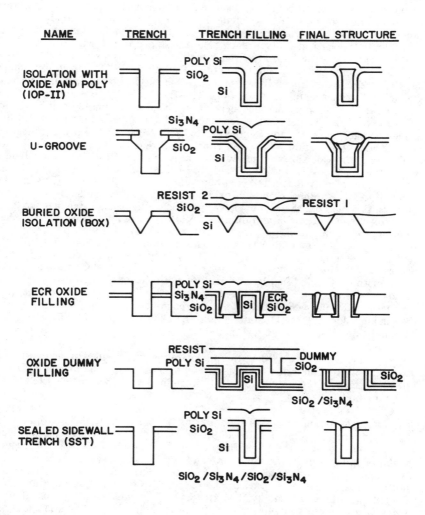

FIGURE 2
TRENCH ISOLATION PROCESSES

filling process is the polysilicon filling of the improved oxide and polysilicon isolation (IOP-II) process, as shown in Figure 2 (43). Because of the difference in trench width, the narrow trench is always filled faster than the wide trench. If the top of the trench is tapered using a U-groove method, or if the simplified buried oxide isolation (BOX) method is used, the surface topography is smoother (9,45). The chance of a reentrant formation in this kind of trench is less than in the vertical-walled trench. But the sloped trench wastes some of the surface territory. The U-groove trench etch takes two steps and the V-groove trench can only supply a limited depth. The Electron Cyclotron Resonance (ECR) plasma oxide trench filling method, as shown in Figure 2, can fill narrow and wide trenches simultaneously (44). The ECR method uses the microwave to generate the plasma and then deposits the film at a remote chamber away from the plasma. Therefore, the deposited film can be very directional and has a high quality, even at room temperature. This trench filling process includes a   nitride   deposition,   a   molybdenum   deposition,   the   etch   of molybdenum/nitride/silicon, the ECR deposition, the lift-off of molybdenum with oxide on top of it, the trench sidewall oxidation, a polysilicon deposition, an oxidation of polysilicon, the etch-back of oxidized polysilicon. This is a tedious process. Another method of oxide dummy filling method was introduced (46). In this method, the thin oxide and nitride coated silicon trenches are filled with polycrystalline silicon and dummy CVD oxide. A photoresist layer is then spun-on and etched-back to leave those trenches half-filled with polycrystalline silicon. The polycrystalline silicon is then totally oxidized to fully fill the trenches. A series of etching and oxidation steps are involved in the whole process. This method suffers for its complexity. The sealed sidewall trench (SST) method is a modified IOP-II method, with the extra deposit of oxide and nitride preventing the vertical bird's beak growth (77). These CVD trench filling methods do not generate a lateral encroachment problem, which increases the packing density. CVD oxide is used in filling trenches of BOX and ECR. Thermal oxide is used in the rest methods.

Two methods were used in the planarization of the filled trench: the mechanical polish method and the plasma etchback method. The former is simple, but the latter is more precise. The lift-off method was used in the ECR oxide filling method.

Trench isolation processes generate far fewer substrate defects than oxide isolation processes. Bipolar and MOS devices built with trench isolation technologies showed very good electric properties (9-11,29,38,43,44,47). Measurements of punchthrough voltage, breakdown voltage, sidewall capacitance, bottom junction capacitance, base resistance, ECL gate delay, and collector-emitter leakage on bipolar devices showed that BOX and U-groove are more efficient than LOCOS and ROI (9,10,46,48). For MOS applications, the following factors were studied: latchup, subthreshold change, junction leakage, interface charge density, and surface inversion of trench isolated devices (11,29,44).

The trench isolation method is more efficient than the oxide isolation method when the structure, the material defect, and the device electrical properties are considered. However, the trench process is usually much more complicated than the oxide isolation process. There were concerns about the n-channel reliability of the IOP-II isolated devices, which was caused by the sidewall parasitic channels and which did not exist in the simplified BOX isolated devices (29,45)

NOVEL ISOLATION TECHNOLOGIES

New isolation technologies are constantly being studied to make improvements in areas such as lowering the material defect level and reducing the number of process steps. Other areas being studied are the latchup immunity and the radiation hardness. Table 3 lists key points of four novel isolation technologies that have been intensively studied in recent years. A more detailed discussion of each technology will follow. There are other novel isolation technologies, such as the full isolation by porous oxidized silicon (FIPOS) that has made great strides in recent years (78). But since these technologies still need more fundamental studies, they are not included in this paper.

Selective Epitaxy Growth (SEG)

An SEG process is distinct from the above isolation processes in that the isolation area is defined first and then the device active area develops (48-51). Figure 3 shows the structure.

An SEG process is composed of three major steps: the oxide growth and etch, the sidewall coating, and the selective epitaxy growth.

An oxide layer of about 2 microns can be thermally grown from the substrate, patterned, and etched until the silicon substrate is exposed. The etched wall is usually vertical.

Facets are usually formed on the SEG epitaxy surface, adjacent to sidewall of the oxide trench. Due to its high defect density and its rough surface topography, the facet area can not be used to build devices. The direction of the oxide trench etch and the coating material on the sidewall of the oxide trench affect the defect density and the surface morphology of the facet area; e.g., the (100) direction etched oxide gave fewer defects to the epitaxy than the (110) direction etched oxide did (48). The polysilicon coated sidewall gave no apparent facet to the adjacent epitaxy while the oxide or nitride coated sidewall generated obvious facets to the adjacent epitaxy (49).

The epitaxy deposition is carried out under LPCVD conditions with HCl being added into the feeding stream. The selectivity and growth rate are affected by the HCl concentration, temperature, pressure, the surface ratio of the masked area to the unmasked area (49-51). Typically a temperature of 950 to 1000 °C, a pressure of less than 100 torr, and a chlorinated silane gas such as dichlorosilane is used for SEG reaction. Because the deposition is reaction-controlled under this condition, the resulting film is uniform. If no HCl is added during the reaction, the area ratio affects the selectivity (50). When the HCl is added, the area ratio becomes less important.

TABLE 3 Novel Isolation Technologies

Issues	SEG	SOS	SIMOX	ZMR
Structure	Figure 3	Figure 4	Figure 4	Figure 4
Dielectric	Oxide/Nitride/Polysilicon	Sapphire	Oxide/Nitride	Oxide/Nitride/Fused Silica/Sapphire
Key Process Issues	Selective dept. (temp., pressure, HCl conc., area ratio), Opening direction, Sidewall coating	Si crystal dept., Interfacial treatment	Si ion implantation (high keV, high dose, raised temp.), High temp. anneal	CVD Si dept. Recrystallization (graphite strip, laser, lamp, e-beam), Cap layer, Temp. profile & gradient
Material Issues	Facets, Defects propagated from interface	Lattice mismatch, Thermal exp. coeff. discrepancy, High dielectric const.	High linear defect density	Subgrain boundaries, Grain boundaries
Device Effects	Junction leakage, Subthreshold change N-channel shift, Small threshold V change, High latchup immunity,	$I_{leakage}$, Low mobilities, Low parasitic C, Latchup immunity, Radiation hardness	Low parasitic C, Low power dissip., High mobilities, Long carrier life, Grounded substrate,	Reduced conductivity, Degraded minority life, $I_{leakage}$, Threshold V uniformity, I-V curve kinks,
Comments	Simple process, High defect density, Delicate dept. cond.,	Simple process, High defect density, Expensive	Simple process, Special implanter	Simple process, Material defects, Film uniformity & topography

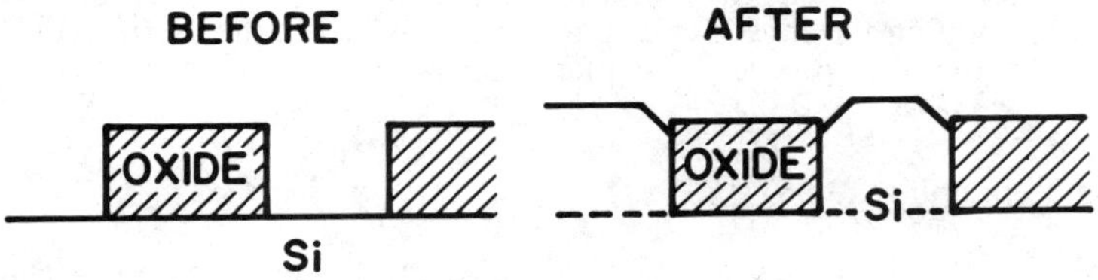

FIGURE 3
SELECTIVE EPITAXY GROWTH (SEG)

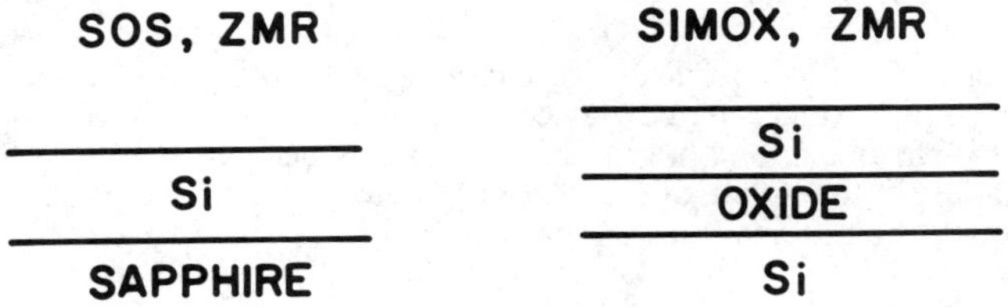

FIGURE 4
SILICON ON INSULATOR (SOI)

MOS and bipolar devices were tested for the SEG technology (48,51,52). A comparison of the n-channel device built on the 2 micron oxide SEG and the 0.65 micron field oxide LOCOS showed that the current leakage of the SEG device was one order of magnitude higher than that of the LOCOS device. However, the n-channel shift, the threshold change, and the latchup immunity of the SEG device are better (48).

Crystal defects originated from the interface of the epitaxy and the oxide wall probably are the biggest problem of the SEG technology. In addition, the facet formation on the edge of the epitaxy pattern wastes the useful area. On the other hand, the SEG process is simpler than the trench isolation process.

Silicon on Sapphire (SOS)

SOS is the most extensively studied SOI technology. Figure 4 shows its structure and Table 3 summarizes its key issues.

The SOS process is a simple CVD epitaxy deposition process. Because this is a heteroepitaxy structure, the lattice mismatch and the thermal expansion coefficient difference are the two major causes of the material defects. The former leads to interfacial defects such as dislocations, stacking faults, microtwins, and the high surface charge (53). The latter generates compressive stress when the wafer is cooled from the deposition temperature of 1000 °C to room temperature because the thermal expansion coefficient of silicon is twice that of the sapphire (53). The compressive stress reduces the carrier mobility within the silicon film. Although a thermal annealing can effectively reduce the current leakage from the interfacial defect, the compressive characteristics can not be changed (54). Recently it was reported that with a high energy silicon ion implantation to the silicon- sapphire interface and a subsequent thermal-regrowth procedure, the interfacial defect density could be reduced one hundred fold and the mobilities could be increased 50% (55).

In spite of its low parasitic capacitance, the speed advantage of the SOS device over the oxide isolated device is eliminated when the minimum device geometry is shrunk to one micron or less. This is because the dielectric constant of SOS is larger than that of the oxide, 11.9 to 3.8, and the carrier mobility in SOS is lower than in the bulk silicon.

The radiation hardness and the latchup immunity are the biggest advantages of the SOS technology. For specific applications the radiation hardness is often required. This is why, although the SOS wafer is several times more expensive and has a higher defect density than the bulk wafer, it is still used. NMOS, CMOS, and lateral bipolar devices have been built on SOS structures (54-56).

Separation by Implanted Oxygen (SIMOX)

Figure 4 shows the structure of SIMOX, which is formed by imbedding a thin oxide layer in the single crystal silicon matrix. The thin oxide layer functions as an insulator layer. Other insulators such as nitride or oxynitride could also be used in similar structures with similar implantation methods (57-59).

The two key process steps of SIMOX are the implantation and the subsequent annealing.

The main goal of the SIMOX process is to keep the single crystal silicon structure on top of the oxide layer for the device manufacture. Therefore, the implantation energy should be high, e.g., higher than 150 keV, to leave some non-implanted top layer (60). In fact, the top layer thickness increases with the increase of the implant energy (61). The implant dose should also be high, e.g., more than 1.0E18 /cm², because when the dose is less than 0.6E18 /cm², the implanted oxygen forms oxide islands after the annealing instead of forming the continuous thin film (62). The size of the islands increases with the increase of the implant dose until a continuous stoichiometric film is formed. When the oxygen dose exceeds the stoichiometric concentration, the extra oxygen diffuses toward the side to oxidize more silicon (60). So the thickness of the top crystal layer decreases with the increase of the implant dose (61). To reduce the amorphization of the top layer during the implantation, the wafer is kept at an elevated temperature during the implant, e.g., 500 °C or above.

The annealing step functions to segregate the implanted oxygen to form the oxide layer and to remove defects in the upper silicon layer. The typical annealing condition is 1150 °C under nitrogen or argon for 2 to 4 hours (63). A higher annealing temperature, e.g., 1405 °C, can remove the oxygen precipitate in silicon in a short time with a sharp silicon-oxide interface (64). Because of the migration and segregation of the oxygen in the upper silicon layer and in the substrate to the buried oxide layer, the width of the upper silicon layer shrinks with the increase of the annealing time while the width of the buried oxide layer increases (65).

Linear dislocations are the main crystal defects of this technology, in contrast to the planar microtwin or stacking fault defects in SOS (64,65).

Devices built on SIMOX have no latchup, high electron and hole mobilities, long carrier lifetimes, and low parasitic capacitance. Because of the thin dielectric structure, SIMOX can dissipate more heat than SOS and the substrate can be grounded. Excellent transient-radiation hardness has been demonstrated for SIMOX SRAMs (66).

SIMOX has been intensively studied by some companies in the past five years. Compared with SOS, SIMOX has fewer material mismatch problems and better device performance. But it takes a special high current, e.g., 200 mA, high energy, e.g., 150 keV or higher, implanter to do the implantation work, which is not commercially available. Even when this kind of machine is available, its economy may be a concern.

Zone Melting Recrystallization (ZMR)

The ZMR structure, as shown in Figure 4, is similar to that of the SOS or SIMOX, except that the processing methods are very different. The ZMR is carried out by a high temperature recrystallization of the polycrystalline or amorphous silicon deposited layer on a dielectric surface (67-71).

A ZMR process is composed of two major steps: the deposition of the polycrystalline or amorphous silicon, and the recrystallization.

A CVD method is used to deposit the polycrystalline or amorphous silicon on the surface of an insulator, which is a thin dielectric layer such as silicon oxide/ nitride on top of a silicon substrate, or on a bulk substrate such as fused silica or sapphire. The thin dielectric can be a blank layer or a patterned layer that is etched to expose some of the underneath silicon crystal to function as the seed during the recrystallization.

The recrystallization temperature should be higher than the melting point of silicon. The temperature gradient and distribution around the heated zone are directly responsible for the final crystal structure. The scan speed and the shape of the heating zone are thus important parameters for the process (67). A variety of heating sources were reported, e.g., a graphite-strip heater (68,79,80), a laser (67), a lamp heater (69,70), and an e-beam (71). The surface reflectivity of the molten silicon is higher than that of the solid silicon, therefore the mechanism of the heat absorption of e-beam is different from the mechanism of the other heating sources. A capping layer of silicon oxide or nitride or both is used to protect the silicon from environmental contamination. The balling up of the molten silicon, the surface roughness and non-uniformity can also be prevented by the use of a capping layer (72-74).

The crystal quality is the main material concern in the ZMR technology nowadays. Subgrain boundaries were observed in crystals prepared from almost all the different heating sources (67,68,70,71). The laser recrystallized film has a polycrystalline structure (72). Precipitates along the subgrain boundaries were observed and were believed to act as pinning points for the subgrain boundaries and as the stress center for the silicon film (70).

MOS devices were manufactured on ZMR substrates. Subgrain boundaries from the graphite-strip heater are responsible for the current leakage, threshold voltage non-uniformity, minority life degradation, and conductivity reduction (75). The lamp ZMR devices have the same kind of threshold voltage non-uniformity, but less current leakage (76). Devices made on laser ZMR substrates have the character of the polycrystalline film (67). P-MOS devices built on e-beam ZMR substrates have electric characteristics similar to those on Ar laser ZMR substrates (71). E-beam ZMR is the least understood of these technologies.

SUMMARY AND FUTURE TRENDS

The main goal of an isolation technology is to protect each device from the interference of the neighboring devices and the environment. The ideal structure is obviously SOI with five dielectric surfaces. Until the SOI technology matures, trench isolation definitely has a better structure than the oxide isolation. Silicon oxide is widely used in almost all the conventional and novel isolation structures, mainly for its appropriate dielectric characteristics, its material compatibility, and its processibility. As the isolation requirement becomes more stringent with the shrinking of devices, the process becomes more complicated. Very often extra steps are added to the original process to mend material defects. Process compatibility with current VLSI fabrication capability can not be neglected. Material defects are the major reason for the poor device performance of current oxide and trench isolations. They are also the main drawbacks of the novel isolation technologies. Most of these defects originate from the dielectric-silicon interface. The basic understanding of interfacial phenomena is the key to solving these material defect problems. For bipolar applications, the device performance is restricted by the crystal structure. For MOS applications, examinations of both the crystal and the thin gate characteristics are necessary. For total latchup immunity and radiation hardness, SOI technologies, specifically the silicon on thin dielectric layer structure, are the solutions.

The future isolation technology should have a self-aligned type of structure similar to the SEG structure, with a well defined isolation area, but without topography problems. The dielectric should be reliable, like silicon oxide, but generate low stress to the adjacent silicon crystal. The process should be simple and generate few interfacial defects and low charge density. Electrical performance is closely correlated with material properties. New process technologies or equipment may be needed to achieve these requirements.

ACKNOWLEDGEMENTS

I would like to thank Dr. W. E. Howard for his useful discussions.

REFERENCES

(1) Runyan, W. R. and Watelski, "Handbook of Materials and Processes for Electronics", Chap. 7, Ed. Harper, C. A., McGraw-Hill, New York, 1970.
(2) Lam, H. W., Technical Digest International Electron Devices Meeting , Washington, DC, Dec. 5-7, 1983, pp 348-351.
(3) Celler, G. K., Solid State Technology , March 1987, pp 93-98.
(4) Oldham, W. G., Technical Digest International Electron Devices Meeting , S.F., CA, Dec. 1982, pp 216-219.
(5) Yau, L.D., Solid State Electron , 16, 1974, p 1059.
(6) Aker, L. A., Begulwala, M, and Custode, F., IEEE Transaction Electron Devices , ED-28, 1981, p 1490.
(7) Wada, M., Shibata, T., Konake, M., Lizulca, H., and Dang, R., Technical Digest International Electron Devices Meeting , 1981, p 223.
(8) Taylor, G. W., IEEE Transaction Electron Devices , ED-25, 1978, p 337.
(9) Hayasaka, A.,Tamaki, Y., Kawamura, Ogiue, K., and Ohwaki, S., Technical Digest International Electron Devices Meeting , S.F., CA, Dec. 1982, pp 62-65.
(10) Vora, M., Ho, Y. H., Bhamre, S., Chien, F., Bakker, G., Hingarh, H., and Schmitz, Technical Digest International Electron Devices Meeting New Orleans, LA, 1985, pp 34-37.
(11) Cham, K. M., Chiang, S., Wenocur, D., Rung, R. D., Technical Digest International Electron Devices Meeting S.F., CA, Dec. 1984, pp 23-26.

(12) Appels, J. A., Kooi, E., Paffen, M. M., Schatorje, J. J., and Verkuylen, W., Philips Research Reports, 25, 1970, pp 118-132.

(13) Iwai, H., Taniguchi, Konaka, M., Maeda, S., and Nishi, Y., IEEE Transaction Electron Devices , ED-29(4), 1983, pp 625-630.

(14) Wang, K. L., Saller, S. A., Hunter, W. R., Chatterjee, P. K., and Yang, P., IEEE Transaction Electron Devices , ED-29(4), 1982, pp 541-547.

(15) Shankoff, T. A., Sheng, T. T., Hasgko, S. E., Marcus, R. B., and Smith, T. E., Journal of Electrochemical Society , 127(1), 1980, pp 216-222.

(16) Bassous, E., Yu, H. N., and Maniscalo, V., Journal of Electrochmeical Society , 133(11), 1976, pp 1729-1737.

(17) Kuo, Y., Proceedings of Science and Technology of Microfabricaiton , Materials Research Society, Vol. 76, 1986, pp 209-214.

(18) Kuo, Y., SPIE Proceedings of Advanced Processing of Semiconductor Devices Vol. 797, Bay Point, FL., March 1987.

(19) Burton, G., Tuntasood, P., Chien, F., Kovacs, R., and Vora, M., Technical Digest International Electron Devices Meeting , S. F., CA, Dec. 1984, pp 582-585.

(20) Sakai, H., Yoshimi, T., and Sugawara, K., Journal of Electrochmeical Society , 124(2), 1977, pp 138-320.

(21) Magdo, I. and Bohg, A., Journal of Electrochmeical Society , 125 (6), 1978, pp 932-936.

(22) Chiu, K. Y., Moll, J. L., and Manoliu, J., IEEE Transaction Electron Devices , ED-29(4), 1982, pp 536-540.

(23) Hui, J. C., Chiu, T., Wong, S., and Oldham, W. G., IEEE Transaction Electron Devices , ED-29(4), 1982, pp 554-561.

(24) Magdo, I. and Bohg, A., Journal of Electrochemical Society , Vol. 125, No. 6, 1978, pp 932-936.

(25) Chiu, K. Y., Fang, R., Lin, J., Moll, J. L., Lage, C., Angelos, S., and Tillman, R., Technical Digest International Electron Devices Meeting , S.F., CA., Dec. 1982, pp 224-227.

(26) Kahng, D., Shankoff, T. A., Sheng, T. T., and Haszki, S. E., Journal of Electrochemical Society , Vol. 127, No. 11, 1980, pp 2468-2471.

(27) Hui, J. C., Chiu, T., Wong, S., and Oldham, W. G., Technical Digest International Electron Devices Meeting , S.F., CA, Dec. 1982, pp 220-223.

(28) Sugino, M. and Akers, L. A., IEEE Electron Letters, Vol. EDL-4, No. 4, April 1983, pp 114-115.

(29) Rung, R. D., Momose, H., and Nagakulo, Technical Digest International Electron Devices Meeting , S.F., CA, Dec. 1982, pp 237-240.

(30) Horwitz, C. M., IEEE Transaction Electron Devices , ED-28(11), Nov. 1981, pp 1320-3123.

(31) Chi-Huang, J., IEEE Transaction Electron Devices , ED-29, 1982, p 554.

(32) Okano, H., Yamazaki, Horrike, Y., Solid State Technology , Vol. 25, No. 4, April 1982, p 166.

(33) Brasseur, G., Coopmans, Proceedings of Electrochemical Society, Fall 1986, Abstract 280, San Diego, CA, 1986, p 419.

(34) Pinto, R., Ramanathan, K. V., and Babu, R. S., Journal of Electrochemical Society , Vol. 134, No. 1, 1987.

(35) Schwartz, G. C., Rothman, L. B., and Schopen, T. J., Journal of Electrochemical Society , Vol. 126, No. 3, 1978, pp 464-469.

(36) Horwitz, C. M., IEEE Transaction Electron Devices , ED-28(11), 1981, p 1320.

(37) Sellamuthu, R., Barkanic, J., and Jaccodine, R, Proceedings Tegal Plasma Seminar , 1986, pp 33-38.

(38) Tang, D. D., Solomon, P. M., Ning, T. H., Isac, R. D., and Burger, R. E., IEEE Journal of Solid-State Circuits , Vol. SC-17, No. 5, Oct. 1982, pp 925-931.

(39) Pogge, H. B., "Deep-Groove Isolation" , Recent News paper, Electrochemical Society Meeting, Boston, MA, 1979.

(40) Pogge, H. B., "CVD Groove Filling of DGI Structures" , ESSDERC 1980 Symp., York, England, Sept. 1979.

(41) Kemlage, B. M., Mauer, and Lechaton, J., "Dual Depth Dielectric Isolation Process" , Recent News paper, Electrochemical Society Meeting, Hollywood, FL., Oct. 1980.

(42) Chiang, S. Y., Cham, K. M., Wenocur, D. W., Hui, A., and Rung, R. D., Electrochemical Society Fall Meeting, paper 174, 1982.

(43) Goto, H., Takada, T., Abe, R., Kawabe, Y., Oami, K., and Tanaka, M., Technical Digest International Electron Devices Meeting , S.F., CA, Dec. 1982, pp 58-61.

(44) Arai, E., Technical Digest International Electron Devices Meeting , Washington, DC, Dec. 1983, pp 19-22.

(45) Shibata, T., Nakayama, R., Kurosawa, K., Onga, S., Konaka, M., and Iizuka, H., Technical Digest International Electron Devices Meeting , Washington, DC, Dec. 1983, pp 27-30.

(46) Mikoshiba, H., Homma, T., and Hamano, K., Technical Digest International Electron Devices Meeting , S.F., CA., Dec. 1984, pp 578-581.

(47) Hirata, K., Ozaki, Y., Oda, M., and Limizuka, M., IEEE Transaction Electron Devices , Vol. ED-28, No. 11, Nov. 1981, pp 1323-1331.

(48) Endo, N., Kasai,N., Ishitani, A., Kitajima, H., and Kurogi, Y., IEEE Transaction Electron Devices , Vol. ED-33, No. 11, Nov. 1986, pp 1659-1666.

(49) Endo, N., Tanno, K., Ishitani, A., Kurogi, Y., and Tsuya, H., Technical Digest International Electron Devices Meeting , S.F., CA, Dec. 1982, pp 241-244.

(50) Voss, H. J. and Kurtan, H., Technical Digest International Electron Devices Meeting , S.F., CA, Dec. 1984, pp 35-38.

(51) Endo, N., Kasai, N., Ishitani, A., and Kurogi, Y., Technical Digest International Electron Devices Meeting , S.F., CA, Dec. 1984, pp 31-34.

(52) Hine, S., Hirao, t., Kayama, S., and Tsubouchi, N., IEEE Technical Digest on VLSI Technology, , 1982, pp 116-117.

(53) Lam, H. W., Tash, Jr., A. F., and Pinizzotto, R. F., VLSI Electronics: Microstrucutre Science , Chapt. 1, Vol. 4, Ed. Einspruch, N. G., 1982.

(54) Roulet, M. E., Schwab, P., Golecki, I, and Nicolet, M. A., Electron Letters , 15, 1979, p 529.

(55) Vasudev, P. K., IEEE Circuits Development , 3(4), July 1987, pp 17-19.

(56) Ipri, A. C., Sokoloski, J. C., and Flatley, D. W., IEEE Transaction Electron Devices , Vol. ED-27, 1980, p 1275.

(57) Izumi, K., Doken, M., and Ariyoshi, H., Electron Letters , Vol. 14, 1978, p 55.

(58) Meekison, C. D., Booker, G. R., Reeson, K. J., Hemment, P., Chater, R. J., Kilner, J. A., and Davis, J. R., Vacuum , Vol. 36, No. 11-12, 1986, pp 925-928.

(59) Reeson, K. J., Hemment, P. L., Kilner, J. A., Chater, R. J., Meekison, C. D., Marsh, C., Booker, G. R., and Davis, J. R., Vacuum , Vol. 36, No. 11-12, 1986, pp 891-895.

(60) Celler, G. K., Solid State Technology , March 1987, pp 93-98.

(61) Gill, S. S. and Wilson, I. H., Proceedings of Materials Research Society , vol. 27, 1984, pp 275-280.
(62) Hemment, P. L., Reeson, K. J., Kilner, J. A., Chater, R. J., Marsh, C., Bookert, G. R., Celler, G. K., and Stoemenos, J., Vacuum , Vol. 36, No. 11-12, 1986, pp 11-12, pp. 877-881
(63) Pinizzotto, R., Proceedings Materials Research Society , Vol. 27, 1984, pp 265-273.
(64) Celler, G. K., Hemment, P. L., West, K. W., and Gibson, J. M., Appllied Physics Letters , Vol. 48, No. 8, Feb. 1986, pp 532-534.
(65) Stonemenos, J. and Margail, J., Thin Solid Films , Vol 135, 1986, pp 115-127.
(66) Tsaur, B. Y., Sferrino, V. J., Choi, H. K., Chen, C. K., Mountain, R. W., Schott, J. T., Shedd, W. M., LaPierre, D. C., and Blanchard, R., IEEE Transaction Nuclear Science , Vol NS-33, No. 6, Dec. 1986, pp 1372-1376.
(67) Celler, G. K, Journal of Crystal Growth , Vol. 63, 1983, pp 429-444.
(68) Fan, J. C., Tsaur, B. Y., and Geis, M. W., Journal of Crystal Growth , Vol. 63, 1983, pp 453-483.
(69) Dutartre, D., Haond, M., and Bensahel, D., Journal of Applied Physics , Vol. 59, No. 2, January 1986, pp 632-635.
(70) Vu, D. P., Haond, M., Bensahel, D., and Dupuy, M., Journal of Applied Physics , Vol. 54, No. 1, 1983, pp 437-439.
(71) Knapp, J. A. and Picraux, S. T., Journal of Crystal Growth , Vol. 63, 1983, pp 445-452.
(72) Colinge, J. P., Demoulin, E., Bensahel, D., and Auvert, G., Applied Physics Letters , Vol. 41, No. 4, 1982, pp 346-347.
(73) Chen, C. K., Geis, M. W., Finn, M. C., and Tsaur, B. Y., Applied Physics Letters , Vol. 48, No. 19, 1986, pp 1300-1302.
(74) Robinson, M., Lischner, D. J., and Celler, G. K. Celler, Journal of Crystal Growth , 1983, pp 484-492.
(75) Tsaur, B. Y., IEEE Circuits and Devices Magazine Vol. 3, No. 4, July 1987, pp 12-16.
(76) Haond, M., Vu, D. P., Agirre, A. M., and Perret, S., IEEE Circuits and Devices , Vol. 3, No. 4, July 1987, pp 27-31.
(77) Teng, C. W., Slawinski, C., and Hunter, W. R., Technical Digest International Electron Devices Meeting , S.F., CA, Dec. 1984, pp 586-589.
(78) Weaver, H. T., IEEE Circuits and Devices Magazine , Vol. 3, No. 4, July 1987, pp 3-5.
(79) Pfeiffer, L., Gelman, A. E., Jackson, K. A., West, K. W., and Balstone, Applied Physics Letters , Vol. 51, No. 16, 1987, pp 1256-1258.
(80) Pfeiffer, L., West, K. W., Paine, S., and Joy, D. C., Proceedings Energy Beam-Solid Interactions and Transient Thermal Processing , Materials Research Society, Vol. 35, 1985, pp 583-592.

Material Defects and Gettering

Peter Eichinger, Heinz J. Rath, and Heinrich Schwenke

APPLICATION OF TOTAL REFLECTION X-RAY FLUORESCENCE ANALYSIS FOR
METALLIC TRACE IMPURITIES ON SILICON WAFER SURFACES

REFERENCE: Eichinger, P., Rath, H.J., Schwenke, H., "Application
of Total Reflection X-Ray Fluorescence Analysis for Metallic Trace Impurities on Silicon Wafer Surfaces", Semiconductor Fabrication: Technology and Metrology, ASTM STP 990, Dinesh C. Gupta,
editor, American Society for Testing and Materialis, 1989.

ABSTRACT: Total Reflection X-Ray Fluorescence Analysis (TXRF) is
presented as a new analytical tool which allows to assess the
metal contamination on silicon wafer surfaces in a non-destructive way. The technique uses a conventional X-Ray tube with a Mo
anode, an energy-dispersive Si(Li) spectrometer, and an alignment
set-up for the exact control of the angle of incidence which is
kept below the critical angle for total reflection. Detection limits in the order of 100 ppm of a monoatomic layer are achieved
e.g. for transistion metals. Application studies include plating
of metals from a high purity liquid process chemical (BHF) and
the adsorptivity of the silicon surface for Br originating from
RCA type cleaning procedures.

KEYWORDS: silicon surface, trace impurities, X-ray fluorescence,
total reflection, transition metals

INTRODUCTION

Traces of metals in the surface layer of silicon wafers are known
to affect seriously performance and yield of integrated circuits. Metal traces may be already present with the starting material, or may
be deposited on the surface during various wet and dry processing
steps or by inadequate handling. Surface contaminants are subsequently
driven in by high temperature processes, leading to the formation of
various kinds of defects [1]. Surface contamination is either locally
concentrated in the form of particles or distributed to a more or less
homogeneous coverage in the submonolayer scale at the outer surface or

Dr. P. Eichinger is head of GeMeTec Gesellschaft für Meßtechnik
und Technologie mbH, Paul-Gerhardt-Allee 50, D-8000 München 60, FRG;
Dr. H.J. Rath is senior scientist at Wacker-Chemitronic GmbH, Postfach
1140, D-8263 Burghausen, FRG; H. Schwenke is research scientist at
GKSS Forschungszentrum, Institut für Physik, D-2054 Geesthacht, FRG.

in the native oxide. Thus, detailed knowledge of the amount and nature of the contamination is essential not only with respect to process contamination control but also for effective cleaning.

Total Reflection X-ray Fluorescence Analysis (TXRF) has been proven to be an effective tool for multielement analysis in analytical chemistry [2]. The technique permits the determination of minute amounts of elements that are placed on a smooth and plane surface, down to the picogram-level (fig. 1).

In this contribution TXRF is presented as a new analytical instrument for the determination of the metal contamination on silicon wafer surfaces in a nondestructive way, and first application studies are shown in order to illustrate the benefits of this technique for the investigation of interactions of the silicon surface with process chemicals.

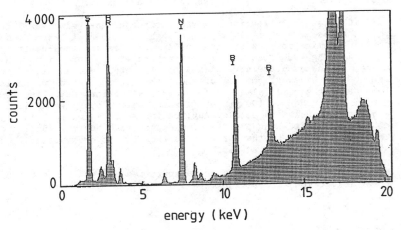

FIG.1:   TXRF-spectrum of 1 nanogram nickel and bismuth deposited from a standard solution on a flat quartz substrate (counting time = 1000 s, minimum detection limit for nickel = 2,3 pg).

EXPERIMENTAL METHOD

The schematic set-up is shown in fig. 2. The X-ray beam of a conventional fine structure tube is directed onto the wafer surface in grazing incidence. The angle of incidence is kept below the critical angle at which total reflection occurs. The critical angle is given by $\Phi_{crit} = \sqrt{2\delta}$, where δ is the small difference to unity of the index of refraction ($n = 1-\delta$). For molybdenum $K\alpha$-radiation and the silicon surface Φ_{crit} is 1.8 mrad.

The fluorescence radiation from the wafer surface is collected by a Si(Li) X-ray detector and processed according to the techniques for

energy dispersive X-Ray fluourescence analysis. The analyzed area of
8 mm in diameter is defined by the aperture of the detector. Quantitation is accomplished by means of a calibration procedure using multielement standard solutions pipetted onto a wafer surface in microliter
volumes and allowed to dry to a thin film. The very slight penetration
of a few nanometers at angles less than the critical angle makes TXRF
a nondestructive method tailored for exploring thin surface layers.

The design of the commercially available instrument [3] considers
exactly controlled incident angles as well as maximum intensity of the
primary radiation at the examined position of the wafer surface. This
results in detection limits in the order of 10^{11} atoms per cm^2 for
transition metals (Fe, Ni, Cu and Zn) (fig. 3) comparable to the sensitivity of neutron activation analysis [4].

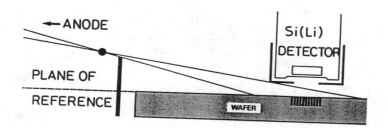

FIG.2: Schematic arrangement for TRXF.

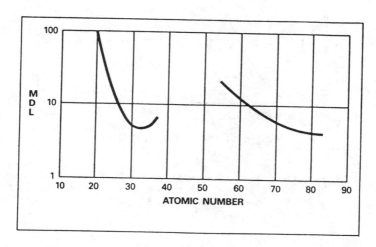

FIG.3:   Detection limits in 1000 s counting time. MDL is given in
10^{10} atoms per cm^2.

Beside its high sensitivity, TXRF offers an inherent capability to
assess the microscopic nature of the impurity from the angular dependence of the fluorescence yield (figs. 4 and 5): Agglomerated impurities, such as particles or droplet residues, do not participate in
the interference phenomenon leading to total reflection; their fluorescence intensity is independent of the angle of incidence below the
critical angle, and drops by a factor of two if the critical angle is
surpassed due to the disappearance of the reflected component in the
exciting beam ("non-reflecting" impurities, fig. 4a). On the other
hand, impurities which are homogneously distributed to a submonatomic
layer within the surface, such als electrochemically plated,
sputtered, or evaporated atoms, are part of the reflecting surface and
show a pronounced dependence in the fluorescent yield as a function of
the incidence angle as shown in fig. 4b [5]. These "reflecting" impurities exhibit basically the same angular dependence below the critical angle as the matrix fluorescence from the bulk silicon (fig. 4c)
but peak at the critical angle.

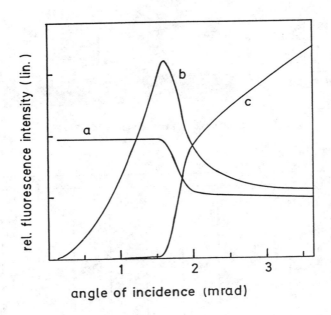

FIG. 4:   Theoretical angular dependence of the fluorescence intensity
for non-reflecting impurities (a), reflecting impurities
(b), and substrate (c: strongly reduced scale).

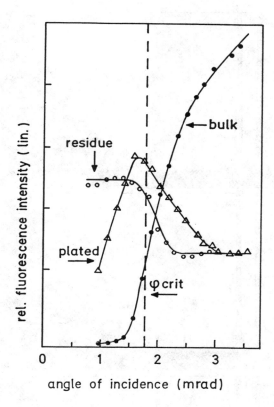

FIG. 5:   Experimental curves for the angular dependence of the fluo-
          rescence intensity from plated or sputtered submonoatomic
          Ni-layers (Δ), layers produced by evaporation of a Ni salt
          solution (o) and the silicon substrate (●).

APPLICATION STUDIES

Metal Plating from Buffered Hydrofluoric Acid (BHF)

        Traces of Cu are often detected on silicon surfaces after a BHF
treatment. In this application of TXRF, silicon wafers with a Fe contamination from a previous reactive ion etching (RIE) step have been
subjected to a BHF (7:1) treatment for 30 s. A fresh solution of semiconductor grade BHF with specified concentrations of Cu and Ni of less
than 10 ppb has been applied. In a parallel step some wafers were
treated with the same chemical doped to a level of 20 ppb Ni and Cu by
addition of diluted solutions of CuCl₂ and NiCl₂ in order to investigate the plating behavior of these metals. Three individual points

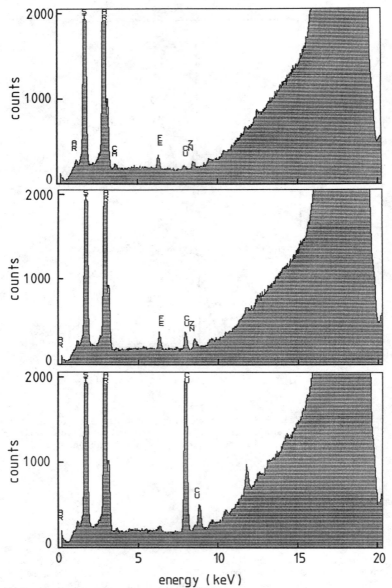

FIG. 6: TXRF spectra of BHF treated wafers
  a) RIE wafer: Fe from dry processing, slight contamination with Cu, Zn,
  b) BHF treatment: Fe unchanged, Cu increased after cleaning in pure BHF,
  c) Contaminated BHF: Substantial increase in Cu, no Ni.

were analyzed by TXRF on each wafer.

Fig. 6 shows the sum spectra for the three points of typical wafers; the numerical results for the individual points are listed in table 1.

TABLE 1 -- Numerical results

Metal concentration, 10^{12} atoms/cm^2

	RIE				BHF (pure)				BHF (doped)			
	mean	1	2	3	mean	1	2	3	mean	1	2	3
Fe	0.60	0.38	0.84	0.59	0.89	0.28	-	2.11	0.22	0.09	0.36	0.22
Cu	0.10	0.09	0.11	0.12	0.44	0.50	0.47	0.36	4.76	4.39	1.98	7.97
Zn	0.18	0.19	0.20	0.14	0.20	0.40	0.11	0.09	0.12	0.17	0.14	0.10
Ni	-	-	-	-	-	-	-	-	-	-	-	-

As a result of this application study it is concluded that Fe is not effectively removed by BHF. On the other hand, Cu is deposited even from semiconductor grade BHF, which probably containes Cu traces below the detection limit (10 ppb) of the analytical technique employed for the specification. The Cu fluorescence signal exhibits a strong angular dependence (not shown) and it is concluded that it is homogeneously plated or diluted in the native oxide (reflecting impurity). In contrast, Ni is not present on the wafer surface even if intentionally added to the solution, probably due to complexation.

Adsorptivity for Bromium

If silicon wafers are subjected to RCA-type cleaning solutions (essentially HCl + H_2O_2) the appearance of Br is regularly observed when analyzing the surface by TXRF. This study was aimed to trace the origin of Br and to investigate the influence of the silicon surface chemistry on the Br coverage. For this purpose, silicon wafers with a hydrophilic surface (as supplied by the manufacturer) and a hydrophobic surface (after an HF-dip) were submersed for 60 s in diluted HCl, in diluted H_2O_2, and in a mixture of the two agents. TXRF analysis was performed 10 hrs after the chemical treatments.

Hydrophyilic surface: No Br detectable on the original surface, nor after immersion in HCl, nor after immersion in H_2O_2. Strong Br signal ($1.4\cdot10^{13}$ at/cm^2) after immersion in HCl + H_2O_2 (fig. 7).

Hydrophobic surface: No Br detected after the HF treatment, moderate Br coverage after immersion in HCl or H_2O_2 ($4\cdot10^{12}$ at/cm^2), very strong Br coverage ($4\cdot10^{13}$ at/cm^2) after immersion in HCl + H_2O_2.

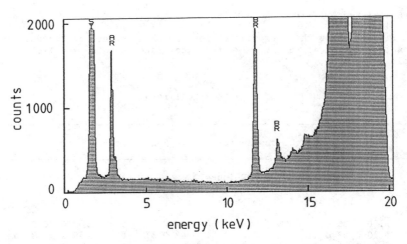

FIG.7:   TXRF spectrum of a hydrophilic wafer after RCA treatment showing a Br coverage of $1.4 \cdot 10^{13}$ at/cm^2

As a result of this study it is concluded that Br may be introduced either by HCl or H_2O_2 but is effectively deposited onto the hydrophilic surface only if two agents are present in a mixture. The hydrophobic surface, however, collects Br from both agents due to its enhanced chemical reactivity. It has been observed that the Br coverage on both surfaces tends to evaporate with a time constant of hours. Thus, the Br coverage in the order of 10^{13} atoms/cm^2 found in these measurements may indicate a considerably higher original value of several tenth of a monoatomic layer immediately after the RCA treatment. Therefore it seems worthwhile to investigate the chemical role of metal bromides for the cleaning efficacy of RCA-type agents.

SUMMARY

TXRF is an analytical technique well suited to inspect on a routine basis silicon wafer surfaces for metal traces due to its high sensitivity, non-destructiveness, and short turn-around time. Furthermore, it seems promising to use this method for systematic studies of the interaction between the chemial environment, such as plasmas or liquid agents, and the silicon surface with regard to metal contamination.

REFERENCES

[1]   Graff, K. and Pieper, H., "The Behaviour of Transition and Noble Metals in Silicon Crystals", Semiconductor Silicon 1981, J.R. Huff, R.J. Krügler, and Y. Takishi, eds., The Electrochemical Society, Pennington N.J., 1981, p. 331.

[2]   Stößel, P.-P. and Prange, A., "Determination of Trace Elements in Rainwater by Total-Reflection X-Ray Fluorescence", _Analytical Chemistry_, Vol. 57, No. 14, December 1985, pp. 2280-2885.

[3]   ATOMIKA Technische Physik GmbH, Postfach 450135, D-8000 München 45, FRG.

[4]   Keenan, J.A., Guade, B.E., and White, J.B., "Instrumental Neutron Activation Analysis of Processed Silicon", _Journal of the Electrochemical Society_, Vol. 132, No 9, September 1985, pp. 2232-2236.

[5]   Iida, A., Sakurai, A., Yoshinaga, A., and Gohshi, Y., "Grazing Incidence X-Ray Fluorescence Analysis", Nuclear Instruments and Methods in Physics Research, A 246, 1986, pp. 736-738.

Toshio Shiraiwa, Nobukatsu Fujino, Shigeo Sumita and Yasuko Tanizoe

CHEMICAL ANALYSIS OF METALLIC IMPURITY ON THE SURFACE OF SILICON WAFERS

REFERENCES: Shiraiwa,T., Fujino,N., Sumita,S., Tanizoe,Y.,"Chemical Analysis of Metallic Impurity on the Surface of Silicon Wafers," Semiconductor Fabrication: Technology and Metrology, ASTM STP 990, Dinesh C. Gupta, editor, American Society for Testing and Materials, 1989.

ABSTRACT: In silicon wafer processing, it is important to decrease the impurity on the wafer after final process. The authors report a method of analysis of impurity only on the top surface of Si wafers. In this study, wafer are contaminated with a cleaning solution containing impurity, and the impurity remains on the wafer is collected into the resulting liquid of the oxide and HF vapor. They are then analysed by atomic absorption spectrophotometer. Detection limits are Na: 5×10^8 atoms/cm^2, Fe: 2×10^9 atoms/cm^2, Al:1×10^{10} atoms/cm^2.

KEYWORDS: silicon wafer, surface analysis, impurity on surface, atomic absorption spectrophotometry, contamination in native oxide.

INTRODUCTION

Silicon wafers are an important material for LSI. Recently the integration grade becomes larger and larger, as Mega bit memory devices are developed. The impurities on the surface of Si wafers which are introduced during the shaping and polishing process and remain after the final cleaning should be lowered. To achieve this, a sensitive method of analysis is needed. SIMS and XPS are effective for surface analysis. SIMS [1] is a highly sensitive method but it is a local analysis and is not good for evaluation of total area of a wafer. XPS can make a state analysis but is not sensitive for impurity on Si wafer. The behavior of impurity on a Si wafer is studied because of its relationship with oxide

Dr.Shiraiwa is executive technical consultant at Osaka Titanium Co.,Ltd; Amagasaki Hyogo, Japan; Dr.Fujino is deputy director of Semiconductor Res. Lab.,Dr.Sumita is manager of material evaluation section, and Ms. Tanizoe is research chemist of Semiconductor Res. Lab. at Kyushu Electronic Metal Co.,Ltd; Kohokucho, Saga, Japan.

breakdown at SiO_2-Si interface [2][3], however, there are few reports of analytical methods of impurity on Si wafers.

In this study, the authors report the method of analysis of impurity only on the top side of the surface of Si wafer. Shimazaki et al. [4] reported a highly sensitive method, but the impurity on the both sides of wafer was collected in that method. The present method is modified from Shimazaki, and it is improved to give only one side analysis. The devices are formed on the one side of Si wafer, so it is important to know the impurity on the top side of wafer. And the back side of a wafer has damage by sand blast for extrinsic gettering effect. So it is important to know the concentration of impurity on the each side.

It is also reported to use the native oxide for collecting the impurity on the wafer. When one uses the thermal oxide for collecting the impurity, some elements diffuse into the substrate during the oxidation and they can not be detected completely. The use of the native oxide can avoid such problem.

In order to know the behavior of the impurity, all wafers are purposely contaminated with some elements, the oxide layer on the wafer containing impurities is dissolved by HF vapor and the impurities are collected into a droplet and analysed by an atomic absorption spectrophotometer(AAS).

EXPERIMENTAL

The amount of impurity on the surface is very small. The impurity has to be collected at enough concentration for analysis. In this study, the two methods of collecting the impurity are tested. One is use of the native oxide and the other is use of the thermal oxide. In the former, metallic impurity in the native oxide layer is dissolved by HF vapor. In the latter, the wafer is oxidized and the impurity in the thermal oxide layer is dissolved by HF vapor. The thermal oxide of about 75nm in thickness is grown by the oxidation with dry O_2 for 2 hours at $1000°C$.

Figure 1 shows one example of the reaction vessel. Wafer is placed horizontally and the surface to be analyzed is set in upper side. The HF is purified through vaporizing, and the solution of 15% HF is used. During the reaction, the vessel is closed containig all vapors.

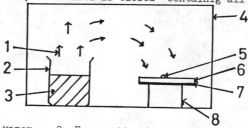

1. HF vapor   2. Evaporation beaker   3. HF solution
4. Sealed container   5. Resolved solution drops
6. Si wafer   7. Oxide layer   8. Wafer supporter

FIG. 1 -- An example of reaction vessel.

Wafers are contaminated purposely after the cleaning of same condition. The contaminating method is that wafers are cleaned in the cleaning solution containg metallic impurity of some concentration levels, and dried by spin dryer. The purposely contaminated elements are Al, Fe and Cu. By this method, all of the contaminated atoms in solution are not attached on the wafer.

After the reaction between the oxide and HF vapor, resulting condensed liquid produces a aqueous droplet because of the hydrophobic of property the surface. In case of the thermal oxide, resulting liquid gathers to a droplet in the center of the surface and it is sampled and its volume is measured by a micro pipette and analysed by AAS of flameless type with tungsten boat (SAS 727, SEIKO I). In case of the native oxide, the resulting liquid dispersed to small droplets so that it is collected with a pure water droplet by rolling on the surface. After that it is same as the case of thermal oxide. In order to know the behavior of metallic elements during oxidation, the depth analysis was made by SIMS (A-DIDA 3000, ATOMIKA).

RESULTS

(1)Reaction between the Oxide and HF

The reaction between the oxide on the surface and HF vapor is as follow;

$$SiO_2 + 6HF \rightarrow H_2SiF_6 + 2H_2O \tag{1}$$

Impurity on the surface is collected into the resulting liquid of eq.(1).

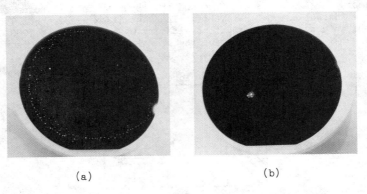

(a)   (b)

PHOTO. 1 Droplet of resulting liquid on the wafer.
(a) 30 min.   (b) 60 min.

In case of the thermal oxide with the thickness of 75 nm, it takes about 2 hours to complete the reaction and the resulting liquid makes a droplet of about 20 μl for 5 inch wafer at the center of wafer. Photo. 1 shows the droplet on the wafer. (a) shows the photograph of the droplet after 30 min. from the start of the reaction, and (b) shows that of after 60 min. The reaction starts at the edge of a wafer and there are many small droplets, and at last the droplets gather to a large one. The completion of reaction is determined by the wettability of wafer surface. That is, the wafer surface with oxide is hydrophilic, and after the reaction with HF it becomes hydrophobic. It is easy to know the end point of the reaction.

In case of the native oxide, however, it takes only 15 min. to complete reaction because of the thin oxide layer, and the resulting liquid is dispersed so that photograph can not be taken. It is collected with a pure water droplet by rolling on the surface.

(2) Top Side Analysis and Both Side Analysis

In both side analysis, the wafer is set vertically and the resulting liquid is dropped along the wafer to a reservoir. It is difficult to avoid the contamination from the reservoir. We tried to collect the resulting liquid without the sampling reservoir, that is to use the wafer itself as a reservoir. This is the method of top side analysis. Table 1 shows the compared results for two methods. Wafers are treated by same procedure except for difference of collectiong of resulting liquid. In this result, there is a difference in alkaline metal. It is concluded that top side analysis can avoid the contamination from the sampling reservoir.

TABLE 1 -- Comparsion of analytical method of both side and top side.

($\times 10^{10}$ atoms $\cdot$ cm^{-2})

	Na	K	Fe
(a) Both side	100	80	10
(b) Top side (This method)	5	3	10

(3) <u>Native Oxide and Thermal Oxide</u>

In this section, We mention about the difference of oxides. The test wafers are purposely contaminated to reveal the difference of the behavior of impurity. The wafers are cleaned by contaminated cleaning solution, dried and analysed. Contamination elements are Al, Fe and Cu. Fig.2 shows the result of Al. The concentration of Al on the surface increases with the increase of Al concentration in cleaning solution for both of thermal and native oxide, and they are almost the same. Fig.3 shows the result of Fe. In case of Fe, it has same tendency as the case of Al.

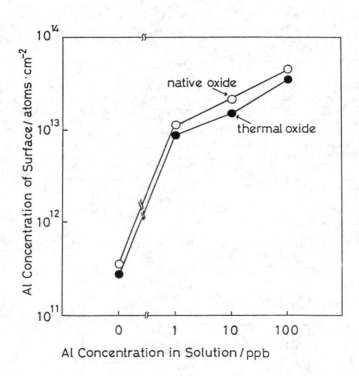

FIG. 2 -- Relation between Al content in cleaning solution
and analysed Al content on the surface.

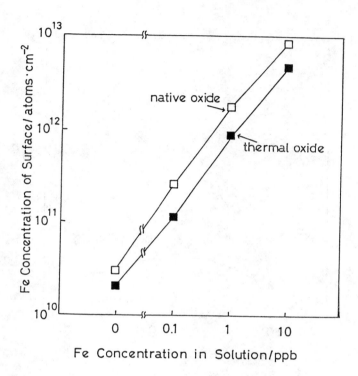

FIG. 3 -- Relation between Fe content in cleaning solution
and analysed Fe content on the surface.

Figure 4 shows the result of Cu. The concentration of Cu of the native oxide increases with the increase of Cu contamination in cleaning
solution, but it does not increase for the use of the thermal oxide. As
both wafers are contaminated with same treatment, the concentration of
Cu on the surface is same for both sample before the thermal oxidation.
But after the thermal oxidation, the amount of Cu on the surface is very
small for large contaminated sample. To know the detail of this difference, SIMS analysis is made for the samples, (a); after the contaminated cleaning and drying (native oxide), and (b); after (a) and
thermal oxidation (thermal oxide).

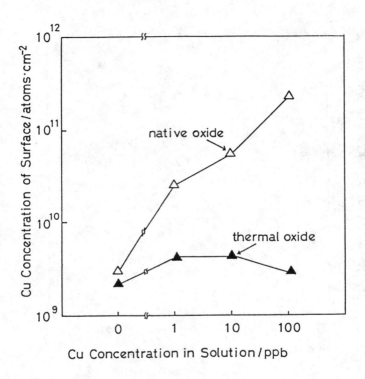

FIG. 4 -- Relation between Cu content in cleaning solution
anf analysed Cu content on the surface.

Figures 5 and 6 show the result of Al and Fe by SIMS respectively.
The impurity of Al or Fe is segregated at the surface of the native
oxide and there is little impurities near the boundary of the oxide
layer and the substrate ((a)). They are also in the oxide layer for the
thermal oxide ((b)). In case of Cu shown in Fig.7, it is same as Al and
Fe for native oxide ((a)). But for the thermal oxide ((b)), Cu
segregates in the substrate near the oxide. Cu shows the different behavior from Al and Fe for the both methods. These are discussed later.

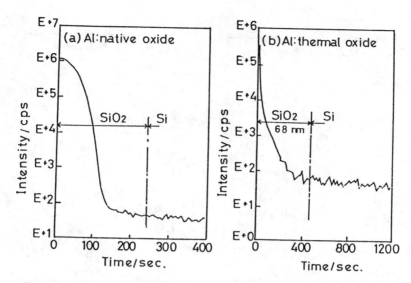

FIG. 5 -- Depth analysis of Al by SIMS.
        (a): after contaminated and dried (native oxide).
        (b): thermally oxidized after (a) (thermal oxide).

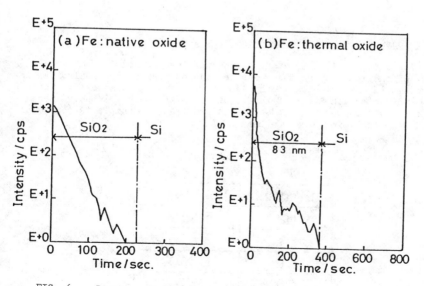

FIG. 6 -- Depth analysis of Fe by SIMS.
        (a): after contaminated and dried (native oxide).
        (b): thermally oxidized after (a) (thermal oxide).

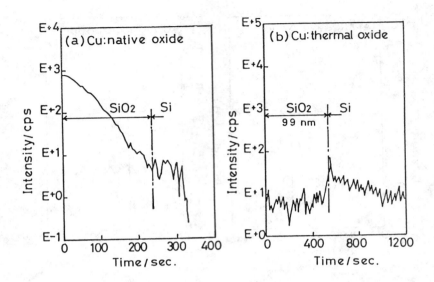

FIG. 7 -- Depth analysis of Cu by SIMS.
          (a): after contaminated and dried (native oxide).
          (b): thermaly oxidized after (a) (thermal oxide).

(4) Detection Limit of the Impurity on the Wafer

The impurity is collected by the explained methods. The detection limit of the impurity on the wafer depends on that of the analytical instrument. In this study, the AAS of flameless type is used. Table 2 shows the detection limit of the impurity on the wafer. These values are achieved by applying the condensing method that the sample is poured and dried repeatedly in the large boat of AAS.

TABLE 2 -- Detection limit of impurity on the surface.

Element	DL/atoms·cm^{-2}
Na	5×10^{8}
Fe	2×10^{9}
Al	1×10^{10}
Cu	4×10^{8}

DISCUSSION

The result of Cu shows a different behavior than Al and Fe by AAS analysis and SIMS analysis. The analytical value of the thermal oxide is smaller than the native oxide. SIMS showed that Cu segregated at the substrate near the interface of SiO_2-Si after the heat treatment. This means that Cu diffuses into the substrate but Al and Fe remain in the oxide layer during the heat treatment. These elements that we added to the cleaning solution are thought to be in the state of ion as they are used the standared solution of AAS. At the surface of Si wafer they are adsorped and there are no change of the state in the native oxide. After the heat treatment, the state of Al and Fe are oxide, considering their free energy of formation of oxide [5], however Cu is thought to be reduced metallic state by Si and metallic Cu diffuses easily into Si substrate. In this analytical method, the oxide on the surface is used to collect the impurity. Al and Fe can be determined by the use of both thermal and native oxide, but Cu is not satisfied by the thermal oxide. It is concluded that the method of use of the native oxide is effective for quantitative determination of such elements.

CONCLUSION

It is important to evaluate the impurity on the surface of Si wafer. In this study, the collecting method of impurity on one side of wafer is reported. The use of the native oxide is also reported to be effective to collect the impurity on the wafer. The detection limits are Na : 5×10^8atoms/cm^2, Fe : 2×10^9atoms/cm^2, Al : 1×10^{10}atoms/cm^2.

REFERENCES

[1] Wittmark,K.,"Secondary Ion Mass Spectrometry as a Means of Surface Analysis", Surface Science, vol.89,1979, pp 668-700.
[2] Ohsawa, A.,Honda, K. and Toyokura, N.,"Metal Impurities near the SiO_2-Si interface", Journal of Electrochemical Society, vol.131, 1984, pp 2964-2969.
[3] Honda, K., Nakanishi, T., Oshawa,A. and Toyokura,N., "Catastrophic Breakdown in Silicon Oxides: The Effect of Fe Impurities at the SiO_2-Si Interface", Journal of Applied Physics, vol.62,1987,pp 1960-1963.
[4] Shimazaki, A., Hiratsuka, H., Matsushita, Y. and Yoshii, S., "Chemical Analysis of Ultrace Impurities in SiO_2 Films", Extended Abstracts of the 16th (1984 International) Conference on Solid State Devices and Materials, Kobe, 1984, pp 281-284.
[5] Darken, L. S. and Gurry, R. W., "Physical Chemistry of Metals", McGraw-Hill, 1953, pp 361.

Vinod K. Khanna, Deep K. Thakur, Khairati L. Jasuja, and Waman S. Khokle

PROCESS - INDUCED INFLUENCE ON THE MINORITY - CARRIER LIFETIME IN POWER DEVICES

REFERENCE : Khanna, V.K., Thakur, D.K., Jasuja, K.L., and Khokle, W.S., "Process - Induced Influence on the Minority - Carrier Lifetime in Power Devices", Semiconductor Fabrication: Technology and Metrology, ASTM STP 990, Dinesh C. Gupta, editor, American Society for Testing and Materials, 1989.

ABSTRACT : Carrier lifetime has been studied as a function of process conditions for power semiconductor devices. The lifetime measurements have been done to see the influence of minority-carrier lifetime on device characteristics under different process conditions such as KOH etching, DI water rinse, deep diffusions, thermal oxidation, phosphorous diffusion and gold diffusion. Open Circuit Voltage Decay (OCVD) and Surface Photovoltage (SPV) techniques have been used to measure minority-carrier lifetime.

It has been observed that the starting-wafer lifetime tends to change strongly during the course of fabrication processes and shows a dependence on the injection level. The typical curves show two-fold effects : (i) The effect of traps and (ii) The carrier density. The injection-level dependence of lifetime is attributed to heavy-doping effects in silicon, and in the absence of traps, is described by an empirical relationship.

KEYWORDS : OCVD, SPV, Ga/Al diffusion, Gettering, Gold diffusion, Shockley - Read-Hall recombination, minority-carrier traps.

1. INTRODUCTION

The performance of virtually every power semiconductor device or integrated circuit is dependent on carrier lifetimes in the semiconductor.

The authors are research scientists in the Semiconductor Devices Area, Central Electronics Engineering Research Institute, Pilani - 333031 (Rajasthan), India.

For example, the forward voltage drop and turn-off time of a rectifier depend on recombination lifetime. In case of thyristor, the important device parameters are its forward and everse blocking voltage, forward drop, turn-off time and dynamic ratings and are strongly dependent on carrier lifetime [1]. Because silicon is the most commonly used semiconductors in the power electronics industry, therefore an understanding that how carrier lifetimes are related to the silicon processing, has practical significance. Therefore, an attempt has been made to measure the minority-carrier lifetime as a function of processing stages with varying carrier injection levels and correlation of these data with diffused layer properties.

Although a number of papers have appeared in the literature on the topic, present studies have attempted to report further investigation of process - induced minority-carrier lifetime in power device structures usisng the Open-Circuit Voltage Decay (acronym OCVD) and Surface Photovoltage (SPV) techniques. A trap-emptying phenomenon has been observed in several measurements on minority-carrier lifetime under different carrier injection levels. It has been found that for a trap-free process, for the range of carrier injection levels 10^3-10^{17} cm^{-3} studied, the decrease in lifetime with carrier concentration (N) agrees well with the equation $\tau = \tau_0(1+N/N_0)$ for Shockley-Read-Hall (SRH) recombination through dopant-generated recombination centers, where τ_0 and N_0 are constants.

2.   CARRIER LIFETIME STATISTICS AND MEASUREMENT TECHNIQUES

2.1   Recombination Statistics

In practice, the lifetime is a quantity which is strongly linked to a certain measurement method and generally is considered to be a constant. From a theoretical point of view, however, it appears from recombination statistics of Shockley-Read-Hall theory that lifetime is not a constant but depends on carrier density and temperature. The recombination and generation carrier lifetimes are defined by the carrier recombination-generation mechanisms [2] : (i) The capture-emission Shockley-Head-Hall process at defects, and thermal generation. (ii) The band-band phonon-assisted Auger impact process, and avalanche multiplication (iii) Direct band-to-band radiative recombination, and optical electron-hole pair generation. The Shockley-Read-Hall recombination involves bound states or traps in the energy band gap resulting from defects in the semiconductor lattice, at surfaces and at grain boundaries. For non-degenerately doped silicon SRH process is generally dominant, and consequently the carrier lifetimes are controlled by the densities of defects in the silicon. To achieve optimal design of power semiconductor devices, it is essential to know how the silicon processing influences the solubility of these defects which define the fundamental limits for carrier lifetime.

2.2   Lifetime Measurement Techniques

The many different approaches or methods (Table 1) for the measurement of carrier lifetime can be categorized into the two generic sub-groups : (i) Device methods and (ii) Bulk semiconductors. In this section, we recall briefly the physical basis of the Open-Circuit Voltage Decay [3-5] and Surface Photovoltage [6,7] methods. Complementary details can be obtained in the references cited.

TABLE 1
LIFETIME MEASUREMENT TECHNIQUES

RECOMBINATION LIFETIME		GENERATION LIFETIME
DEVICE METHODS	BULK SEMICONDUCTOR	DEVICE METHODS
A. Open Circuit Voltage Decay (OCVD)	A. Surface Photovoltage (SPV)	A. Pulsed MOS Capacitor (MOS-C)
B. Reverse Recovery of a Diode (RR)	B. Photoconductive Decay	B. Leakage Current of a Reverse Biased Diode (I_r)
C. Admittance of a Diode	C. Contactless Eddy Current Measurement following Photo-induced Injection	
D. Base-Width Modulation of a Transistor (BWM)	D. Photoelectromagnetic effect	
E. Scanning Electron Microscope-Electron Beam Induced Current (SEM-EBIC)	E. Luminiscence Decay after Laser Pulse Excitation	
	F. Decay in Microwave Reflection after Photoinjection	

The Open-Circuit Voltage Decay Method, Fig. 1, sets the initial conditions by exciting the device with forward voltage or with incident light in negative time. Then, at time t = 0, one switches off the excitation and observes the decay of voltage. The voltage V(t) across the diode is the junction voltage as all ohmic drops disappear. It is assumed that the carrier concentrations are uniform throughout the n region, then using the current and continuity equations combined with Boltzmann relation, carrier lifetime can be related to the time variation of the diode voltage:

$$\tau^{-1} = \frac{1}{(2kT/q)}\frac{dV}{dt} \tag{1}$$

The open-circuit voltage decay method can be used as a routine technique to determine minority-carrier lifetime. It offers the following advantages : (i) It is simple and rapid and is applicable to determining recombination lifetime following key processing steps in manufacturing. (ii) It gives measurements under conditions approximating those of the actual fabricated p-n junction. (iii) The measurement immediately yields excess carrier lifetime as a function of injection level.

In the Constant Magnitude Steady State Surface Photovoltage method, a semiconductor surface barrier is illuminated with spectrally resolved light of variable wavelength λ (hc/λ > E_g). The advantages of the Surface Photovoltage method are : (i) The method is non-destructive. (ii) Sample preparation is minimal i.e., no contacts or junctions or high-temperature processing steps are required. (iii) The method is based on steady-state

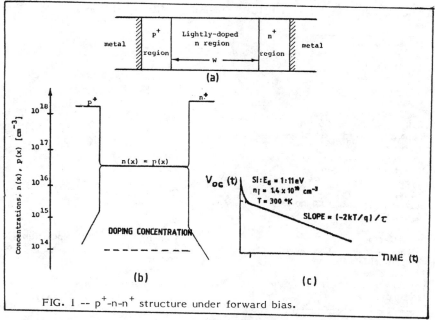

FIG. 1 -- p^+-n-n$^+$ structure under forward bias.

transport and is relatively immune to the slow trapping and detrapping difficulties that affect lifetime measurements by the photoconductive decay and other transient methods. SPV method has been used for determination of minority-carrier lifetime in diffused layers of silicon and bulk lifetime of intrinsic silicon. The determined diffusion length L_p gives the carrier lifetime according to the relation.

$$\tau_p = 8.13 \times 10^{-4} L_p^2$$

presuming that the mobility is a constant parameter.

3. EXPERIMENTAL PROCEDURE

The sample characteristics and the process parameters used in this study are listed in Table 2. The starting material is n-type Float-Zone (F-Z) silicon with orientation (1 1 1). For experimental investigation, monitor samples of thyristor and transistor have been fabricated using conventional sealed tube diffusion and thyristor technology.

To evaluate the process, an array of mesa diodes has been made on the wafer of measuring lifetime of p-n junction using OCVD method, as follows : (i) The thyristor structure has been appropriately lapped to obtain the proper p^+-n$^-$n$^+$ test configuration with constant n$^-$ width

TABLE 2 - PROCESS PARAMETERS OF THE DEVICES USED IN THIS STUDY

Thyristor	Transistor
Starting silicon slices n-type, 154 ohm-cm, 800 um thick	Starting silicon slices n-type Epitaxial 40-60 ohm-cm Epi-layer 100 um Substrate 300 um
KOH etching	
Ga/Al diffusion 1230°C, 25 hours, 80 um deep, Evacuated quartz ampoule, 2×10^{-6} torr	Non-epitaxial 80-120 ohm-cm 300 um thick
	Ga/Al sealed tube diffusion 1200°C, 3 1/2 hours 25 um deep
Phosphorous diffusion in dry oxygen/nitrogen ($POCl_3$ source) Predeposition 1150°C, 90 min. Drive-in 1235°C, 10.5 hours 20 um deep	Oxidation 1200°C 90 min. wet, 10 min. dry 0.6 um thick
Au diffusion Wafer coating by dipping in gold chloride solution 710°C, 2 hours Quenched after diffusion time is completed	Phosphorous predeposition 1100°C, 1 hour Drive-in 1200°C, 2 hours 9 um deep

for the different stages. (ii) A series of dots, about 6 mm in diameter have been applied with apiezone wax on the p^+ side. The n-side has been completely covered with wax and fixed onto a large teflon disc. (iii) The samples have been etched in CP4 (3HF : $5HNO_3$: 3 CH_3 COOH) to produce mesa type diodes. Deep etching for 5 min. at room temperature ($\sim$100 μm) has been performed to avoid any surface leakage. (iv) The wax has been removed in trichloroethylene followed by acetone and water rinsing. The test structures have been subjected to hot HNO_3 to passivate the etched surface and then rinsed thoroughly in D.I. and Millipore water. (v) Ohmic contacts to the surface of p-n junction have been made by applying tin-indium solder in regions of about 0.3 cm^2 area on one face of the sample by a properly tuned ultrasonic soldering tip. (vi) Lifetime measurements have been performed on wafers haing a number of diodes at constant current density.

4. RESULTS AND DISCUSSIONS

Fig. 2 presents the variation of measured minority-carrier lifetime with different processing treatments using the SPV (refer to Table 1) and OCVD (refer to Table 1) methods. It is observed that the lifetime falls appreciably from 188 μ sec. to 65 μ sec. during KOH etching. The presence of alkali ions on the etched surface (which is always covered with a thin layer of native oxide) produces surface states. The alkali ions such as K^+ on freshly etched surface are known to be stubborn impurity

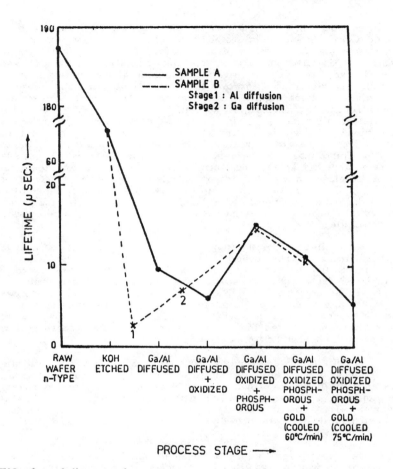

FIG. 2 -- Influence of process steps on lifetime for thyristor fabrication
         fabrication.

in the thin layer of SiO_2.   When these space charges (K^+ ions) move
from surface to the bulk silicon, they are again strongly trapped. These
space charges are responsible for introducing such surface states.   The
effect of these surface states is analogous to that of introducing defect
bulk states and they impart charge to the Si/SiO_2 interface. Recombination on the etched surface is greatly enhanced by these states resulting
in a drastic reduction in lifetime.

         To study the influence of Ga/AL diffusion on lifetime two samples
A and B (refer in Fig. 2) have been prepared. In case of sample A, Ga/Si
source, AL/Si source and silicon wafers all together have been sealed
in Quartz capsule. So that simultaneous diffusion of Ga and AL could

be carried out.   In preparation of sample B, silicon wafers have been diffused using AL source in sealed quartz capsule.   These AL-diffused silicon wafersand Ga source have been loaded in separate quartz capsule to carry out Ga diffusion.   It is observed that AL diffused wafers (Marked Stage 1) have low lifetime compared to Gallium diffused wafers (Marked Stage 2).   Though Ga itself improves lifetime after AL diffusion, it appears that major cause for degradation in lifetime is AL impurity.   In sealed--tube diffusion, Al and quartz are certain to react and reduce the partial presssure of aluminum [8].   In vacuum, the evaporated Al molecules could travel considerable distances undergoing any collisions most of which occur at the quartz walls.   Thus a layer of Si and Al_2O_3 builds up on the quartz tube wall, which becomes passivated. This is only possible if the system has an O_2 and moisture content and thus an impervious skin is developed along with donor complexes i.e. $(SiO_4^+Al^-SiO_4^+)$ or $AlO_4SiO_4^+$.   In principle, Al in Si can form two basic defects : Interstitial atoms (Ali) and substitutional atoms (AlSi).   The formation of these aluminum neutral complexes or deep levels can be a major cause to deteriorate the carrier lifetime.

      The lifetime deterioration for the oxidation step is ascribed to deep level impurities like copper, iron, nickel etc. which diffuse primarily by an interstitial mechanism with a diffusion constant 5 to 6 orders of magnitude higher than the substitutional impurities.   These impurities are present in large quantities in chemical solutions, glassware and gases and in the quartz diffusion tubes themselves.   During processing, they condense around dislocations forming metallic precipitates.   The amount of impurities incorporated into silicon depends upon the processing time and temperature and the diffusion-induced stress.

      The lifetime is enhanced by phosphorous diffusion. Phosphosilicate glass getters mobile ionic impurities.   For halogenic dopant sources, Meek et. al [9] have shown that the phosphorous diffusion gettering operates by solubility enhancement and ion pairing of the substitutional metal acceptors.   The impurities and other heavy metals which are acceptors on substitutional sites are paired with phosphorous donors and gettered in the form of volatile halides.

      The effect of gold killing has been studied for two cooling cycles. In present study, the recombination centers of interest are provided by gold atoms in the silicon lattice.   The diffusion constant of gold is substantially larger than gallium or phosphorous at temperatures upto 1300°C.   Thus, it is possible to diffuse gallium, aluminum and phosphorous into silicon wafer, then plate the wafer with a thin gold layer using $AuCl_3$ solution and diffuse in the gold without producing substantial changes in the p or n type impurity distribution.   Gold killing has been done at temperatures ranging from 830° - 850°C in vacuum and a sufficient time of two hours has been allowed for gold diffusion so that concentration of gold can approach to its solubility limit corresponding to its killing temperature.   According to Bemski [10], recombination in gold-doped silicon is facilitated by two trapping levels associated with each atom. These are acceptor level located at 0.54 eV below conduction band and donor level about 0.35 eV above valence band.   In n-type silicon, this acceptor level influences the minority-carrier lifetime and the lifetime is inversely proportional to the recombination center density.

      A last-cooling effect has been observed. The wafers were cooled at

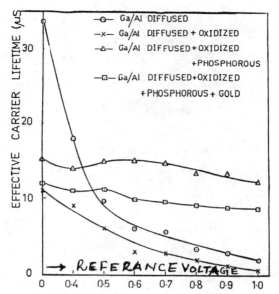

FIG. 3 -- Dependence of lifetime on OCVD reference
voltage for a thyristor process.

60°C/min. and 75°C/min.   During fast cooling, the induced surface
states are created in the fast cooled samples.   These surface states
appear to be due to thermal stress owing to a rapid cooling.   These
temperature-induced surface states are responsible for the low lifetime
obtained.

The dependence of lifetime on injection level can be expressed
in terms of OCVD reference voltage or the injected carrier density.
Fig. 3 illustrates the measured OCVD lifetimes for different thyristor
fabrication stages as a function of reference voltage.   In Fig. 4, the
carrier lifetimes for an epitaxial collector transistor fabrication are
shown.   Very frequently, the lifetime-injection level characteristic
exhibits a peak followed by a sharp decline in lifetime.   This peak
in Fig. 4 occurs in the range 10^{13}-10^{14} cm^{-3}.   Such behaviour is explained in terms of capture cross-section of minority-carrier traps [3].
The trapping effect in phosphorous doped NTD-Si, in which the conductivity has not fully recovered, is a phenomenon common to samples of
high-resistivity starting materials used for power devices.   In the study
of EPR for NTD Si [11], it is proposed that the non-substitutional phosphorous atoms transmuted by the NTD process are constituent parts of
the electron trapping centers, capable of trapping two electrons.   The
defects of this type must act to reduce part of the conductivity.   The
lifetime is dominated by recombination processes of excess carriers
through trapping centers.   In a diode p^+nn^+ sample, hole is injected
from p^+ side and it is temporarily lost to the trap.   The probability per unit
time of the hole capture with all the empty traps is very high and thus associated lifetime is low.   When the injection level exceeds 10^{14} cm^{-3} (high-level)

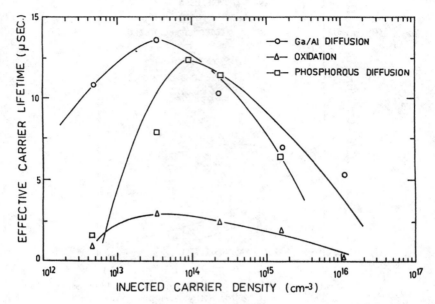

FIG. 4 -- Study of lifetimes for transistor fabrication.

injection), the traps are filled. A trap is occupied by a hole for a similar length of time as it is occupied by an electron. The probability per unit time of electron/hole capture with all traps full is << the probability when they are all vacant. The lifetime begins to recover after the trapping effect disappears i.e., after the trap density becomes smaller than 0.2-0.4 % of the injection level. Consequently, the observed lifetime is higher and the lifetime is virtually saturated around 10^{14} cm^{-3}. The subsequent fall of lifetime is a heavy doping effect, and is explained below.

The lifetimes for the collector-base diode and emitter-base diode of a transistor, fabricated using triple diffusion, are plotted in Fig. 5. The lifetime curves show that the lifetime of the emitter-base diode is less than the collector-base diode for a wide range of carrier injection 5×10^{12} to $\sim 10^{17}$ cm^{-3}. The lifetime decreases monotonically with increasing injected carrier density. This is because the OCVD gives an effective lifetime which is a combined result of the recombination in the p^{+}, n^{-} and n^{+} regions.

Taking the p^{+}-n^{-}-n^{+} OCVD test structure (Fig. 1) and considering the effects of recombination in the p^{+} and n^{+} regions and for a uniform carrier distribution in the n^{-} region, the effective lifetime can be expressed as

$$\tau_{eff.} = \tau_{B} / [\, 1 + 2h\, \bar{p}/w\,] \qquad (3)$$

$$\text{where} \quad h = (1/2)\, (h_{P} + h_{N}) \qquad (4)$$

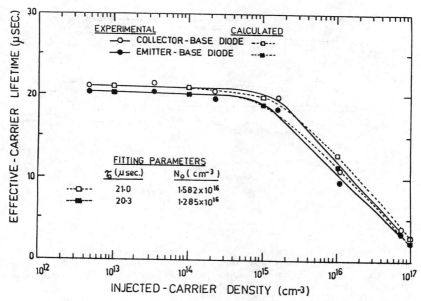

FIG. 5 -- The lifetimes for the collector-base and emitter-base diodes in a transistor.

$$h_P = (1/p^+) \sqrt{[D_n (P)/\tau_n]} \qquad (5)$$

$$h_N = (1/n^+) \sqrt{[D_p (N) /\tau_p]} \qquad (6)$$

τ_B, τ_p and τ_n are the lifetimes in the n^- region, p^+ and n^+ region. D_n (P) and D_n (N), the diffusion coefficients of minority carriers in the outer layers of concentrations p^+ and n^+, $\bar{p}$ the mean concentration of holes in the n^- region and w is its width.

For a given device, τ_B, h and w are constants so that eq. (3) reduces to the form [12,13]

$$\tau = \tau_o /[1+N/N_o] \qquad (7)$$

where τ_o and N_o are fitting parameters. Eq. (7) gives good agreement with the measured lifetime data. A comparison of experimental and theoretically calculated points is given in Fig. 5. Thus, in the absence of traps, eq. 7 can be used for modeling and prediction of device performance.

The physical interpretation of the decrease in lifetime can be given in reference to eq. 3. The underlying cause is the recombination in the p^+ and n^+ regions. In these regions, a high concentration of dopant atoms increases the density of energy levels in the forbidden band which may be created by lattice defects or by an increased solubility of deep-level impurities like iron and gold in heavily-doped silicon. As a result, τ_n

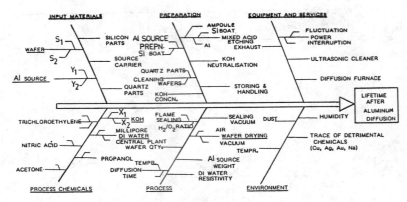

FIG. 6 -- Cause and effect diagram.

and τ_D are $\ll \tau_B$. h_P and h_N and thus h increases becoming comparable in magnitude to $\bar{p}$/w whereby the effect of $2h\bar{p}$/w cannot be ignored. Thus, physically the behaviour represents SRH type phononic mechanisms in heavily doped Si.

It appears from lifetime measurement results that in fabrication of thyristor and high-voltage transistor, principal step of Al diffusion deteriorates carrier lifetime.   Optimal semiconductor design requires a reliable and reproducible manufacturing process for thyristor and thus needs to know the fundamental limit of carrier lifetime and its correlation with diffused layer properties.   Therefore, in initial phase, efforts have been put to identify the critical factors affecting carrier lifetime during aluminum diffusion and to fix their optimum levels.   A cause and effect analysis has been carried out (Fig. 6).   The following 8 factors have been selected for the experiment and each factor is at two levels.   The factors and their levels are : (i) Wafer source : S_1, S_2; (ii) KOH source : X_1, X_2; (iii) Aluminum source Y_1, Y_2; (iv) Water used for cleaning : DI water + Millipore, Millipore; (v) Drying of wafer: Air 120°C, Vacuum 160°C; (vi) Cleaning after KOH etching : with HCl, without HCl ; (vii) Temperature and time of aluminum diffusion : 1230°C for 25 hours, 1238°C for 20 hours; and (viii) Weight of aluminum source in each boat : 135 mgm, 472.5 mgm.

The factors which have been kept constant during the experiment are : (i) Resistivity of DI water 5 M ohm-cm, Millipore water 18 M ohm-cm, (ii) Sealing vacuum level $2x10^{-6}$ torr and (iii) Source of trichloroethylene.

The above-mentioned factors have been arranged in a Latin array. The plan for the Latin square design with t^2 experimental units is to form a square with t rows and t columns and then to apply t treatments in the cells in such a way that each treatment occurs once in each column and once in each row.   In this way, each row and each column contains a complete replication of the treatments.   Table 3 illustrates the experimental layout for the Latin square design.

TABLE 3 -- Experimental layout for Al diffusion

Expt. No.	Type of water	KOH source	Cleaning of wafer	Drying of wafer	Aluminum source	Weight of Aluminum in each boat	Diffusion Temp.&Time (^{o}C) (Hrs.)		Mean carrier lifetime (μsec.)
1.	DI water + Millipore (DIM)	X_1	With HCl (WH)	Vacuum 160°C (V)	Y_1	135 mgm. (W_1)	1230 (P_1)	25	τ_1= 4.2
2.	Millipore (M)	X_2	Without HCl(WOH)	Air 120°C (A)	Y_1	135 mgm.	1230	25	τ_2= 3.5
3.	DI+Millipore	X_1	Without HCl	Air 120°C	Y_1	472.5 mgm. (W_2)	1238 (P_2)	20	τ_3= 1.6
4.	Millipore	X_2	With HCl	Vacuum 160°C	Y_1	472.5 mgm.	1238	20	τ_4= 4.7
5.	Millipore	X_1	Without HCl	Vacuum 160°C	Y_2	472.5mgm.	1230	25	τ_5= 5.7
6.	DI + Millipore	X_2	With HCl	Air 120°C	Y_2	472.5mgm.	1230	25	τ_6= 5.0
7.	Millipore	X_1	With HCL	Air 120°C	Y_2	135 mgm.	1238	20	τ_7= 2.5
8.	DI + Millipore	X_2	Without HCl	Vacuum 160°C	Y_2	135 mgm.	1238	20	τ_8= 2.7

Grand mean τ_m = 3.7

The lifetime measurements have been performed using OCVD. From each source of wafer (X_1 and X_2), two wafers have been taken for measurement of lifetime and 5 independent measurements of carrier lifetime have been made on each wafer. In total, 160 measurements have been done. The injected carrier density for the full measurement is kept constant.

Table 4 presents the influence of process steps on lifetime for this factorial experiment. For the analysis, the lifetime for each experiment in Table 3 is considered as the additive effect of the constituent steps e.g.,

$$\tau_1 = \tau_{DIM} + \tau_{X_1} + \tau_{WH} + \tau_V + \tau_{Y_1} + \tau_{W_1} + \tau_{P_1} \qquad (8)$$

where the symbols are explained in Table 3.

The use of Millipore water has been found to be superior to D.I. water, obviously because of its higher resistivity (low ionic contamination) and the low degree of particulate and microbiological contamination. Further experimentation showed the effect of rinse time on carrier lifetime; a longer rinse time decreases τ . The KOH source X_2 and the aluminum source Y_2 resulted in better lifetimes than the sources X_1, Y_1. This can be correlated to the degree of purity of these sources.

HCl cleaning improves lifetime in two ways : (i) It neutralizes the alkali and reduces the level of alkali ion contamination. (ii) The small percentage of HCl left participates in a gettering process. During subsequent high-temperature processing, HCl provides an atmosphere for the formation of volatile halides. The HCl gettering process removes the remaining alkali ions from SiO_2 and also the fast-diffusing interstitial contaminants from silicon, thus improving bulk lifetime and the device properties.

TABLE 4
INFLUENCE OF PROCESS STEPS ON LIFETIME FOR Al DIFFUSION

S. No.	Difference in lifetime (μsec.)	% deviation from grand mean
1.	$\tau_{DIM} - \tau_M = (\tau_1 - \tau_2 + \tau_3 - \tau_4 - \tau_5 + \tau_6 - \tau_7 + \tau_8)/4$ = -0.7	-18.9%
2.	$\tau_{x_1} - \tau_{x_2} = (\tau_1 - \tau_2 + \tau_3 - \tau_4 + \tau_5 - \tau_6 + \tau_7 - \tau_8)/4$ = -0.5	-13.5%
3.	$\tau_{WH} - \tau_{WOH} = (\tau_1 - \tau_2 - \tau_3 + \tau_4 - \tau_5 + \tau_6 + \tau_7 - \tau_8)/4$ = 0.7	18.9%
4.	$\tau_V - \tau_A = (\tau_1 - \tau_2 - \tau_3 + \tau_4 + \tau_5 - \tau_6 - \tau_7 + \tau_8)/4$ = 1.2	32.4%
5.	$\tau_{y_1} - \tau_{y_2} = (\tau_1 + \tau_2 + \tau_3 + \tau_4 - \tau_5 - \tau_6 - \tau_7 - \tau_8)/4$ = -0.5	-13.5%
6.	$\tau_{w_1} - \tau_{w_2} = (\tau_1 + \tau_2 - \tau_3 - \tau_4 - \tau_5 - \tau_6 + \tau_7 + \tau_8)/4$ = -1.0	-27.0%
7.	$\tau_{P_1} - \tau_{P_2} = (\tau_1 + \tau_2 - \tau_3 - \tau_4 + \tau_5 + \tau_6 - \tau_7 - \tau_8)/4$ = 1.7	45.9%

Vacuum drying has been found to give better lifetime as compared to air drying because it reduces the surface state density. A large weight of aluminum source used for diffusion improved lifetime because of the Al degradation reactions outlined above. It is also observed (refer to Table 3) that for same amount of AL weight (W_1, W_2), the measured lifetime (τ_{P_1} and τ_{P_2}) varies with diffusion temperature (P_1 and P_2). The measured lifetime (τ_{P_1}) of the silicon p^+nn^+ sample diffused at $1230^{\circ}C$ (P_1) is high compared to the lifetime (τ_{P_2}) of the sample diffused at $1238^{\circ}C$ (P_2). The Table 4 shows that temperature effect on minority carrier lifetime is high and has maximum percentage deviation ($\tau_{P_1} - \tau_{P_2}$) of 45.9% from grand mean τ_m. In the present study, it is revealed that temperature profile has been also a significant factor to influence the minority carrier lifetime of the power semiconductor device, when other process parameters are same.

5. CONCLUSIONS

In fabrication of power semiconductor devices (thyristors and high voltage transistors) AL diffusion, high diffusion temperature and the wet oxidation have been found to be the principal steps deteriorating lifetime. Gallium diffused pnn^+ silicon structure has high carrier lifetime compared to AL diffused pnn^+ structure. It has been found that silicon processed through KOH cleaning, HCl neutrilization, vacuum drying and diffusion temperature ($1230^{\circ}C$), followed with phosphorus getering and slow cooling gives improved minority carrier lifetime. HCl neutrilization improve minority carrier lifetime by 32.4% and vacuum drying yields 18.9% enhancement in minority carrier lifetime. It has been observed that amount of aluminium weight and temperature profile are also other factors to influence the minority carrier lifetime.

Traps in the silicon appear at any stage in a process and considerably complicate the variation of lifetime with injection level.   In the absence of traps, for the range of concentrations examined in this paper, the dependence of effective-carrier lifetime on injected-carrier density conforms to phonon-assisted Shockley-Read-Hall recombination through energy levels introduced at high-doping levels.

ACKNOWLEDGEMENT

The authors gratefully acknowledge the help of BHEL, Bangalore for supplying the monitor samples of thyristor used in this study. They are also thankful to Dr. G.N. Acharya, Director, CEERI, Pilani, for his constant encouragement and valuable discussions during the course of this work.

REFERENCES

[1]   Cornu, J. Sittig, R. and Zimmermann, W., "Analysis and Measure-ment of Carrier Lifetimes in the Various Operating Modes of Power Devices", Solid State Electronics, Vol. 17, Oct. 1974, pp. 1099-11106.

[2]   Schroder, D.K., "The Concept of Generation and Recombination Lifetimes in Semiconductors", IEEE Transactions on Electron Devices, Vol. ED-29, No. 8, Aug. 1982, pp. 1336-1338.

[3]   Wilson, P.G.,"Recombination in Silicon p- -n Diodes", Solid State Electronics, Vol. 10, Feb. 1967, pp. 145-154.

[4]   Schlangenotto, H. and Gerlach, W., "On the Effective Carrier Life-time in p-s-n Rectifiers at High Injection Levels", Solid State Electronics, Vol. 12, April 1969, pp. 267-275.

[5]   Lindholm, F.A., Liou, J.J., Neugroschel, A. and Jung, T.W., "Deter-mination of Lifetime and Surface Recombination Velocity of p-n junction Solar Cells and Diodes by Observing Transients, IEEE Transactions on Electron Devices, Vol. ED-34, No. 2, Feb. 1987, pp. 277 - 285.

[6]   Goodman, A.M., Goodman, L.A. and Gossenberger, H.F., "Silicon-Wafer Process Evaluation Using Minority-Carrier Diffusion Length Measurement by the SPV Method", RCA Review, Vol.44, June 1983 , pp. 326-341.

[7]   Chiang, C-L, Schwarz, R., Slobodin, D.E., Kolozey, J. and Wagner, S., "Measurement of Minority-Carrier Diffusion Length in Thin Semiconductor Films", IEEE Transactions on Electron Devices, Vol. ED-33, No. 10, Oct. 1986, pp. 1587-1592.

[8]   Rai-choudhury, P. Selim, F.A. and Takei, W.J., "Diffusion and Incorporation of Aluminum in Silicon", Journal of the Electrochemical Society, Vol. 124, No. 5, May 1977, pp. 762-766.

[9]   Meek, P.L., Seidel, T.E. and Cullis, A.G., "Diffusion Gettering of Au and Cu in Silicon", Journal of the Electrochemical Society, Vol. 122, No. 6, June 1975, pp. 786-796.

[10]   Remski, G., "Recombination Properties of Gold in Silicon", Physical Review, Vol. 111, No. 6, Sept.1958, pp. 1515-1518.

[11]   Maekawa, T., Inoue, S., Aiura, A. and Usami, A., "Carrier Lifetime of Silicon Wafers Doped by Neutron Transmutation", Semiconductor Science and Technology, Vol. 1, No. 5, Nov. 1986,pp. 305-312.

[12]   Fossum, J.G. and Lee, D.S., "A Physical Model for the Dependence of Carrier Lifetime on Doping Density in Nondegenerate Silicon", Solid State Electronics, Vol. 25, No. 8, Aug. 1982, pp. 741-747.

[13]   Roulston, D.J., Arora, N.D. and Chamberlain, S.G., "Modeling and Measurement of Minority-Carrier Lifetime Versus Doping in Diffused Layers of n[+] - p Silicon Diodes", IEEE Transactions on Electron Devices, Vol. ED-29, No. 2,Feb. 1982, pp. 284-291.

Pankaj K. Sinha and William S. Glaunsinger

THE ROLE OF OXYGEN PRECIPITATES IN THE GETTERING OF
IRON IN SILICON

REFERENCE: Sinha, P. K. and Glaunsinger, W. S., "The Role of Oxygen
Precipitates in the Gettering of Iron in Silicon," Semiconductor Fabrication:
Technology and Metrology, ASTM STP 990, Dinesh C. Gupta, editor,
American Society for Testing and Materials, 1989.

ABSTRACT: The gettering of iron in silicon has been reported to occur at
dislocations and stacking faults in the vicinity of oxygen precipitates. The
iron-containing phase has also been identified. For heat treatments between
800 $^{\circ}$C and 1025 $^{\circ}$C for 24 hrs, only one phase was identified in argon-
implanted as well as oxygen-implanted samples. The gettered particles 30
nm to 100 nm in size were analyzed using EDS, EELS and micodiffraction,
and the only phase was identified as FeSi. It is proposed that the role of
oxygen precipitates in the gettering process is only to generate defects in the
matrix, which ultimately getter the transition metal.

KEY WORDS: Intrinsic gettering, oxygen precipitates, ion implantation,
TEM and SIMS.

The role of oxygen precipitates in intrinsic gettering of transition metals in
silicon has been debated for over a decade [1-4, 7-12]. According to a recent
report, oxygen precipitates react with iron to form iron silicate [3] at
temperatures of 900 - 1200 $^{\circ}$C. Earlier reports show gettering in samples
without oxygen precipitates as well [2, 5, 6]. It has been suggested that oxygen
precipitates are not essential for intrinsic gettering of metallic impurities [2,5].
However, observations also indicate that the gettering process is enhanced by the
presence of such precipitates [7-12]. Since oxygen precipitates enhance
gettering and also decrease the mechanical strength of a silicon wafer [13], it is
desirable to optimize their performance.

Based on various indirect observations, it has been hypothesized that self-
interstitials, which are ejected due to the volume-misfit, release the strain
associated with oxygen precipitates and getter metallic impurities [2,5,6].
However, there is a paucity of definitive evidence for this hypothesis. In

Dr. Sinha is a postdoctoral research associate in the Department of
Chemical, Bio and Materials Engineering; Dr. Glaunsinger is Chairman of the
Department of Chemistry, Arizona State University, Tempe, AZ 85287-1604.

this work, ion implantation of oxygen and argon have been used to explore the gettering of iron in the presence of oxygen precipitates and self-interstitials. The results of this systematic study suggest that direct gettering involves self-interstitials, rather than oxygen precipitates, which supports the hypothesis of Ourmazd and Schroter [2].

EXPERMENTAL TECHNIQUE

A boron doped, p-type, float-zone (FZ) silicon wafer with an initial oxygen concentration below 0.1 ppma (ASTM F121-83) was implanted with 2.5×10^{15} Ar^{++} /cm^2 at 280 keV at the APRDL, Motorola, Inc., Texas. A Czochralski (CZ) silicon wafer with an initial oxygen concentration of 16.55 ppma (ASTM F121-83) was implanted with 5×10^{15} O^- /cm^2 at 190 keV at SRDL, Motorola, Inc., Phoenix. The oxygen-implanted samples were annealed at 1050 °C for 30 min in order to remove any implant damage.

TABLE 1 -- Annealing and metal deposition parameters.

Silicon Wafer	Implant species	First Anneal		Iron film	Second anneal		Third anneal		Sample
		°C	Hrs	Thickness Angstrom	°C	Hrs.	°C	Hrs.	
CZ	oxygen	1050	0.5	...	...	...	...	...	OXY
		1050	0.5	...	800	24	...	...	OXY-1
		1050	0.5	90	800	24	...	...	OXYFE-1
		1050	0.5	90	750	20	1025	24	OXYFE-2
FZ	Argon	...	...	...	...	...	...	...	AR
		...	...	...	800	24	...	...	AR-1
		...	...	90	800	24	...	...	ARFE-1
		...	...	90	1025	24	...	...	ARFE-2

The samples were cleaned in a solution of 1:100 HF in doubly deionized water for 5 min. After rinsing thoroughly in doubly deionized water, the samples were stored under freon until placed in an ultrahigh vacuum chamber (10^{-9} Torr) for metal deposition. Iron was deposited by thermal evaporation on the back surface of samples taken from the wafers. Two sets of samples (OXY-1 and AR-1, and OXYFE-1 and ARFE-1) were annealed at 800 °C for 24 hrs. OXYFE-2 was annealed at 750 °C for 20 hrs prior to a third anneal at 1025 °C. ARFE-2 was annealed directly at 1025 °C for 24 hrs. The silicon wafer types and treatments for the samples used in this study are summarized in Table 1.

A piece from each wafer type, ARFE and OXYFE, was sealed under a helium atmosphere in the same quartz tube. For the second anneal, the ampoule was placed horizontally in a pre-heated tube furnace, so that the two samples were not in contact. The ampoule was quenched to ambient temperature by immersion in water after the gettering anneal. Cross-sectional specimens with (110) orientation were prepared for transmission electron microscopy and analytical electron microscopy studies using standard techniques described by Shinde and De Jonghe [14]. High-resolution imaging was performed on a JEOL-200 CX microscope with an operating voltage of 200 kV and 0.25 nm resolution. A Philips 400 microscope, equipped with super-twin lenses and a field-emission gun, was used for microanalysis of the gettered particles having sizes in the range 30-100 nm using a 10-nm probe size.

A CAMECA IMS-3F secondary ion mass spectroscope (SIMS) was used for depth profiling of iron. The   Fe-54 isotope of iron (5.8 %   natural abundance) was analyzed using a primary beam energy of 12.5 keV and secondary beam extraction voltage of 4.5 keV.

RESULTS

The distribution of iron below the polished surface of wafer ARFE-1 was obtained using SIMS. The presence of iron close to the surface, as shown in Fig. 1, suggests that iron diffused from the back surface to the front surface of the wafer as a result of the heat treatment at 800 °C for 24 hrs. The iron peak is close to the implant projection depth of 300 nm, which implies gettering at the defects associated with argon implantation. A study of the sample using transmission electron microscopy revealed that the ARFE- 1 sample contained most of the iron-precipitated particles at the defect layer (see Fig. 2a), with a few particles near the surface. A high-resolution image of the particle is presented in Fig. 2(b). The particle sizes ranged from 30 to 60 nm. Electron microdiffraction and energy dispersive X-ray spectroscopy (EDS) results on one of the gettered particles are shown in Figs. 3 and 4, respectively. A comparison of the lattice spacings calculated from the diffraction pattern to that of FeSi is shown in Table 2.

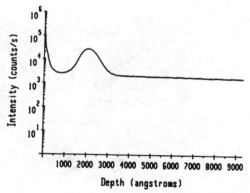

Fig. 1 -- A SIMS depth profile of iron in the ARFE-1 sample. Zero depth corresponds to the wafer polished surface.

Fig. 2(a) -- A TEM cross-sectional view of the defect layer in the ARFE-1 sample.

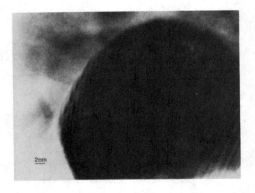

Fig. 2(b) -- A HREM image of the particle marked FeSi in Fig. 2(a).

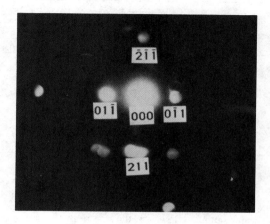

Fig. 3 -- An electron microdiffraction pattern from the particle in Fig. 2.
Reflections from the particle were identified by dark-field imaging.

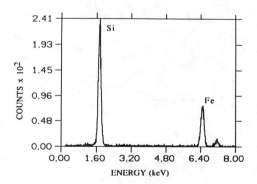

Fig. 4 -- An EDS spectrum indicating the presence of iron in the particle in
Fig. 2.

TABLE 2 -- A comparision of the measured lattice spacings and angles in ARFE-1 with that of FeSi.

Reflections	Measured		For FeSi	
	angle	spacing	angle	spacing
	degrees	Ångstrom	degrees	Ångstrom
211		1.81±0.04		1.82
	90±1		90.0	
01$\bar{1}$		3.13±0.1		3.15
	90±1		90.0	
$\bar{2}\bar{1}\bar{1}$		1.81±0.04		1.82
	90±1		90.0	
0$\bar{1}$1		3.13±0.1		3.15

The gettering of iron in silicon samples implanted with oxygen display similar macroscopic and microscopic characterstics. As indicated by the SIMS spectrum of samples OXYFE-1 in Fig. 5, iron diffused from the back surface to the front surface of the wafer sample. However, the iron peak appears to occur before and after the projection depth of oxygen implantation at 490 nm. No iron peak was observed at the projection depth, where the density of oxygen precipitates was highest. A microscopic investigation of the OXYFE-1 wafer showed gettering to occur primarily at stacking faults (see Fig. 6). The phase was identified as FeSi by EDS and microdiffraction (see Figs. 7 and 8). A comparison of the lattice parameters is given in Table 3.

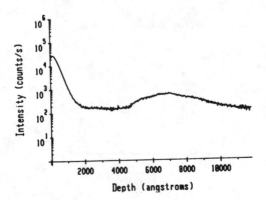

Fig. 5 -- A SIMS depth profile of iron in the OXYFE-1 sample. Zero depth corresponds to the wafer polished surface.

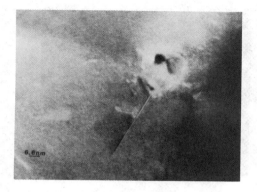

Fig. 6 -- A HREM image of an iron-gettered particle in the OXYFE-1 sample.

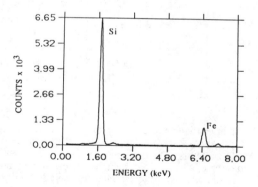

Fig. 7 -- An EDS spectrum from the particle in Fig. 6.

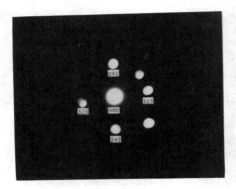

Fig. 8 -- An electron microdiffraction pattern from the particle in Fig. 6.

TABLE 3 -- A comparision of the measured lattice spacings and angles in OXYFE-1 with that of FeSi.

Reflections	Measured		For FeSi	
	angle	spacing	angle	spacing
	degrees	Ängstrom	degrees	Ängstrom
$\bar{3}\bar{2}3$	81 ± 1	0.94 ± 0.03	80	0.95
$\bar{2}4\bar{2}$	100 ± 1	0.94 ± 0.03	100	0.91
323	81 ± 1	0.94 ± 0.03	80	0.95
$2\bar{4}2$		0.94 ± 0.03		0.91

In order to investigate the stability of the gettered phase at elevated temperatures, a piece from each sample type, ARFE and OXYFE, was heat treated at 1025 °C for 24 hrs. The gettered particles were of the order of 100 nm or larger in each sample, which is reasonable for an essentially infinite source of reactants. The phase was again determined to be FeSi, as described earlier. Therefore, the gettered phase (FeSi) is stable to a temperature of at least 1025°C in this system, which is consistent with the phase equilibria data available for FeSi [15].

DISCUSSION

It is useful to consider some important features of oxygen precipitation and induced-defect phenomena briefly before discussing the results of this study. The growth of oxygen precipitates above a critical dimension (10 nm) ejects silicon atoms from their regular lattice sites to interstitial sites [16,17]. The condensation of such self-interstitials results in the generation of extrinsic stacking faults and dislocation loops in oxygen-precipitated samples [18]. Therefore, an oxygen-precipitated sample contains the following major defects: oxygen precipitates, self-interstitials, stacking faults, and dislocation loops. In order to investigate the role of oxygen precipitates in the gettering process in this study, thermally aged silicon samples were simulated by implantation of oxygen and subsequent annealing. The concentration of self-interstitials not associated with oxygen precipitates was simulated by the implantation of argon ions. Only qualitative comparisons are possible in this study due to the lack of a direct measurement of the self-interstitial concentration in silicon.

It is well known that a low-energy implantation of species in silicon at ambient temperature results in the generation of self-interstitial point defects [19,20]. Sample AR-1, which was annealed at 800 °C for 24 hrs, contained a very large number of extrinsic stacking faults and microtwins in the defect layer. Such stacking faults result from the condensation of self-interstitials [18]. Therefore, the as-implanted AR sample contained a higher density of self-interstitials in the defect layer without having oxygen precipitates associated with them. In contrast, the defect layer of OXY contained fewer stacking faults and microtwins compared to AR-1, but the former sample had a higher density of oxygen precipitates which may be attributed to the consumption of self-interstitials by implanted oxygen. In this way, self-interstitials, which play an important role in the gettering process, were reduced (compared to AR samples) in the oxygen-precipitated samples (OXY samples). Although the OXY samples should contain self-interstitials, their concentration should be reduced substantially.

A large difference in the extent of gettering of iron in OXY and AR-type starting materials is believed to originate from the aforementioned differences in the concentration of self-interstitials. Since iron diffusion was sufficient to easily traverse the 600-micron-thick wafer (0.5 cm rms displacement at 800 °C for 24 hrs), the extent of gettering may be limited by the availability of the other reactant, i.e., self-interstitials. As mentioned earlier, self-interstitials in OXYFE were significantly lower than in ARFE samples. The enhanced gettering of iron in ARFE compared to OXYFE suggests that the availability of self-interstitials indeed determines the extent of gettering.

As shown in Fig. 6, gettering occurs at stacking faults in the OXYFE-1 sample. The association of gettering with the stacking faults could not be obtained in AR samples due to the high density of imperfections in the defect layer. Therefore, the results of this study indicate that stacking faults are favorable sites for gettering and that gettering is enhanced by increasing the self-interstitial concentration.

The SIMS depth profile of iron concentrations in OXYFE-1 (Fig. 5) suggests that gettering did not occur at oxygen precipitates, since no iron peak was observed at the implantation projection depth. Instead, gettering occurred in the tail region of the implant damage, where the oxygen concentration is low [21]. Also, the presence of an iron peak close to the wafer surface where again the concentration of oxygen is low [21], suggests that gettering was not favored at oxygen precipitates. This was also substantiated by the presence of a FeSi particle at the edge of a stacking fault. The above evidence leads to the conclusion that oxygen precipitates do not getter directly. Also, the presence of a FeSi phase in the OXYFE-2 sample suggests that the gettering mechanism at $1025^{\circ}C$ is the same as that at $800\ ^{\circ}C$.

CONCLUSIONS

On the basis of the results of this study as well as other works [2,5,6], it is possible to elucidate the primary role of thermally grown oxygen precipitates in the gettering process. In particular, a growing oxygen precipitate ejects silicon from its regular site to an interstitial site, and the ejected silicon atoms condense to form stacking faults and other types of defects. The excess self-interstitials subsequently react with iron atoms to form FeSi at such defect sites in the vicinity of oxygen precipitates. Therefore, oxygen precipitates apparently enhance the gettering process by supplying self-interstitials rather than by gettering directly.

ACKNOWLEDGEMENTS

The authors would like to thank Mr. Ray-Chern Deng for SIMS analyses. The electron microscopy was carried out at the NSF/ASU High Resolution Electron Microscopy Facility. This research was funded by NSF Grant No. DMR-8605937 and a Grant-in Aid of Research from Sigma Xi, The Scientific Research Society.

REFERENCES

[1] Buck, T. M., Poate, J. M., and Pickar, K. A., "A Rutherford Scattering Study of the Diffusion of Heavy Metal Impurities in Silicon due to Ion Implanted Surface Layers," Surface Science, Vol. 35, 1973, pp 362- 79.

[2] Ourmazd, A. and Schroter, N., "Gettering of Metallic Impurities in Silicon," Mat. Res. Soc. Symp., Vol. 36, 1985, pp 25-30.

[3] Colas, E. G., Weber, E. R., and Hahn, S., "Intrinsic Gettering of Iron in Silicon," Mat. Res. Soc. Symp. Proc., Vol. 71, 1986, pp 13-20.

[4] Schmalz, K., Kirscht, F.-G., Niese, S., Richter, H., Kittler, M.,Seifert, W, Babanskaya, I., Klose, H., Tittelbach-Helmrich, K., and Schoneich, J., "On the Intrinsic Gettering in Fe-Contaminated CZ-Si,"Phys. Stat. Sol. (a), Vol. 100, 1987, pp 69-85.

[5] Nauka, N., Lagowski, J., Gatos, H. C., and Li, C.-J, "Intrinsic Gettering in Oxygen Free Silicon," Appl. Phys. Lett., Vol. 46, No. 7, 1985, pp 673-75.

[6]   Ueda, O., Nauka, K., and Gatos, H. C., "Nature and Generation
      Mechanisms of Butterfly-type Intrinsic gettering Centers in Oxygen Free
      Silicon Crystals," Defects in Semiconductors, Edited by H. J. Von
      Bardeleben, Materials Science Forum, Vol. 10-12, 1986, pp 145-50.
[7]   Jastrzebski, L., Soyaden, R. McGinn, J., Kleppinger, R., Blumenfeld,
      M., Gillespie, G., Armour, N., Goldsmith, B., Henry, W., and
      Vecrumba, M., "A Comparision of Internal Gettering during Bipolar,
      CMOS, and CCD (High, Medium, Low Temperature) Processes," J.
      Electrochem. Soc., April 1987, pp1018-25.
[8]   Wong, C.-C. D., Malwah, M. L., and Pollock, L., "Nucleation Time
      Effects on Intrinsic Gettering," Mat. Res. soc. Symo. Proc., Vol. 36,
      1985, pp 239-43.
[9]   Borland, J. O., "Activation of the Intrinsic gettering Mechanism by the
      Growth of Oxygen Related Precipitates in CZ-Grown Silicon Wafer,"
      Proc. Electrochem. Soc. Symp. - Defects in Silicon, 1983, pp 194-203.
[10] Soydan, R. and Jastrzebski, J., "Internal Gettering in Bipolar Process:
      Part II-Oxygen Precipitation Kinetics,"Proc. Electrochem. Soc. Symp.-
      Defects in Silicon,1983, pp 153-5.
[11] Huff. H. R., Schaake, H. F., Robinson, J. T., Baber, S. C., and Wong,
      D., "Some Observations on Oxygen Precipitation/Gettering in Device
      Processed Czochralski Silicon," J. Electrochem. Soc., July 1983. pp
      1551-5.
[12] Swaroop, R. B., and Fish, T., "Oxygen Control and Intrinsic Gettering
      in CZ Silicon,"Proc. Electrochem. Soc. Symp.-Defects in Silicon,
      1983, pp 180-4.
[13] Tan, T. Y., and Tice, W. K., "Oxygen Precipitation and the generation of
      Dislocations in Silicon," Phil. Mag., Vol. 34, No. 4, 1976, pp 615-31.
[14] Shinde, S. L. and De Jonghe, L. C., "Cross-sectional TEM from Metal-
      Ceramic Composites," J. Elect. Micro. Tech., Vol. 3, 1986, 361-3.
[15] Hansen, M., Constitution of Binary Alloys, Metallurgy and Metallurgical
      Engineering Series, McGraw Hill Book Co., New York, 1958, pp 711-7.
[16] Schaake, H. F., Baber, S. C., and Pinizzotto, R. F., "The Nucleation
      and Growth of Oxide Precipitates in Silicon," Semiconductor Silicon 81,
      Proc. Fourth International Symp. on Silicon Mat. and Techn., The
      Electrochemical Society, Vol. 81-5, 1981, 273-81.
[17] Wada, K., and Inoue, N., "Growth Kinetics of Oxide Precipitates in
      Czochralski Silicon," J. Cryst. Growth, Vol. 71, 1985, 111-7.
[18] Maher, D. M., Staudinger, A., and Patel, J. R., "Characterization of
      Structural Defects in Annealed Silicon Containing Oxygen," J.
      Appl.Phys., Vol. 47, No. 9, 1976, pp 3813 -25.
[19] Madakson, P., and Angilello, J.,"Stress and Radiation Damage in Ar++
      and Ti+ Ion-implanted Silicon," J. Appl. Phys., Vol. 62, No. 5, 1987,
      pp 1688-93.
[20] Waddell, C. N., Spitzer, W. G., Fredrickson, J. E., Hubler, G. K., and
      Kennedy, T. A., "Amorphous silicon Produced by Ion Implantation:
      Effects of Ion Mass and Thermal Annealing," J. Appl. Phys., Vol. 55,
      No. 12, 1984, pp 4361-66.
[21] Ryssel, H., and Ruge, I.,Ion Implantation, John Wiley & Sons
      Publications, 1986.

Michael Goldstein and Joseph Makovsky

THE CALIBRATION AND REPRODUCIBILITY OF OXYGEN
CONCENTRATION IN SILICON MEASUREMENTS USING SIMS
CHARACTERIZATION TECHNIQUE.

REFERENCE: Goldstein, M. and Makovsky, J., "The
Calibration and Reproducibility of Oxygen
Concentration in Silicon Measurements Using SIMS
Characterization Technique", Semiconductor
Fabrication: Technology and Metrology, ASTM STP 990,
Dinesh C. Gupta, editor, American Society for Testing
and Materials, 1989.

ABSTRACT: A "Load Line Calibration" (LLC)
methodology for [O] in silicon determinations by SIMS
is introduced. The LLC uses two (or more) p- silicon
dice characterized by FTIR as calibration standards
that are incorporated into each load of analytical
samples. Repeated measurement of p- control samples
with an [O] = 27.7 ppma [1] shows that with a two-
point-LLC methodology the "load to load" relative
error is 2.6% (σ = 0.7 ppma). Measurement results are
presented and compared with those obtained by other
calibration methodologies. The results have been
obtained under experimental conditions that are
adaptable for large scale production of controlled
oxygen n+ and p+ silicon substates.

KEYWORDS: Oxygen content, Silicon, SIMS, Load Line
Calibration.

Usage of epitaxial silicon on heavily doped n+ and p+
substrates for CMOS applications has been steadily
growing. The main force driving this trend has been the
epitaxial wafers' inherent capability for reducing
latchup effects.

Dr. Joseph Makovsky is a senior scientist, manager
of the Silicon Material Technology (SMT) and Dr. Michael
Goldstein is a SMT staff scientist at Intel Corp., 2250
Mission College Blvd., P.O. Box 58125, M/S SC9-05, Santa
Clara, CA. 95052-8125.

The advantages of controlling oxygen concentration - [O]-and its precipitation in silicon in IC manufacturing processes are well established. With the increased recognition and understanding of the roles of oxygen in silicon, silicon wafer manufacturers have developed the capability to provide silicon to tight [O] specifications.   Today, lightly doped silicon wafers specified to ±3 ppma (ASTM - 121-79 [1]) are offered by silicon manufacturers as standard items. Nevertheless, achievement of similiar control over [O] in heavily doped substrates used for epitaxial n/n+ and p/p+ wafers has lagged far behind.

A major obstacle in achieving the desired oxygen control in heavily doped substrates was lack of a reliable measurement technique that may be applicable to large scale production needs.   Fourier Transform Infrared Spectrometry **(FTIR)**,which has become the industry's work horse for measuring interstitial oxygen concentration in lightly doped silicon material, cannot be applied to heavily doped silicon due to the inherent free carrier noise level. Other measuring techniques, such as Photon Activation Analysis, Charged Particle Activation Analysis and Secondary Ion Mass Spectrometry **(SIMS)** have been considered as being non-manufacturable and having day to day measurements low reproducibility characteristics.

Characteristics that are directly measured in -[O]- in silicon determinations by SIMS are oxygen and silicon isotope ion count rates. The oxygen to silicon isotope ion count ratio is converted into [O] in silicon concentration units using a calibration methodology. Two calibration methodologies that have been reported are the "Relative Sensitivity Factor" **(RSF)** [2,3] and the "Load Factor" **(LF)** [4] methodologies.

The **RSF** methodology uses oxygen implanted silicon specimens as calibration standards. In   this methodology, a multiplicative factor - the oxygen "Relative Sensitivity Factor" - is calculated utilizing the standard's known oxygen implant dose and the oxygen and silicon counts measured in a depth profile mode for same. Once determined, the relative sensitivity factor is used for calibration in subsequent measurements of analytical samples.

In the **LF** methodology, a p- calibration standard with a known [Oi] level (characterized by FTIR), is incorporated into each SIMS load of analytical samples. The FTIR/SIMS measurement ratio is used to normalize analytical sample SIMS results into their FTIR equivalents.

With the **RSF** calibration methodology, **"load**

to load" relative measurement error has been shown to be high, in the best case in the 10-20% range [4,5,6,7]. The main reason for this level of irreproducibility is the high susceptibility of this methodology to instrumental variations, particularly to background oxygen noise level.

The **LF** methodology as presented by Bleiler et al [4,5], succeeded in improving the oxygen signal to noise ratio to a value between 10:1 and 20:1, the noise is not negligible and significantly affects the load to load reproducibility. Though with the improved experimental conditions utilized by Bleiler et al, the **"in load"** relative error was significantly improved, the long range **"load to load"** relative error remained high at 10% level [4,5].

As will be shown in our results, meticulous attention to experimental detail can decrease the above mentioned relative error figures. However a new calibration methodology, the Load Line Calibration **(LLC)** methodology introduced in this presentation, resolves to a great extent some of the irreproducibility problems inherent in the RSF and the LF methodologies.

The LLC methodology utilizes two (or more), well characterized by FTIR, p- silicon dice calibration standards that are incorporated into each load of analytical samples to be measured. Using the LLC methodology, the load to load relative error is reduced down to about a 2.5% level. Results validating this conclusion are presented and compared with results of the RSF and LF methodologies obtained under identical experimental conditions.

EXPERIMENTAL

The measurements were carried out using a CAMECA IMS - 3f Ion Microanalyzer and a Cs+ ion source. For the reported experiments two different instruments of the same type were used. The primary ion beam was focused to a spot size of about 150 μm in diameter and rastered over an area of 250 μm X 250 μm. The primary beam's typical current was 5 μA. It was accelerated to a 14.5KV impact energy. The effective sputtering rate was about 200 Å/sec. The secondary ion accelerating voltage was 4.5KV. The oxygen and silicon ion counts were measured by an electron multiplier and a Faraday cup, respectively.

The silicon specimens used in these experiments were 4mmX4mmX1mm dice cut from lapped and polished wafers. A SIMS sample **"load"** was a group of sixteen silicon specimens loaded into the instrument in a sample holder and measured in one run under the same applied conditions. In each of the loads one of the specimens was a Float Zone (FZ) sample, two were p- samples with known [O] levels and the remaining thirteen were analytical samples.

The two pre-characterized p- samples were used in this study for calibration of the SIMS oxygen measurements and will be referred to hereafter as the **"standards"**. The p- calibration standard specimens were diced off the central areas of mirror polished 150mm silicon wafers that had been well characterized for their [Oi] level and [Oi] homogeneity. [Oi] levels of p- wafers used for the generation of calibration standards were in the $21 \leqslant [Oi] \leqslant 34$ ppma range [1]. As a rule, a calibration standard pair was chosen so that it spanned both ends of the [O] range to be studied.

To monitor the **"load to load"** measurement reproducibility an analytical sample in each of the participating loads was replaced by an additional p- **"control"** sample. The p- control specimens were cut from well characterized 150mm wafers as described for the generation of the calibration standards; thus, each such wafer could be a source for hundreds of control samples with the same [O] level.

The mounted sample holder was baked at 100° C prior to analysis to remove adsorbed moisture. The holder was loaded into the instrument chamber and pumped to a vacuum of about 3×10^{-9} mm Hg by a turbomolecular pump. The specimen target surfaces had been sputtered in situ and the native oxide removed prior to measurements.

The measurements of specimens in a "load" were performed sequentially, one measurement per sample. This measurement sequence was repeated 3 - 4 times and the mean value and standard deviation for each specimen were calculated. The mean value and standard deviation thus obtained are the specimen's **"load value"** and **"in load standard deviation"**, respectively. In a typical two shift working day 60 - 70 analytical samples could be analyzed.

The calibration methodology developed in this study to convert the SIMS load values to FTIR equivalent values has been the Load Line Calibration method **(LLC)**. "SIMS Oxygen Values" of the samples in a load were calculated from the ^{16}O to ^{30}Si ion count ratio.

A calibration line equation of FTIR oxygen values versus load values as measured by SIMS is derived separately for each load; for this we utilize the known standards'FTIR values and their load values as measured by SIMS.

The measured values of the analytical samples are converted into their FTIR oxygen concentration equivalent using the calibration line equation.

In the LLC methodology the value obtained for the load's FZ sample is not used for [O] evaluation; the sole purpose of including the FZ samples is to get a "go/no go" signal relevant to the noise level in the system.

RESULTS and DISCUSSION

The methodology and instrument combined performance was monitored via two main test vehicles:

1. Repeated measurements of p- control samples with the same known [Oi] level incorporated into a number of loads.
2. Repeated measurements of samples with the same [O] level taken from randomly chosen heavily doped n+ and p+ silicon wafers.

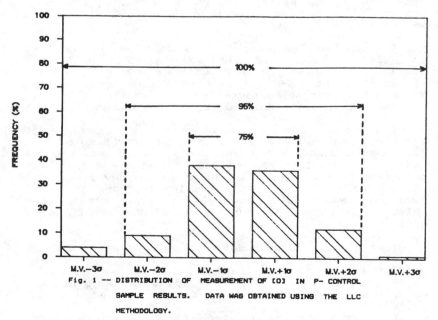

Fig. 1 -- DISTRIBUTION OF MEASUREMENT OF [O] IN P- CONTROL SAMPLE RESULTS. DATA WAS OBTAINED USING THE LLC METHODOLOGY.

n = 150, M.V. = 27.7 PPMA, σ = 0.7 PPMA, RSD = 2.6%

About 150 loads that incorporated **"same - [O]"** control samples have been analyzed during a six month period. In accumulating the data two instruments operated by ten alternating analysts were used. During this period several p- calibration standard sets were used. Using the LLC methodology, analysis of the 150 data points for the control sample shows a mean value M.V. = 27.7 ppma and a "load to load" RSD of 2.6%. The "in load" RSD was typically $\simeq$ 2%. A histogram of measurement result dispersion about the average is presented in Fig.1; as immediately indicated, this complies with a normal distribution. Using the same basic measurement results but with the LF and the RSF calibration methodologies, RSD "load to load" values of 3.3% and 7.0% respectively have been obtained. Analysis of the data indicated for both the LF on RSF calibration had normal distributions; the difference in the RSD values between the LLC and the LF methodologies was statistically valid with a confidence level greater than 97.5%.

TABLE 1 -- [O] IN CONTROL SAMPLES BY SIMS. USING THE LLC , LF AND RSF CALIBRATION METHODOLOGIES.Q4/1987.ALL CONTROL SAMPLES WERE 4mm X 4mm X 1mm SAMPLES DICED FROM CENTRAL REGIONS OF TWO ADJACENT P-WAFERS SHOWING SAME [Oi] VALUES BY FTIR.

INSTRUMENT	ANALYST	CONTROL SAMPLE [O],ppma			INSTRUMENT	ANALYST	CONTROL SAMPLE [O],ppma		
		RSF	LF	LLC			RSF	LF	LLC
2	F	18.6	29.2	29.1	1	C	18.5	27.7	28.1
2	F	18.5	27.6	28.3	2	K	15.3	27.0	27.0
1	C	18.0	27.4	27.7	2	K	16.2	28.2	28.2
1	C	16.7	27.1	27.5	2	K	16.2	28.4	28.2
1	J	17.3	29.5	28.2	2	C	17.5	26.8	26.7
1	A	16.8	27.2	28.0	2	K	18.1	29.7	28.6
2	E	14.0	25.7	26.2	1	C	19.5	26.4	27.2
2	E	16.7	26.7	27.0	2	K	17.4	27.4	27.0
2	E	19.9	27.3	27.5	2	J	18.1	29.3	28.9
2	E	19.5	26.6	26.6	2	K	18.1	28.5	28.2
2	N	20.6	29.2	29.3	2	C	18.4	27.7	28.0
2	K	17.5	27.8	27.6	2	G	16.9	27.2	27.4
2	K	18.0	27.2	27.5	1	C	17.9	27.3	26.9
2	K	17.4	27.8	28.0	1	N	19.3	27.5	28.0
2	K	17.0	28.3	27.7	2	K	18.9	26.8	27.1
2	K	17.8	28.5	28.4	2	K	17.7	27.4	27.3
2	D	17.8	27.9	28.5	2	K	18.4	28.3	28.3
2	K	17.0	27.6	27.5	2	E	19.4	28.9	28.7
2	C	16.4	28.4	28.2	2	D	17.8	28.1	28.4
2	C	16.2	28.2	27.3	2	N	18.2	27.2	27.2
2	C	16.1	28.2	28.2	2	E	19.4	27.3	27.4
2	C	16.1	27.2	27.3	1	N	19.6	28.4	28.2
2	C	16.5	27.9	27.9	2	H	18.4	26.8	27.4
1	J	17.8	27.2	27.3	1	K	18.4	28.0	27.4
1	J	17.4	26.6	27.0	1	K	17.5	27.2	27.9
2	E	18.5	26.3	26.9	2	E	18.4	27.5	27.4
2	E	18.8	27.6	27.6	2	J	16.8	27.4	27.6
2	G	18.0	27.3	27.3	2	H	18.6	27.6	27.7
2	D	19.1	27.7	27.7	2	H	18.1	27.4	27.1
1	C	15.6	29.1	28.2					
2	K	18.6	29.4	28.9					

	RSF	LF	LLC
MEAN VALUE (ppma)	17.8	27.7	27.7
STD (ppma)	1.2	0.8	0.6
RSTD (%)	6.9%	3.1%	2.3%

Table 1 summarizes the results obtained during the last three months with measurements about evenly spread over this period. In the "LLC" column we present the measurement results when applying the LLC methodology. The mean value (M.V.) of these determinations is 27.7 ppma with σ = 0.6 ppma and RSD = 2.3% (Identical to the measured FTIR value). A plot of these [O]

TABLE 2 -- VARIABILITY OF [O] IN SILICON MEASUREMENTS RESULTS DERIVED FOR RANDOMLY CHOSEN
N+ AND P+ SUBSTRATES USING THE LLC , LF AND RSF CALIBRATION METHODOLOGIES.

			[O]								
			LLC			LF			RSF		
SAMPLE	WAFER TYPE	# OF LOADS	MEAN (ppma)	STD (ppma)	RSD (%)	MEAN (ppma)	STD (ppma)	RSD (%)	MEAN (ppma)	STD (ppma)	RSD (%)
A	P+	4	25.0	0.3	1.2	24.7	1.0	4.0	16.1	1.1	6.9
B	P+	5	23.7	0.7	3.0	23.5	0.8	3.3	15.4	1.1	6.9
C	P+	4	24.9	0.2	0.8	24.8	0.8	3.2	15.8	1.1	6.7
D	P+	4	23.4	0.5	2.1	23.4	0.7	3.0	15.7	0.8	4.0
E	P+	4	26.7	0.9	3.4	27.2	1.3	4.8	17.4	1.7	9.5
F	N+	3	28.4	0.3	1.1	28.0	0.7	2.3	19.3	1.9	9.8
G	N+	4	32.1	0.5	1.6	32.2	1.4	4.3	22.0	2.4	10.9
H	N+	3	28.1	0.4	1.4	27.9	1.1	3.9	18.6	1.9	10.2
I	N+	4	32.0	0.6	1.9	31.7	1.4	4.4	21.0	2.5	11.9

Table 2 summarizes result data obtained by repeated
measurements of samples taken from some randomly picked
p+ and n+ wafers.   For each wafer the samples were
4mmX4mmX~1mm pieces diced from the central region of the
wafer.   These measurements were collected over an eight
month period by two operators.

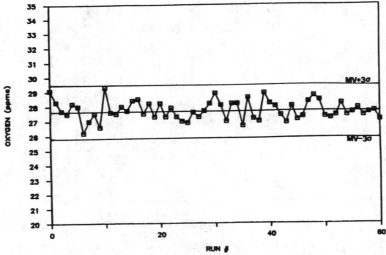

Fig. 2 -- [O] IN P- CONTROL SAMPLES vs. RUN # (Q4/1987).

RESULTS OBTAINED USING THE LLC METHODOLOGY. n = 61, M.V. = 27.7 PPMA, σ = 0.6 PPMA, RSD = 2.3%

The RSD = 2.3%, obtained in monitoring [O] in the control samples using the LLC methodology, constitutes a significant improvement over the RSD 10% figure [4,5,6,7] which was, until lately, considered typical of SIMS determinations of [O] in silicon.   This accomplishment should be partially attributed to improvements in experimental conditions and meticulous attention to detail.   Therefore, it is of special interest, in this report, to evaluate the "net" positive impact on the "load to load" reproducibility of the LLC methodology when compared to the RSF and LF methodologies.   In the "RSF" and "LF" columns in Table 1 we give the [O] determinations obtained on employing the RSF and the LF calibration methodologies, respectively; for these determinations, the same $^{16}O/^{30}Si$ ratios as for the determinations in the LLC column have been used. When applying the LF methodology any one of the two standards in the load can be used for calibration without a significant difference between the calculated values.   For the presented analysis all the data was calculated using the calibration standard having the low [O] value.   The mean value obtained with the LF methodology is the same as with the LLC methodology i.e., M.V.=27.7 ppma with σ=0.8 ppma and RSD = 3.1% for LF, compared with 0.6 ppma or 2.3% for LLC.   The mean value obtained with the RSF methodology is 17.8 ppma with σ=1.2 ppma and RSD = 6.9%.   The 17.8 ppma figure is in good agreement with the Figure of 17.5 ppma that can

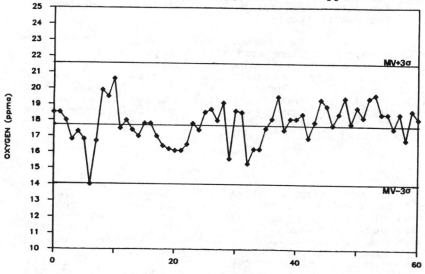

Fig. 3 -- [O] IN P- CONTROL SAMPLES vs. RUN # (Q4/1987).

RESULTS OBTAINED USING THE RSF CALIBRATION

METHODOLOGY. n = 61, M.V. = 17.8 PPMA [8], σ = 1.2 PPMA, RSD = 6.9%.

be obtained on converting the 27.7 ppma (ASTM F121-79) into its ppma equivalent according to the JEIDA convention [8]. Figure 3 gives the plot of [O] vs. the run number for the RSF calibration methodology case.

Based on the data in Table 1 we can deduce that the net impact of the various calibration methodologies to the [O] measurement reproducibility as measured by their RSD values relates to one another as in the proportion 1.0:1.35:3.0 (LLC:LF:RSF).

The RSD Figures of 6.9% and 3.1% achieved with the RSF and LF methodologies respectively prove that better experimental conditions did indeed contribute to the improved reproducibility results; nevertheless, the advantage in using the LLC methodology is also clearly demonstrated. Description and analysis of the improved conditions will be published elsewhere.

The advantage of the LLC methodology stems from the following main reasons:
(a)   Minimization, to almost complete elimination, of the background oxygen noise level effect. This is achieved without having to resort to actual physical elimination of the noise.
(b)   As with the LF methodology, elimination of the Sensitivity Factor from calculations (discards a major possible error source).
(c)   Minimization of the variability due to operators systematic errors.

A way to further improve reproducibility of the LLC methodology is to use more than two points to draw the Load Line i.e., utilization of 3 (or more) calibration standards with each load. Basic statistics considerations indicate that with the usage of 3 calibration standards the standard deviation can be improved by a factor of $\sqrt{3/2}$; preliminary results indicate that with "3 point" calibration line an RSD smaller then 2% is achievable.

CONCLUSION

The Load Line Calibration methodology for [O] in silicon determinations by SIMS has been introduced. Analysis of a large number of measurement results obtained over an extended time period show the measurement standard deviation, of a control sample of 27.7 ppma [O] level, to be 0.7 ppma; i.e., a relative standard deviation of 2.6%. This figure should be compared with the RSD values of 3.1% and 6.9% obtained in this work for the LF and RSF methodologies, respectively.

This result was obtained using two instruments operated by ten alternating operators with a relatively high throughput of 60-70 analytical samples per instrument per day.

Though [O] in silicon determinations utilizing the LLC methodology have been performed, so far, in only one laboratory [9], the conditions under which the measurements have been carried out, we trust, is a fair depiction of a working environment appropriate for adaptation by the industry for control of [O] in silicon in production of heavily doped p+ and n+ silicon wafers.

Work in progress shows that using the LLC method with a "3 point line" RSD <2%, and thus better accuracy of oxygen in silicon measurements by SIMS, is a goal achievable in the near future.

ACKNOWLEDGEMENTS

The SIMS measurements were performed at Charles Evans and Associates Analytical Laboratory in Redwood City, Ca. The authors are grateful to all staff members for their support in performing the SIMS determinations and thank E. Strathman, P. Chiu, R. Bleiler and R. Hockett for useful discussions. Special thanks also to S. Michaels and D. Narvaes of Intel's SMT group for the fabrication and FTIR-characterization of the p- control samples and calibration standards.

REFERENCES

[1]   F121-79,"Standard Test Method for Interstitial Atomic Oxy gen Content of Silicon By Infrared Absorption," Annual Book of ASTM Standards, Part 43, American Society for Testing and Materials, Philadelphia, Pennsylvania, 1979,pp. 519-521.
[2]   Deline, V.R., "Quantitative Aspects of Secondary Ion Mass Spectrometry", Phd Thesis, University of Illinois, Urbana - Champaign, 1978.
[3]   McHugh, J.A., "Empirical Quantitation Procedures in SIMS", in Secondary Ion Mass Spectrometry, NBS Spec. Publ. 427, K.F.J. Heinrich, and D.E. Newbury, Eds., National Bureau of Standards, Washington D.C., 1975, PP. 129-134.
[4]   Bleiler, R.J., Hockett, R.S., Chu, P. and Strathman, E., "SIMS Measurements of Oxygen in Heavily Doped Silicon", in Oxygen, Carbon, Hydrogen and Nitrogen in Crystalline Silicon, Mat. Res. Soc. Symp. Proc., Vol. 59, 1986, MRS, Pittsburgh, Pen., PP. 73-79.

[5]   Hockett, R.J., private communication, Monsanto
       Electronic Corp., St. Louis Miss., 1986.

[6]   Matlock, J., private communication, S.E.H. America,
       Inc., Vancouver, Wa., 1987.
[7]   Rath, H. J., private communication, Wacker
       Chemitronic GmbH, Burghausen, Germany, 1986.
[8]   Inoue, N., Arai, T., Nazaki, T., Endo, K., Mizama,
       K., "High Reliability Infrared Measurements of
       Oxygen and Carbon in Silicon", Emerging
       Semiconductor Technology, ASTM STP 960, D.C. Gupta
       and P.H. Langer, Eds., American Society for Testing
       and Materials, Philadelphia, Pennsylvania, 1986, pp.
       365-377.
[9]   Charles Evans and Associates, Analytical Lab.,
       Redwood City, California.

George A. Rozgonyi, Ratnaji R. Kola, Kenneth E. Bean, and Keith Lindberg

DEFECT, DOPANT, AND DEVICE MODIFICATION USING Si(Ge,B) EPITAXY

REFERENCE: Rozgonyi, G. A., Kola, R. R., Bean, K. E., and Lindberg, K., "Defect, Dopant, and Device Modification Using Si(Ge,B) Epitaxy," Semiconductor Fabrication: Technology and Metrology, ASTM STP 990, Dinesh C. Gupta, Ed., American Society for Testing and Materials, Philadelphia, 1989.

ABSTRACT: In order to eliminate strain and dislocation generation in heavily boron-doped epitaxial silicon films, co-doping with germanium, a strain counterbalancing element with a larger covalent radius has been utilized. By adjusting the ratios of germane and diborane in a dichlorosilane/hydrogen CVD reactor we can sequentially achieve extrinsic gettering (XG) using controlled introduction of interfacial misfit dislocations with Si(Ge), as well as buried, highly conducting Si(Ge,B) layers which are strain-free and lattice matched to the silicon substrate. It is now possible to perform "Defect Engineering" by strategically positioning singly, or in tandem, either XG or co-doped Si(Ge,B) layers. The p^{++} layers act as recombination zones or buried field plates to suit the needs of MOS latch-up control, high speed and radiation hard devices, as well as providing defect free p^{++} etch stops for thin membranes and three-dimensional silicon structures. A variety of these epitaxial structures have been characterized using chemical etching and optical microscopy, X-ray topography and rocking curves, cross-section TEM, SEM/EBIC, SIMS, RBS and Spreading Resistance Profiling. An additional defect engineering program has been initiated in which individual misfit dislocations have been exposed and positioned under oxide mesas by anisotropically etching V-grooves in Si(Ge) XG samples. These structures will be used to examine the basic electrical properties of clean and decorated dislocations. More exotic applications for the creation of electrically useful misfit dislocations as active components in simple devices are being explored.

KEYWORDS: silicon epitaxy, co-doping, strain compensation, buried layers, misfit dislocations, chemical etching, micro-wires

George Rozgonyi and Ratnaji Kola are Professor and graduate student respectively, in the Department of Materials Science and Engineering at North Carolina State University, Raleigh, NC 27695; Ken Bean is with the Central Research Labs., Texas Instruments Inc., Dallas, TX 75265; Keith Lindberg is with the Advanced Products Group, Texas Instruments Inc., Sherman, TX 75090.

Extrinsic gettering (XG) via the controlled introduction of epitaxial misfit dislocations has been described by the authors[1] as a complementary approach to conventional back-side and intrinsic gettering techniques. The procedure is readily compatible with any technology which incorporates epitaxial substrates and is particularly well suited for gettering during lower temperature/shorter time thermal processing. The XG material has proven to be very effective in improving epitaxial minority carrier lifetime and gated diode leakage current[2]. Due to enhanced recombination at buried sheets of interfacial misfit dislocations, XG material also offers the device designer localized minority carrier lifetime control, which may be particularly beneficial for latch-up protection in CMOS circuits, as well as in very high speed and radiation hard devices. In these devices thin, lightly doped epitaxial layers are grown on highly conducting substrates to improve device performance. The closer the highly conductive substrate is placed to the active device region (meaning thinner epitaxial layer) the higher is the resistance to latch-up. Alternatively, strategic positioning of heavily boron-doped buried epilayers will relax some of the heavy doping requirements for substrates. In addition, p^{++} layers are becoming increasingly important in the fabrication of thin membranes and three-dimensional structures in silicon, since these layers have extremely low etch rates with certain anisotropic selective etchants[3,4]. New applications for SOI using bonded wafers require even more accurate control of the etching process. In many of these applications, the high boron concentrations causes significant lattice mismatch between the doped layer and undoped substrate. The resulting stress gives rise to uncontrolled nucleation of misfit dislocations[5]. However by co-doping with germanium, a strain counterbalancing element with a larger covalent radius, it is possible to compensate the boron induced lattice contraction and eliminate the dislocation generation[6,7]. Germanium was also a suitable element because of its high solubility and electrical inactivity in silicon[4]. Utilizing our understanding of germanium induced lattice expansion from our previous extrinsic gettering (XG) work, we have compensated the lattice contraction and defect formation in boron-doped p^{++} layers by a simultaneous vapor phase co-doping of silicon epilayers with germanium and boron. The electrical properties of misfit dislocations were examined using SEM/EBIC, minority-carrier lifetime and gated diode structures.

EXPERIMENTAL

The epitaxial layers were deposited by chemical vapor deposition (CVD) in an AMC 7810 barrel-type reactor on 4 inch diameter p- and n-type (100) substrates employing the SiH_2Cl_2-B_2H_6-GeH_4-H_2 chemical system. The growth temperature was $1080°C$. For the XG case, the resistivity of the epilayers was maintained at about 10 Ω-cm by doping with either B or P. The misfit dislocations were introduced in a controlled fashion by the incorporation of ~2% Ge into layers ~2 μm thick. Pure Si layers 4 to 8 μm thick were grown on top of Ge-alloyed layers for use in device fabrication. Pure Si buffer layers (2 μm thick, 10 Ω-cm) were also placed between the Ge-doped layers and the substrates to separate the electrical effects of misfit dislocations from those of heavily doped substrates. For the co-doping case, single 5 μm thick epilayers were grown on p-type (10 and 0.04 Ω-cm) substrates and the B and Ge contents adjusted. The boron concentration in the epilayers was varied from 5 x 10^{19} to 5 x 10^{20} cm^{-3}, whereas the germanium concentration was varied from 5 x 10^{20} to 5 x 10^{21} cm^{-3}. Heavily boron-doped, 2 μm thick buried layers with 4 μm intrinsic cap layers were also grown. The resistivity of all heavily boron-doped layers was in the 0.001 ohm-cm range.

The XG and co-doped epilayers were characterized using Nomarski optical microscopy after preferential etching on plan view and angle polished surfaces. X-ray topography was employed for large area defect observation, while cross-sectional and plan-view electron microscopy (TEM) were used for the critical analysis of misfit dislocation interactions and boron precipitation. Double-crystal X-ray rocking curves were obtained in (+,-) parallel arrangement using Cu radiation. In addition, a rapid single crystal X-ray diffraction substrate/layer peak shift analysis was obtained using Cu Kß radiation. Scanning Electron Microscopy (SEM) in the EBIC (electron beam induced current) mode provided in-depth mapping of the electrical activity of defects. Schottky contacts 30 nm thick and 1 mm in diameter were fabricated by Au evaporation onto shallow angle polished n-type samples, whereas Al was evaporated on the backside for ohmic contacts. The boron concentration of the deposited layers was measured by SIMS and the Ge concentration was determined by Rutherford Backscattering (RBS) and channeling techniques. Carrier concentration profiles were obtained by spreading resistance measurements. Anisotropic etching with 10% KOH at 80°C[8] was used to etch V-grooves in Si(Ge) XG samples to expose the ends of misfit dislocations for electrical evaluation of individual defects.

RESULTS AND DISCUSSION

An optical micrograph of an XG structure with misfit dislocations obtained on a sample which has been angle polished in two orthogonal directions and then preferentially etched is shown in Fig. 1. The micrograph gives a three-dimensional perspective of the dislocations at both the upper and lower interfaces of the buried XG layer. The epitaxy consists of a Si(2% Ge) layer for the generation of misfit dislocations, and a pure silicon capping layer which hosts the device and provides electrical separation from the underlying interfacial defects; although a chemical gettering and clean-up of the capping layer proceeds easily. The micrograph shows an orthogonal cross-grid network

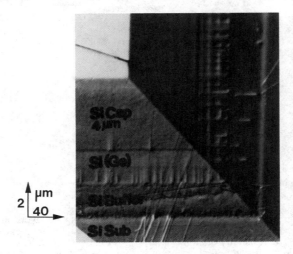

Fig. 1.   Optical micrograph of a double angle-polished XG structure showing buried layers of misfit dislocations.

of misfit dislocations, which are confined to the Ge-alloyed layer interfaces, or to the buffer layer. The extended linear etch ridges in orthogonal <110> directions disappear as the wedge thickness of the angle polished capping layer increases. Note that the epitaxial capping layer is free of etch ridges or of any etch pits representative of threading defects. This is also confirmed by the SEM/EBIC micrograph in Fig. 2, which was obtained with a beam energy of 20 KeV (penetration depth ~5 μm) using Schottky diodes fabricated on an angle polished XG sample. The dislocations appear as dark lines at and slightly above the XG interface due to their strong recombination activity for the electron-hole pairs generated at the surface by the electron beam. This single micrograph not only provides information on the electrical activity of the interfacial dislocation array, but also proves that none of these buried defects penetrate the capping layer, since no localized recombination sites are visible in the thicker capping layer. Further evidence of the absence of surface defects has been described in Ref[2], which verified the stability and gettering efficiency of the interfacial misfit dislocations by measuring leakage currents of less than 1 nA/cm^2 for both gate depletion and accumulation for a large number of large area gated diodes.

4 μm Si + 1.5 μm Si(2%Ge) + 2 μm Si   on   Si

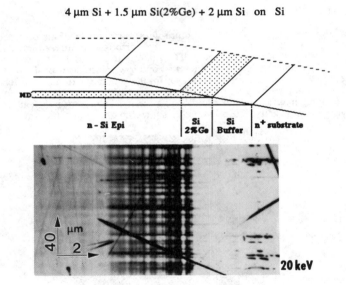

Fig. 2. SEM/EBIC image of an angle-polished XG sample at a beam energy of 20 KeV.

Heavily boron-doped and boron and germanium co-doped epitaxial layers on (100) p-type silicon substrates were investigated for the range of epitaxial doping and alloying outlined in Table 1. The resistivity of all the epilayers was in the 0.001 ohm-cm range. A typical SIMS profile for boron and germanium is shown in Fig. 3, which depicts the abrupt interface between the buried co-doped layer and the capping layer. Fig. 4 shows a typical RBS spectrum obtained using 2 MeV He^{2+} ions, from which the germanium concentrations were obtained. The χ_{min} value is around 5% indicating good crystalline quality of the co-doped layer. The carrier concentration profiles were obtained by spreading resistance measurements on angle polished samples. These profiles showed uniform doping of the layers with a linear carrier concentration relationship with layer boron content up to 1×10^{20} cm^{-3}, indicating full dopant activation. The ability to create

TABLE 1 -- Parameters of co-doped epitaxy*

| Sample | Buried/Co-doped layer | | | Cap layer | |
No.	B	Ge	t (μm)	Dopant conc.	t (μm)
1	5E19	...	2	8E14	4
2	5E19	5E20	2	8E14	4
3	5E19	...	5	...	...
4	5E19	5E20	5	...	...
5	1E20	...	2	1E15	4
6	1E20	1E21	2	1E15	4
7	1E20	...	5	...	...
8	1E20	1E21	5	...	...
9	5E20	...	2	1E17	4
10	5E20	5E21	2	1E17	4
11	5E20	...	5	...	...
12	5E20	5E21	5	...	...

* All wafers are 4-inch diameter, (100) p-type.

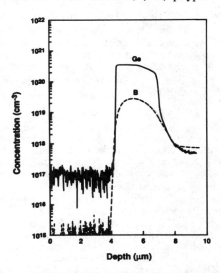

Fig. 3. A typical SIMS profile of a Si(Ge,B) co-doped sample.

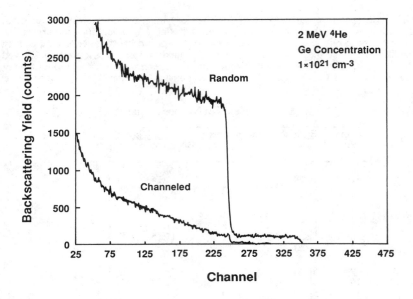

Fig. 4.   RBS spectrum of a Si(Ge,B) co-doped sample.

very low resistance buried "field-plates" is shown in the spreading resistance profile of Fig. 5, for a sample with a 2 μm buried layer co-doped with 1×10^{20} cm^{-3} boron and 1×10^{21} cm^{-3} germanium. The profile indicates a sharp interface with minimum interdiffusion, as was also observed from the SIMS profile. Sheet resistance values obtained by four-point probe method indicated a 20% lower resistivity in the co-doped samples at boron levels $\geq 1 \times 10^{20}$ cm^{-3}. This is due to increased electrical activation upon strain compensation and/or enhanced carrier mobility of silicon doped with germanium.

Extensive X-ray topography coupled with TEM were employed to study the confinement and interactions of boron-induced misfit dislocations. In boron-doped samples, unlike the Ge-alloyed XG case[1], the misfit dislocations strongly interact forming a tangled dislocation network with threading defects[9]. In order to determine the growth parameters for complete strain compensation and dislocation elimination, the boron concentration in the epilayer was fixed at 1.2×10^{20} cm^{-3} and the germanium concentration was varied from 5×10^{20} to 1.2×10^{21} cm^{-3}. Figure 6a is an optical micrograph of a preferentially etched sample with a Ge/B ratio of 4, showing a high density of misfit dislocations still remains. As the Ge/B ratio is increased to 6.7, the misfit dislocation density decreased. Although total defect elimination was not achieved at this Ge/B ratio, as expected from lattice-contraction coefficient calculations using covalent radii, it was only possible to have zero strain and zero defects at a Ge/B ratio of 8, as shown in Fig. 6b. This is discussed further in the double-crystal peak shift data below.

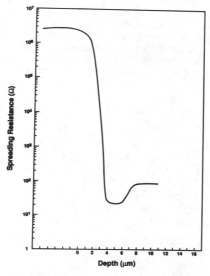

Fig. 5.   Spreading Resistance Profile of a 1 x 10^{20} cm^{-3} boron-doped,
2 μm buried layer.

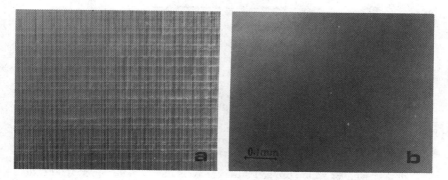

Fig. 6.   Optical micrographs of preferentially etched, co-doped samples
with a) Ge/B ratio = 4   b) Ge/B ratio = 8.

Small differences between the lattice constants of the epitaxial layers and the substrate
can be measured with high accuracy by means of double crystal X-ray rocking curve
analysis, where two Bragg reflections are obtained, one each from the substrate and the
layer. Figure 7 shows the (400) rocking curves, obtained in a (+,-) parallel arrangement,
of boron-only doped and B and Ge co-doped samples. Rocking curve (a) is from a 1 x
10^{20} cm^{-3} boron-only doped sample showing a peak shift of 70 arcsec, indicating a large
lattice mismatch. Complete strain compensation was achieved at a Ge/B ratio of 8,
resulting in a single overlapping layer/substrate peak. The ability to adjust the strain to

any desired level is shown by the rocking curve (b) for an over compensating Ge/B ratio of 10. Here the layer peak is located to the left of the substrate peak indicating a transition from tensile to compressive strain. Single crystal rocking curves were also obtained using Cu Kß radiation to facilitate ease of operation and avoidance of the $K\alpha_1$ and $K\alpha_2$ peak overlaps typically encountered in a single crystal diffractometer.

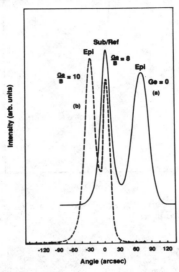

Fig. 7. Double-crystal (400) rocking curves from a) 1×10^{20} cm^{-3} boron-only doped sample b) co-doped sample with Ge/B ratio = 10.

Using dislocations as active elements in simple electrical devices would be the penultimate defect engineering application. In fact, the "diode" effect for dislocations in n-type silicon has been reported[10], and Shockley[11] has speculated on the physical properties of these dislocation micro-wires. Because of the unique Si(Ge) materials system and the current level of microfabrication technology, we have made some exploratory attempts at fabricating a device with a dislocation having a positive electrically active role in the device function. This was done by growing a 120 nm thick oxide on XG samples with 4 μm and 8 μm epilayers by dry oxidation at 1000°C for 2 hours. Squares 1mm on a side were separated by 10 μm and 20 μm windows via photolithography. The edges of the squares were aligned along <110> directions. V-grooves whose depths were 7 μm or 14 μm and controlled by the 10 or 20 μm oxide openings were anisotropically etched with 10% KOH at 80°C[8]. Figure 8 shows an SEM micrograph of the V-grooves with arrays of co-linear dislocatioin etch pits delineated by 1 min Secco etching. The one-to-one correspondence of the etch pits in adjacent V-grooves indicate the continuity of the misfit dislocations from edge to edge of the 4 inch dia. wafer. The absence of etch pits in the mesa regions indicates that there are no threading defects. Metallization to form MOS structures and to evaluate the conductivity of clean and Au, Ni, and Co decorated misfit dislocations is in process.

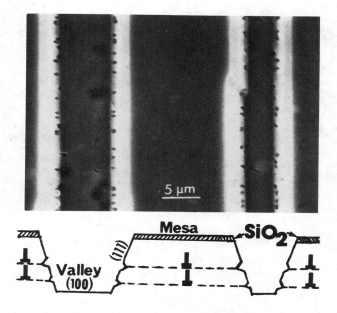

Fig. 8.   A SEM micrograph showing misfit dislocation etch pits on the side
walls of anisotropically etched V-grooves.

CONCLUSIONS

Defect, dopant, and device modification have been implemented by lattice adjustments during silicon epitaxy using boron and/or germanium for extrinsic gettering and defect engineering. Heavily boron-doped, strain-compensated epitaxial layers of high conductivity were produced by co-doping. The strain in the epilayers could be adjusted to any desired level. Misfit dislocations were shown to be electrically active by SEM/EBIC and a model system to test their use for micro-wiring and MOS structures is being fabricated to evaluate the properties of clean and metal or silicide decorated misfit dislocations.

ACKNOWLEDGEMENTS

The authors wish to thank B. Rogers and R. Subrahmanyan of Duke University, B. Jiang and Z. Radzimski of North Carolina State University for valuable discussions and assistance. We gratefully acknowledge R. Kuehn and E. Condon of North Carolina State University for their help with the photolithography. This research was supported by the Semiconductor Research Corporation and the Texas Instruments, Inc.

REFERENCES

[1]   Salih, A. S. M., Kim, H. J., Davis, R. F., and Rozgonyi, G. A., in "Semiconductor Processing", ASTM STP 850, D. Gupta, Ed., p.272, ASTM, Philadelphia, (1984).

[2]   Salih, A. S. M., Radzimski, Z., Honeycutt, J., Rozgonyi,G. A., Bean, K. E., and Lindberg, K., Appl. Phys. Lett.., Vol. 50, 1678 (1987).

[3]   Petersen, K., Proc. IEEE, Vol. 70, 420 (1982).

[4]   Herzog, H. -J., Csepregi, L., and Seidel, H., J. Electrochem. Soc., Vol. 131, 2969 (1984).

[5]   Queisser, H. J., J. Appl. Phys., Vol. 32, 1776 (1961).

[6]   Yeh, T. H., and Joshi, M. L., J. Electrochem. Soc., Vol. 116, 73 (1969).

[7]   Lee, Y. T., Miamoto, N., and Nishizawa, J. I., J. Electrochem. Soc., Vol.122, 530 (1975).

[8]   Bean, K. E., IEEE Trans. Electron Devices, Vol. ED-20, No.10, 1185 (1978).

[9]   Rozgonyi, G. A., Salih, A. S. M., Radzimski, Z., Kola, R. R., Honeycutt, J., Bean, K. E., and Lindberg, K., J. Cryst. Growth., Vol. 85, 300 (1987).

[10] Mil'shtein, S., and Nikitenko, V., JETP Lett., Vol. 13, 233 (1971).

[11] Shockley, W., Solid State Technology, Vol. 26, No. 1, 75 (1983).

Witawat Wijaranakula, Steven Shimada, Howard Mollenkopf, John H. Matlock, and Michael Stuber

EFFECT OF PRE- AND POST-EPITAXIAL ANNEALING ON OXYGEN PRECIPITATION AND INTERNAL GETTERING IN N/N+(100) EPITAXIAL WAFERS

REFERENCE: Wijaranakula, W., Shimada, S., Mollenkopf, H. Matlock, J.H., and Stuber, M., "Effect of Pre- and Post-epitaxial Annealing on Oxygen Precipitation and Internal Gettering in N/N+(100) Epitaxial Wafers", Semiconductor Fabrication: Technology and Metrology, ASTM STP 990, Dinesh C. Gupta, editor, American Society for Testing and Materials, Philadelphia, 1989.

ABSTRACT: Oxygen precipitation in silicon heavily-doped with antimony, particularly at the concentration range higher than 7×10^{17} atoms/cm^3, is known to be severely suppressed because of the doping concentration effect. This results in a reduction in internal gettering (IG) efficiency in the N/N+ epitaxial wafers. In this work, substrate wafers heavily-doped with antimony were pre-annealed prior to the epitaxial deposition process. Post-epitaxial annealing was used for enhancing precipitation in as-deposited epitaxial wafers. The results indicate that both pre- and post-epitaxial annealing can improve oxygen precipitation and IG efficiency. The relationship between oxide breakdown, generation lifetime and bulk defect density is observed.

KEYWORDS: silicon epitaxy, oxygen precipitation, internal gettering.

During the past several years the usage of epitaxial silicon wafers for the application of integrated circuit (IC) devices such as high density CMOS (Complementary Metal Oxide Semiconductor) [1-2] and CCD (Charge-Coupled Device) [3] has increased steadily because of several

Dr. Wijaranakula is a senior engineer/R&D Materials Characterization, Mr. Shimada is an application engineer, Dr. Mollenkopf is the department manager, Dr. Matlock is the Vice President of Technology at SEH America, Inc., 4111 NE 112st Avenue, Vancouver, WA 98662; Mr. Stuber is a process engineer at UNISYS, Corp., 10850 Via Frontera, San Diego, CA 92127

advantages compared to polished silicon wafers. Although the epitaxial layer deposited on a heavily-doped substrate wafer can provide a high quality surface for IC device fabrication, significant yield loss due to metallic contaminants can still be observed. It is conceivable that this yield loss could be reduced after internal gettering is fully embodied into the device processing steps. In N/N+ epitaxial wafers where the substrate is heavily-doped with antimony, internal gettering is extremly limited because of the antimony doping concentration effect. The oxygen precipitation in antimony doped substrate is retarded, particularly when the doping concentration is higher than 7×10^{17} atoms/cm^3 [4-7]. This phenomenon has been explained by several proposed models, [5,8-9], but the whole picture is still unclear and controversial. Precipitation enhanced annealing schemes for the epitaxial substrate wafers heavily-doped with antimony have been developed [6-7]. Nevertheless, these schemes might be too complicated and less feasible for typical IC device fabrication.

Present studies on oxygen precipitation in P/P+ and N/N+ epitaxial wafers indicate that both pre- and post-epitaxial annealing performed at temperatures between 650 and 800 °C can be used to generate sufficiently large amounts of bulk defects for IG purposes [10-12]. Other unrelated studies have shown that the secondary bulk defects, namely the bulk stacking faults (BSFs), are considered to be one of the most effective gettering sites found in CMOS and Bipolar processes [13]. Despite the above information, the principle understanding of the IG process with respect to the annealing procedures (pre- or post-annealing) for N/N+ epitaxial wafers needs to be studied further.

The purpose of this paper is to extend our previous investigations [10-12] on the effect of pre- and post-annealing on the oxygen precipitation process in N/N+ epitaxial wafers. The interpretation of the IG efficiency, which will be discussed here, is based upon minority carrier generation lifetime results.

EXPERIMENTAL PROCEDURES

In this experiment 100 mm Czochralski (CZ) grown N+(100) wafers, heavily-doped with antimony at the concentration between 7×10^{17} atoms/cm^3 and 4×10^{18} atoms/cm^3, were used as the substrate wafers. The oxygen concentration in the substrate wafers was determined by SIMS (Secondary Ion Mass Spectrometry) analysis and calibrated according to ASTM F121-79 using the calibration factor of 4.815×10^{17} 1/cm^3. Only substrate wafers having the oxygen content in the range between 1.45×10^{18} atoms/cm^3 and 1.6×10^{18} atoms/cm^3 were used. Two IG annealing (pre- and post-annealing) schemes were investigated. In the pre-annealing experiment, substrate wafers were annealed at 800 °C in nitrogen ambient for times up to 24 hours and then processed through epitaxial deposition. From our previous study, high BSF density can be generated in silicon having the above specification when pre-annealing is performed at 800°C (see Fig. 1) [12]. For the control purpose, one group of the wafers without pre-annealing was set aside. After being annealed, the front surface of substrate wafers was mirror polished. Approximately 20 to 30 μm was removed during this operation. The polishing step was necessary because epitaxial layer cannot be deposited directly on the lapped surface of as-received substrate wafers due to the surface roughness.

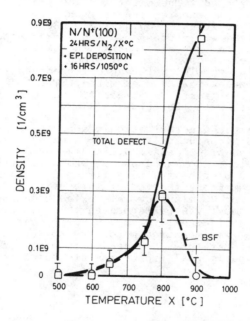

FIG. 1 -- Relationship between bulk defect density and pre-annealing temperature.

During epitaxial deposition, a thin epitaxial silicon layer, approximately 6 microns thick, doped with phosphorus at the concentration of 1.5×10^{16} atoms/cm^3 was deposited. Epitaxial deposition was performed at 1150°C using trichlorosilane as the gas source. Prior to epitaxial deposition, substrate surface of approximately 1 and 2 microns was removed by in-situ HCl etching [14]. As-deposited epitaxial wafers were annealed at 1050°C in dry O$_2$ for 16 hours. This annealing cycle should represent the well drive-in step of a typical CMOS device process.

In the post-annealing experiment, substrate wafers were first polished and processed through epitaxial deposition. The epitaxial layer which was deposited on these substrate wafers was doped with phosphorus at the concentration of 1.5×10^{15} atoms/cm^3. This doping concentration is one order of magnitude lower than that in the epitaxial layer of pre-annealed wafers. As-deposited epitaxial wafers were annealed at 750°C for times up to 48 hours. One group of control wafers without post-annealing was set aside. Following the post-annealing, wafers were annealed at 1050°C in dry O$_2$ ambient for 16 hours.

After being annealed, the oxide grown on the wafer surface was stripped. The wafer surface was inspected for crystallographic defects under the optical light microscope after Wright etching [15]. Bulk defects were examined on the wafer cross-section and counted at 200X magnification. In the area containing high bulk defect density, the defect count was performed at 400X magnification. Selected samples were angle-lapped and the defect-free denuded zone (DNZ) was examined. The DNZ width was measured at the location between 20 and 30 mm from the wafer edge underneath the epitaxial layer.

Electrical characterization was performed on the MOS (Metal Oxide Semiconductor) capacitors which had a gate oxide thickness of 450 angstroms and a doped polysilicon gate. The gate oxide was grown at 920°C in dry O$_2$ (+ 2% HCl) ambient. Doping of the polysilicon gate took place in a POCl$_3$ system where the temperature of the wafers was held at 950°C for 22 minutes. Gate oxide breakdown voltage (BV$_{ox}$) measurement was performed on the capacitor which had a gate area of 6.46×10^{-2} cm^2. Minority carrier generation lifetime was measured according to Zerbst's method [16] at room temperature on a capacitor with a diameter of 0.6 mm. The experimental procedures are summarized in Fig. 2.

RESULTS AND DISCUSSION

Growth Kinetics of the Bulk Defects

No surface defects can be counted using the nine-points counting technique as described in ASTM F47-84 publication. This method was found to be unsuitable for counting the surface microdefects at a low density level (below 30 defects/cm^2). Therefore, the surface defect density was determined by cross scanning the wafer surface. This was done under the microscope at 200X magnification starting at approximately 5 mm from one wafer edge and ending at approximately 5 mm from the other edge. The inspection was repeated crosswise. The surface defect density was determined by dividing the total number of the defects by the actual scanned surface [17]. The surface defect observed here was primarily stacking faults of approximately 2-3 μm in length.

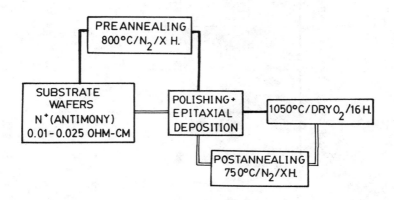

FIG. 2 -- Summary of the experimental procedures.

Figs. 3a and 3b show the surface defect density as a function of pre- and post-annealing time, respectively. The surface defect density in pre-annealed wafers increases with increasing annealing time, whereas in post-annealed wafers this relationship reverses. No surface defect was observed in the control wafers from the pre-annealing experiment. Theoretically, the surface defect density in the control wafers from both experiments should be identical. This does not agree with the results shown in Fig. 3. The discrepancy could arise from the fact that the 1050°C annealing of both experiments was performed at a different time. It is likely possible that during the 1050 °C annealing cycle more contaminants are introduced into the post-annealed wafers than the pre-annealed wafers. This could contribute to high surface defect density in the control post-annealed wafers. The reason that the surface defect density increases with increasing pre-annealing time is unclear and will be discussed later. A reduction in the surface defect density as the post-annealing time increases could be related to the gettering effect.

Figs. 4a and 4b show a series of the optical micrographs of the sample cross-section of the pre- and post-annealed wafers. From the figures, the bulk defect density in both pre- and post-annealed wafers increases with increasing annealing time. Generally, the bulk defect size in the pre-annealed wafers is much larger than that in the post-annealed wafers. Under the SEM (Scanning Electron

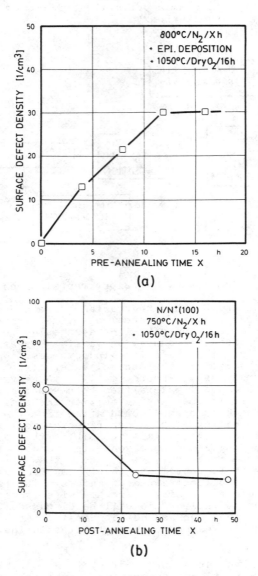

FIG. 3 --   Surface defect density as a function of a) pre-
and b) post-annealing time.

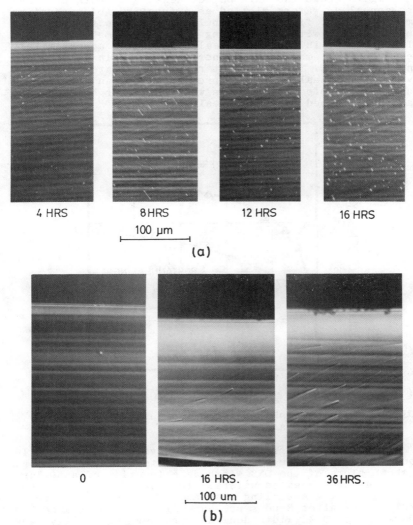

FIG. 4 -- Photomicrographs of the sample cross
         sections in the a) pre- and b) post-
         annealed wafers.

Microscope), two different types of the bulk defects are
identified: (i) BSFs and (ii) small etch pits which are
believed to have originated from precipitate particles
and/or small stacking faults [18-20].

Fig. 5 shows the bulk defect density in both pre- and post-annealed wafers plotted as a function of annealing time. From the figure, the bulk defect density increases exponentially with increasing annealing time. The bulk defect density in the pre-annealed wafers is approximately one order of magnitude higher than that in the post-annealed wafers. The present results indicate that for a given total annealing time, pre-annealing can generate a much higher defect density as well as larger bulk defects than that induced by post-annealing.

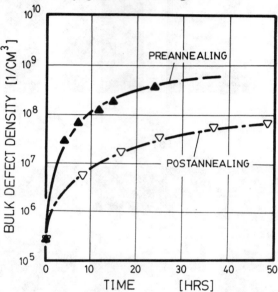

FIG. 5 -- Relationship between the bulk defect density and the annealing time.

In order to perform a complete evaluation of the IG process, data of the DNZ width needs to be included. Fig. 6 shows plots of the DNZ width as a function of annealing time. In pre-annealed wafers, the DNZ width decreases with increasing annealing time and levels off at approximately 20 μm after 8 hour pre-annealing. In post-annealed wafers, the DNZ width declines rather gradually and levels off also at approximately 20 μm after 48 hour post-annealing. In interpreting these observations, it is necessary to include "grown-in" microprecipitates in the discussion. It is well accepted that "grown-in" microprecipitates exist in CZ-grown silicon [11]. During epitaxial deposition, a dissolution of "grown-in" microprecipitates occurs, particularly in the subsurface region where oxygen concentration decreases drastically due to out-diffusion. Assuming such a mechanism to prevail, the DNZ formation

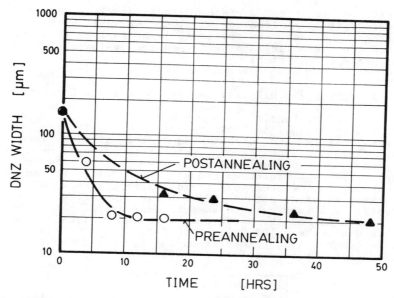

FIG. 6 -- Relationship between DNZ width and the annealing time.

will be governed by the following parameters [21]:   i) the "grown-in" microprecipitate size,   ii) the epitaxial deposition time   and   temperature and iii)   the   bulk   oxygen concentration. An increase in the "grown-in" microprecipitate size for example,   would result in a decrease in the DNZ width.

The   reason that pre-annealing causes a reduction   in the DNZ width is because pre-annealing enhances growth   of "grown-in"   microprecipitates   [11].   As a   result,   fewer microprecipitates   are dissolved in the subsurface   region compared to wafers without pre-annealing. In post-annealed wafers,   "grown-in"   microprecipitates   dissolve   rapidly during the epitaxial deposition. Small residual   precipitates   grow at a much slower rate than large   precipitates [22].   Consequently,   the   DNZ width in the   post-annealed wafers   will   decrease at a much slower rate than   in   the pre-annealed wafers.   More detailed explanation related to this specific effect can be found elsewhere [23].

As   observed earlier,   surface defect density in pre-annealed   wafers increases with   increasing   pre-annealing time.   This could be related to a drastic reduction in the DNZ width as observed in Fig.   6. The relationship between the   microdefect density on the epitaxial surface and   DNZ width   has   been observed and reported [24].   Lack of   DNZ contributes to high surface defect density. Residual microprecipitates located at the epitaxial-substrate interface grow into the epitaxial layer during the high temperature annealing and appear on the epitaxial surface after preferential etch.

Oxide Integrity and Minority Carrier Generation Lifetime

The oxide integrity with respect to the oxide breakdown voltage (BV_{OX}) is known to depend strongly upon the surface quality and cleanliness of the silicon wafer. Figs. 7a and 7b show the BV_{OX} statistics measured on the pre- and post-annealed wafers, respectively. In this study, breakdown voltages equal to or below 15 volts correspond to low breakdown fields which are believed to be related to oxide defects. High breakdown voltages above 15 volts are intrinsic to the silicon oxide materials. (The criteria of the oxide breakdown has already been described elsewhere [25-26]). Therefore, the discussion will be concentrated primarily on the low breakdown fields (breakdown voltages equal to or below 15V).

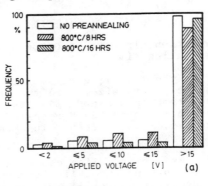

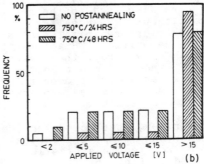

FIG. 7 -- BV_{OX} statistics of a) pre- and b) post-annealed wafers.

In pre-annealed wafers, the relationship between BV_{OX} and pre-annealing time cannot be established. This could be due to the fact that pre-annealing is performed prior to the polishing and epitaxial deposition steps. Any possible deterioration of the surface quality induced by pre-annealing could have been removed by polishing. In addition, the epitaxial layer was deposited on the pre-annealed substrate at the same time. Therefore, the surface quality with respect to BV_{OX} should not depend upon the pre-annealing time.

In the post-annealed wafers, some improvement in the gate oxide integrity is observed on wafers post-annealed for 24 hours. In contrast, a post-annealing cycle for 48 hours causes degradation in the gate oxide quality. An improvement in BV_{OX} could be interpretated as the result of an increase in the gettering efficiency. An extended post-annealing leads to an increase in surface contaminants and thus degradation in the gate oxide quality. In the absence of further experimental data this hypothesis should be regarded as unproven. Fig. 3 shows that no correlation can be established between the oxide integrity and the surface defect density.

Figs. 8a and 8b show the minority carrier generation lifetime (tg) as a function of annealing time. In both experiments, tg increases first with increasing annealing time and then decreases gradually after an extended annealing. Generation lifetime measured on the control wafers from the pre- annealing experiment is 58 μsec.

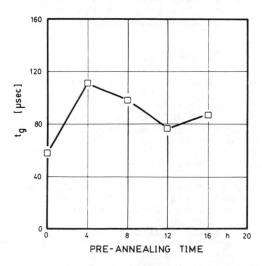

FIG. 8a -- Generation lifetime as the function of annealing time in pre-annealed wafers.

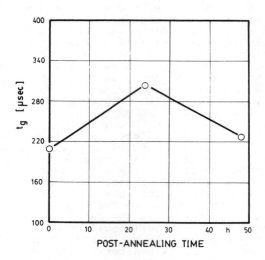

FIG. 8b -- Generation lifetime as the function of
annealing time in post-annealed wafers.

This number is lower than that measured on the control
wafers from the post-annealing experiment, 210 μsec. The
reason for this can be due to the dependence of generation
lifetime on the impurity doping concentration of the epitaxial layer [27]. Note that the doping concentration of
the epitaxial layer deposited on the pre- annealed wafers
is one order of magnitude higher than the post-annealed
wafers.

For the pre-annealing process, the ratio between
maximum generation lifetime, observed after 4 hour pre-
annealing, and generation lifetime measured on the control
wafers is 1.91. This ratio is only 1.38 for the post-
annealing process. Maximum generation lifetime for the
post-annealing process is observed after 24 hour
annealing. By comparing these results and those in Fig. 5,
an increase in generation lifetime after some pre- or
post-annealing could be due to an increase in the bulk
defect density and hence IG effectiveness.

There are several reasons that the results from the
pre- and post-annealing experiments cannot be compared
directly. One reason is that the surface quality with
respect to pre- and post-annealing processes is quite
different. This could possibly lead to differences in the
bulk oxide trap concentration. The bulk oxide traps,
particularly those located at the Si–SiO$_2$ interface, are
known to have an effect on the minority carrier generation
lifetime [28]. Secondly, differences in the impurity

doping concentration of the epitaxial layer influences the generation lifetime. Evaluation and comparison of the gettering efficiency of the pre- and post-annealing processes based on the generation lifetime results should be done with precaution.

As observed in Fig. 8, a reduction in generation lifetime after an extended annealing in both pre- and post-annealed wafers could occur because of either lack of DNZ width (see Fig. 6) or other influential factors such as a non-getterable metallic contamination or a loss of gettering effectiveness when the precipitation stops. This subject is beyond the scope of this project and will not be discussed here. Generally, these results agree well with results from pre-annealed epitaxial experiments conducted by Tsui, et al [29]. It was found that both a sufficiently large DNZ and high bulk defect density must be created in order to obtain the most effective gettering.

Summary

Both pre- and post-epitaxial annealing can lead to precipitation of oxygen and thus improvement in the gettering efficiency. Post-annealing can have some disadvantages compared to pre-annealing. For example, post-annealing takes considerably longer than pre-annealing before any sufficiently high bulk defect density and improvement in lifetime can be observed. Extended post-annealing could lead also to deterioration of the surface quality. Two critical parameters for the effective gettering process have been determined: (i) high bulk defect density and (ii) sufficiently large DNZ width.

In view of these results, a combination between moderate pre- and post-epitaxial annealing might be the ideal solution. Pre-annealing should be performed as long as necessary to cause growth of the precipitate nuclei to a thermodynamically stable size that can withstand the heat cycle of epitaxial deposition. Residual nuclei can be successfully re-grown by a short post-annealing step. With the results of short pre- and post-annealing time, the DNZ width can be better controlled. In addition, the surface contamination and deterioration of epitaxial surface quality caused by post-annealing could be reduced.

REFERENCES

[1]   Mohsen, A., Kung, R., Schultz, J., Madland, P., Simon-
      son, C., Hamdy, E., and Yu, K., "C-MOS 256-K Ram
      with Wideband Output Stands By on Microwatts", Elec-
      tronics, Vol.57, 14 June 1984, pp.138-143.
[2]   Yamaguchi, T., Morimoto, S., Kawamoto, G., and Dela-
      cy, J.,"Process and Device Performance of 1 um-Chann-
      el n-Well CMOS Technology", IEEE Transaction Electro-
      nic Devices, Vol.ED-31, No. 2, Feb. 1984, pp.205-214.
[3]   Slotboom, J.W., Theunissen, M.J., and de Kock, A.J.R.,
      "Impact of Silicon Substrates on Leakage Currents",
      IEEE Electronic Device Letters, Vol.EDL-4, No.11,
      November 1983, pp.403-406.
[4]   Wijaranakula, W., Matlock, J.H., and Mollenkopf, H.,
      "Retardation of the Oxygen Precipitation Process in
      N/N+(100) Epitaxial Silicon Wafers", an Extended
      Abstracts, the Electrochemical Society, Vol.87-1,
      1987, pp.352-353.
[5]   Shimura, F., Dyson, W., Moody, J.W., and Hockett,
      R.S.,"Oxygen Behavior in Heavily Sb-Doped CZ-
      Silicon", VLSI Science and Technology - 1985, W.M.
      Bullis and S. Broydo, Eds., Electrochem. Society,
      1985, pp.507-516.
[6]   Tsuya, H., Kondo, Y., and Kanamori, M., "Behaviors of
      Thermally Induced Microdefects in Heavily Doped Sili-
      con Wafers", Japanese Journal of Applied Physics,
      Vol. 22, No.1, January 1983, pp.L16-L18.
[7]   Dyson, W. and Makovsky, J., "Oxygen Precipitation in
      N+ Silicon", Oxygen Carbon, Hydrogen and Nitrogen in
      Crystalline Silicon, J.R. Mikkelsen, Jr., S.J. Pear-
      ton, J.W. Corbett, and S.J. Pennycook, Eds., Mate-
      rials Research Society, Vol. 59, 1986, pp.293-300.
[8]   De Kock, A.J.R. and Van de Wijgert, W.M., "The Effect
      of Doping on the Formation of Swirl Defects in Dislo-
      cation-Free Czochralski-Grown Silicon Crystals", Jou-
      rnal of Crystal Growth, Vol.49, 1980, pp.718-734.
[9]   Hahn, S., Arst, M., Rek, Z.U., Stojanoff, V., Bulla,
      D.A., Castro, Jr., W.E., Tiller, W.A., "Effect of
      450C Thermal Annealing Upon Oxygen Precipitation in
      Heavily Doped B- and Sb-Doped Czochralski Si",
      Applied Physics Letters, Vol.50, No.7, 16 Feb. 1987,
      pp.401-403.
[10] Wijaranakula, W., Burke, P.M., Forbes, L., and
      Matlock, J.H., "Effect of Pre- and Postepitaxial
      Deposition Annealing on Oxygen Precipitation in
      Silicon", Journal of Material Research, Vol.1, No.5,
      September/October 1986, pp.698-704.
[11] Wijaranakula, W., Matlock, J.H., Mollenkopf, H.,
      Burke, P., and Forbes, L., "Oxygen Precipitation in
      P/P+(100) Epitaxial Silicon Material", Journal of
      Electrochemical Society, Vol.134, No.9, September
      1987, pp.2310-16.

[12] Wijaranakula, W., Matlock, J.H., and Mollenkopf, H., "Oxygen Precipitation and Bulk Microdefects Induced by the Pre- and Postepitaxial Annealing in N/N+(100) Silicon Wafers", Journal of Applied Physics, Vol. 62, 15 December 1987, pp.4897-4902.

[13] Jastrzebski, L., Soydan, R., McGinn, J., Kleppinger, R., Blumenfeld, M., Gillespie, G., Armour, N., Goldsmith, B., Henry, W., and Vecrumba, S., "Comparison of Internal Gettering during Bipolar, CMOS, and CCD (High, Medium, Low Temperature) Processes", Journal of Electrochemical Society, Vol.134, No.4, April 87, pp.1018-1025.

[14] Boydston, M.R., Gruber, G.A., and Gupta, D.C., "Effects of Processing Parameters on Shallow Surface Depressions During Silicon Epitaxial Deposition", Silicon Processing, Gupta, D.C., ed., American Society for Testing and Materials, ASTM STP 804, 1983, pp.174-189.

[15] Wright Jenkins, M., "A New Preferential Etch for Defects in Silicon Crystals", Journal of Electrochemical Society, Vol. 124, No. 5, May 1977, pp.757-762.

[16] Zerbst, M., Zeitschrift fuer Angewandten Physik, Vol. 22, 1966, pp.948.

[17] Wijaranakula, W., Matlock, J.H., and Mollenkopf, H., "Effect of Post-Annealing on the Oxygen Precipitation and Internal Gettering Process in N/N+(100) Epitaxial Wafers", to be published in the Journal of Electrochemical Society.

[18] Maher, D.M., Staudinger, A., and Patel, J.R., "Characterization of Structural Defects in Annealed Silicon Containing Oxygen", Journal of Applied Physics, Vol.47, No.9, September 1976, pp.3813-25.

[19] Wada, K., Takaoka, H., Inoue, N., and Kohra, K., "Growth of Stacking Faults by Bardeen-Herring Mechanism in Czochralski Silicon", Japanese Journal of Applied Physics, Vol.18, No.8, 1979, pp.1629-30.

[20] Rozgonyi, G.A., Jaccodine, R.J., and Pearce, C.W., "Oxygen Precipitation Effects in Degenerately - Doped Silicon", in Defects in Semiconductors II, Mahajan, S. and Corbett, J.W., Eds., Materials Research Society, 1983, pp.181-185.

[21] Wijaranakula, W., Matlock, J.H., and Mollenkopf, H., "The Role of Antimony on Oxygen Precipitation and Formation of Defect-Free Denuded Zone in Epitaxial Substrate Wafers", submitted for publication in Advanced Materials for ULSI, Scott, M., Akasaka, Y., and Reif, R., The Electrochemical Society, 1988.

[22] Reed-Hill, R.E., "Physical Metallurgy Principles", Second Edition, D. Van Nortrand Company, New York, 1973.

[23] Murray, E.M., "Denuded Zone Formation in p<100> Silicon", Journal of Applied Physics, Vol. 55, No. 2, 15 January 1984, pp.536-541.

[24] Rossi, J.A., Dyson, W., Hellwig, L.G., and Hanley, T.M., "Defect Density Reduction in Epitaxial Silicon", Journal of Applied Physics, Vol.58, No.5, 1 September 1985, pp.1798-1802.

[25] Osburn, C.M. and Ormond, D.W., "Dielectric Breakdown in Silicon Dioxide Films on Silicon: I. Measurement and Interpretation", Journal of Electrochemical Society, Vol. 119, No.3, March 1972, pp.591-597.

[26] Osburn, C.M. and Ormond, D.W., "Dielectric Breakdown in Silicon Dioixde Films on Silicon: II. Influence of Processing and Materials", Journal of Electrochemical Society, Vol. 119, No.3, March 1972, pp.597-603.

[27] Dyson, W and Makovsky, "N/N$^+$ Epitaxial Silicon Lifetime Dependence on Epitaxial and Substrate Resistivity", an "Extended Abstracts", Vol.87-2, Electrochem.Soc., Pennington, 1987,p.988.

[28] Nicollian, E.H. and Brews, J.R., "MOS (Metal Oxide Semiconductor) Physics and Technology", John Wiley & Sons, New York, 1982.

[29] Tsui, R.K., Curless, J.A., Secco d'Aragona, F., and Fejes, P.L., "The Effects of Substrate Oxygen Content and Preannealing on the Properties of Silicon Epitaxial Layers, Journal of Electrochemical Society, Vol.131, No.1, January 1984, pp.180-185.

Albert Derheimer, S. Takamizawa , John H. Matlock, and Howard Mollenkopf

ELECTRICAL CHARACTERIZATION OF ELECTRICALLY ACTIVE SURFACE CONTAMI-
NANTS BY EPITAXIAL ENCAPSULATION

REFERENCE: Derheimer, A., Takamizawa, S., Matlock, J., and Mollenkopf, H. "Electrical Characterization of Electrically Active Surface Contaminants by Epitaxial Encapsulation", Semiconductor Fabrication : Technology and Metrology, ASTM STP 990, Dinesh C. Gupta, editor, American Society for Testing and Materials, 1989.

ABSTRACT: Electrically active contaminants have been successfully detected on the surface of substrates using an
epitaxial layer for encapsulation. P-type <100> wafers were
deliberately contaminated with phosphorus and aluminum. The
substrates were then subjected to a modified epitaxial
growth cycle to preserve the contaminant on the surface
High frequency C-V dopant profiles were performed, and
electrically active contaminants were detected.

KEYWORDS: CV method, epitaxial encapsulation, contaminants,
Schottky diode, depletion layer width, semiconductor

INTRODUCTION

With the emphasis in the semiconductor field on MOS devices in
VLSI, it has become necessary to maintain tight control on the
resistivity of the material on, or near the surface. This is
essential to keep the characteristics of implant devices, such as
junction capacitances, threshold voltages, and the like, well
defined. These parameters can be greatly affected by impurities on
the wafer surface, especially those that are electrically active.

Mr. Derheimer is the Electrical Characterization R and D Engineer,
Dr. Mollenkopf is the manager of Materials Characterization R and D,
and Dr. Matlock is the Vice-President of Technology at SEH America,
4111 NE 112th Ave., Vancouver Wash. 98682-6776. Mr. Takamizawa is
Technical Service Manager at Shin Etsu Handotai Company, LDT, Isobe,
Annaka, Gunma 379-01, Japan.

In an effort to characterize electrically active surface contaminants on semiconductive material, one would prefer a technique that is sensitive, rapid, and straight forward to analyze. Such a technique should distinguish between the type of dopant the contaminating species represent, and also provide information about the concentration, depth of penetration into the material surface, as well as lend itself to well established methods of electrical characterization for the purpose of precisely identifying the unknown species.

Secondary Ion Mass Spectroscopy (SIMS), Ion Scattering Spectroscopy (ISS), Rutherford Backscattering Spectroscopy (RBS), and charged particle induced nuclear reaction analysis (NRA) are examples of proven methods for detecting and characterizing surface contaminants, while SIMS and RBS are also capable of providing depth profiling of the same sample.

Capacitance - Voltage measurement techniques (CV) are most useful for determining the concentration of contaminants within the bulk of a semiconductor, as well as producing a dopant profile of the semiconductor. The minimun depth of profiling and the effect of the extrinsic Debye screening length will unfortunately place limitations on the use of a diffused p-n junction or a Schottky barrier diode as a test structure in the C-V method.

An alternate method using a MOS capacitor has been demonstrated by Ziegler, Klausmann, and Dar [1], which would permit analysis to the SiO_2/Si interface. However, this would require thermal processing which could cause excess diffusion of surface impurities.

In this paper, we present a capacitance technique which has been used in the past in determining dopant profiles after ion implantation, and to study the diffusivity of various species in semiconductors [2]. It will be demonstrated here, that the same technique can be used to study electrically active surface contaminants. This method, which we will call Epitaxial Encapsulation Capacitance - Voltage (EECV) has been demonstrated to be fast, reliable, and relatively economical, making it highly useful as a material acceptance test at the front end of a device fabrication process.

In Section II, a brief review of conventional C-V will be given. The fabrication of the test device, and the experimental procedure will be addressed in Section III, and representative examples of data on several silicon samples will be presented in Section IV. Finally, in Section V, a summary of the contents of the paper will be given.

THEORY

In order to explain EECV, one must consider conventional C-V methods. One must also consider the assumptions which were made to obtain the final derivation of the doping profile equations, and the results if these constraints were removed to address abrupt changes in dopant concentration.

Because much work has been done in the past [3, 4, 5, 6] to derive the dopant profile, only a brief overview will be given here.

It will be assumed that a n-type semiconductor is uniformly doped to a concentration much greater than the intrinsic carrier concentration as indicated by equation (1).

$$N_D \gg n_i \qquad\qquad\qquad (1)$$

It will also be assumed that the donor impurities are completely ionized.

With the deposition of a suitable metal, to form a Schottky barrier diode, a depletion region will be generated under the contact. Figure 1a shows the band bending and the charge distribution for a Schottky barrier diode. Figure 1b depicts a two dimensional Schottky barrier diode with the depletion region. Here N^+ is equal to Q_{sc}, the semiconductor charge density.

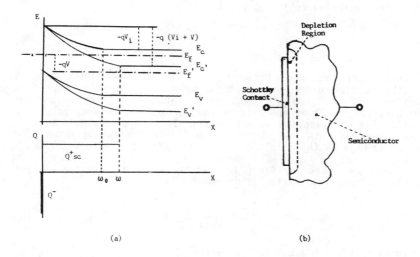

(a)   (b)

Figure 1. (a) Band bending and charge distribution with, and without external biasing potential.   (b) Schottky barrier diode with exaggerated depletion width and edge effect. (No external bias applied)

As usual, it is necessary to solve Poisson's equation:

$$\frac{\partial^2 \phi (x)}{\partial x^2} = \frac{-\rho}{\epsilon} \tag{2}$$

where ρ is the space charge density, and $\epsilon = \epsilon_{sc} \epsilon_0$ Here ϵ_{sc} is the dielectric constant of the semiconductor, and ϵ_0 is the permittivity of free space.

If $0 < X < \omega_0$, the charge density in the depletion region is

$$\rho = qN^+ \tag{3}$$

where   is equal to the charge density. Outside the depletion region, the semiconductor is in equilibrium. If equation (3) is inserted into equation (2), and the results integrated twice with respect to x, equation (4) is obtained.

$$\phi (x) = \frac{-qN^+}{2\epsilon} x^2 \tag{4}$$

The boundary conditions of figure (1a) show that the total potential across the depletion region is V_i, thus

$$V_i = \frac{qN^+}{2\epsilon} \omega_0^2 \tag{5}$$

This points out one of the limitations of a p-n junction or a Schottky barrier diode in C-V measurement. It can be seen from equation (5), that o will not equal zero in a Schottky barrier configuration, and that analysis at the surface can be done only if a forward bias were applied to negate Vi. If this were done one would need to address both the measured capacitance due to the conduction current as well as the displacement current through the test device.

It has been shown by Sze [7], that the minimum depletion - layer width at thermal equilibrium is determined by:

$$\omega_0 = \left[\frac{2\epsilon}{qN^+} \left(V_i - \frac{2kT}{q} \right) \right]^{\frac{1}{2}} \tag{6}$$

For an example, if $N^+ \approx 2.5 \times 10^{14}$ atom/cm^3, T = 300° K, and $V_i \approx .6$ volts, then equation 6 yields a minimum depletion width of 2 μm.

In order to overcome the minimum depth limitation of 2 μm produced by the built-in voltage, an epitaxial layer with the same type of dopant and similar resistivity was grown onto the contaminated front surface of the specimen. By choosing an epitaxial thickness greater than the largest expected, zero bias, depletion layer width, it will be possible to look from ω_0' through the interface (Note Figure 2).

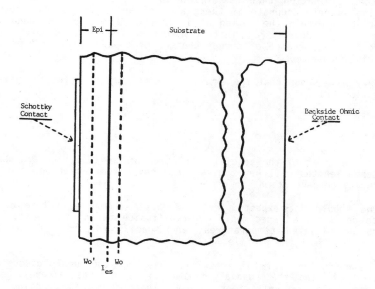

Figure 2. Specimen with EPI layer grown on the contaminated surface. Ies is the location of the EPI/substrate interface, and ω_0 and ω_0' is the location of the zero bias depletion depth for a Schottky contact on the substrate and EPI, respectively.

At the same time, the capacitance across the junction will be

$$C_{sc} = \frac{\varepsilon A}{\omega_0} \tag{7}$$

where A is the area of the Schottky Contact. This assumes that the radius of the device is at least 2 orders of magnitude greater than the width of the depletion region, reducing the edge effect.

Now, if an incremental voltage ΔV is applied across the junction which causes an increase in the depletion width ($\omega_0 +\Delta \omega$), the dopant concentration can be determined by equation (8):

$$N = \frac{2}{\varepsilon q A^2} \left(\frac{\partial^1 / C_{sc}^2}{\partial v} \right)^{-1} \tag{8}$$

and the depletion depth from equation (9) will yield

$$\omega = \frac{\varepsilon A}{C_{sc}} \tag{9}$$

Again, it must be emphasized, that this solution is applicable to material with a uniform dopant concentration. This presents us with the other limitation that was indicated in the introduction. CV profiling is only accurate if there are no abrupt changes in dopant concentration within the region of interest. Work has been done by Johnson, and Panovsis [8] that illuminates the problem which is created by the presence of abrupt changes of dopant concentration in the region under test.

They have shown that the extrinsic Debye screening length, given in equation (10)

$$\lambda_\eta = \left(\frac{\epsilon kT}{q^2 N} \right)^{\frac{1}{2}} \tag{10}$$

will be the limit of the spacial resolution of the CV method and that five Debye lengths will be required to recover from an abrupt change in impurity concentration.

One should not expect a delta function from the profile of a surface contaminated specimen. Both diffusion during the epitaxial process at elevated temperatures, and spacial response of the CV method will affect the profile.

The diffusion of metal impurities has been thoroughly discussed by Fair [2], and the spacial resolution of CV has already been addressed. It is sufficient to say that thermal processing is essential to diffuse the impurities over greater than   five Debye lengths if quantitative data is to be obtained.

Experimental Procedure

In this experiment silicon specimens were treated under conditions that would enhance the surface contamination with known acceptor and donor inpurities. Immersion in chemical baths produced either aluminum or phosphorus at levels much higher than inherent in the silicon itself.

The starting material was taken from an ingot having a <100> orientation. It was P-Type (Boron doped), with a mean resistivity of 50 -cm. The oxygen content is $\leq$ 30 ppma as per ASTM F121-79, measured at the wafer stage. All specimens were subjected to a RCA cleaning process. [9]

After cleaning, the specimens were subjected to known contaminant sources. In the case of the acceptor impurity, a 2:7 ratio of $NH_4OH:H_2O_2$ was placed in a pyrex bath and held at 80°C. The specimens were then immersed for 30 minutes, followed by D.I. water rinsing and nitrogen blow dry. This produced an aluminum contamination as predicted by Kawado, et.al [10], and verified by SIMS [11] and photoluminescence analysis (P.L.). [12]

In the case of the donor impurity, a Quartz bath was prepared containing 1 Liter of deionized water and $1X10^{-3}$ mliters of 85% concentrated phosphoric acid. This bath was maintained at 23°C throughout the immersion period. The specimens were immersed in the solution for 30 minutes to insure thorough contamination of the surface. Subsequent rinising took place in a flowing D.I. water bath for 10 minutes, followed by a filtered dry nitrogen "blow dry" process.

Where both species were desired a dilute phosphoric acid bath was prepared in a pyrex container, and held at 40°C.

Verification of the presence of phosphorus was also performed independently by PL analysis.

Upon drying, the specimens were subjected to a CVD epitaxial silicon process cycle which was modified to preserve the condition of the contaminated surface.

This growth cycle was performed with the elimination of any pregrowth in-situ cleaning step, to avoid stripping the impurity from the surface. Such steps usually are performed with the injection of HCl while the reactor is held at the growth temperature to prepare the specimen for deposition. With many elements being reactive with HCl, the contaminant could be reduced or removed by the presence of the gaseous reactant in the cycle.

The cycle consisted of a room temperature purge in dry Nitrogen followed by Hydrogen. This was followed by a ramp to a growth temperature of 1130° C. This temperature was selected to optimize crystal quality while reducing the surface impurity diffusion and evaporation. Deposition of the epitaxial layer by hydrogen reduction of trichlorosilane proceeded immediately after the specimen had equilibrated at the growth temperature, and continued until the desired EPI thickness of 10 μm was obtained. The growth rate was on the order of 1 μm/minute.

As indicated, the total cycle time was kept to a minimum to reduce the time of diffusion of the surface impurities.

It is also during the growth cycle that activation of surface impurities take place. The electrically active contaminants are now detectable by CV methods.

Creation of the Schottky barrier diode was done after the specimen was precleaned by immersion in a solution of $NH_4OH-H_2O_2-H_2O$ for 10 minutes, followed by a dilute $HF-H_2O$ etch to remove the native oxide. The specimen was then rinsed for 10 minutes in flowing deionized water, and dry nitrogen blow dried.

Metal deposition was performed by resistance heating evaporation, at a pressure lower than $3x10^{-6}$ Torr, thru a non-contact shadow mask. The contact diameter was 2000 μm ± 20 μm. Because the specimen is P-type, Samarium was used with a barrier height of χ .85 eV [13, 14].

When using Samarium, electrical testing should be performed immediately after deposition, because of the high oxidation rate of this metal at room temperature in air.

CV testing was performed using a standard CV system with computer interface to transpose the data into a dopant profile with no corrections in the software for abrupt transitions.

DISCUSSION

Specimen With Aluminum Impurity

A typical representative of a specimen which was deliberately contaminated with aluminum is shown in Figure 3. The epitaxial film thickness was measured on a monitor wafer, and was found to be 10.6 μm. The dopant concentration of the substrate and the epitaxial film were nearly matched at 3×10^{14} atom/cm^3 and 2.3×10^{14} atom/cm^3 respectively.

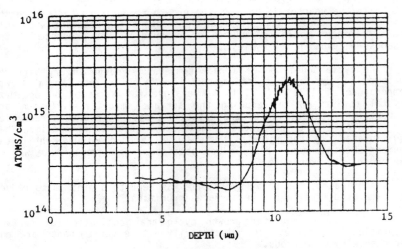

Figure 3. Specimen deliberately contaminated with aluminum.

It is possible to obtain an estimation of the dose of aluminum at the original surface by assuming that the impurity has a Gaussian distribution about the interface, and that a non contaminated interface can be represented by a Complementary Error Function as discribed by Grove, Roder, and Sah [15], and given in equation (11)

$$N = \frac{Q_D}{2\sqrt{\pi D t}} \, \exp\left(\frac{-x^2}{4Dt}\right) \qquad (11)$$

and (12), respectively.

$$N = N_f + \tfrac{1}{2} N_s \quad . \quad erfc \left[\frac{x}{2(Dt)^{\frac{1}{2}}} \right] \qquad (12)$$

with t=20 minutes, X=0 (at the interface), D=.024 μ^2/min, and considering equation (12) to represent the baseline, an approximate value of Q=6.7X10^{11} atom/cm^2 is obtained. A simple integration of the area under that portion of the curve in Figure (2) which represents the aluminum peak yields a surface concentration of Q=5.4X10^{11} atom/cm^2. (Simpsons rule). [16]

In order to verify that this peak is primarily due to the surface contaminant, a control specimen with no surface contamination was prepared. It can be seen in Figure (4) that no abrupt transition exist at the epitaxial/substrate interface. This verifies the absence of significant surface contamination.

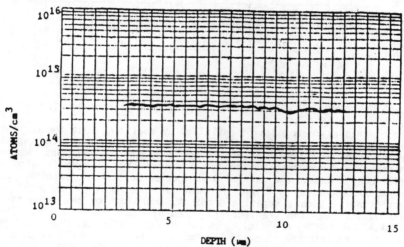

Figure 4. Doping profile of uncontaminated specimen.

The limit of detectability is therefore set at the noise level of the C-V system, which is on the level of 1X10^9 atom/cm^2.

Specimens With Phosphorus Impurity

The phosphorus contaminated specimens presented a different signature.

As indicated in Figure (5), the abrupt change in dopant concentration is asymetrical. The epitaxial film thickness was determined by a monitor wafer to be 10µm thick. A near matching of the substrate and epitaxial film dopant concentration, 3.2×10^{14} and 2.1×10^{14} atom/cm^3 respectively, was obtained.

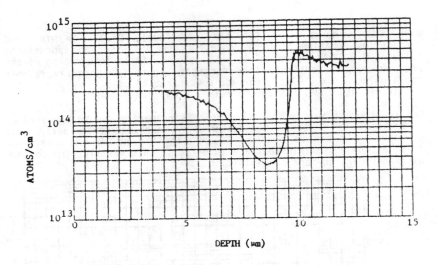

Figure 5. Specimen deliberately contaminated with phosphorus.

Some of this asymmetry can be explained by realizing that the carrier distribution in a region containing an abrupt change in dopant concentration will be different from a region of constant dopant concentration when that region is CV tested [8]. There is also a difference in dopant and carrier distribution depending on whether the dopant concentration gradient is negative (decreasing) or positive (increasing). With a negative gradient, the slope of the transition is shallower than the gradient predicted by equations 7 and 8. The opposite holds for a positive dopant concentration gradient. This would help explain the shape of the abrupt transition in Figure 5, but it does not explain the apparent inability of the phosphorus to diffuse into the substrate. Therefore, only a simple integration of the area under the curve (Simpson's rule) was possible for determining the dose of the contaminant. This was calculated to be 6.33×10^{10} atom/cm^2.

Specimen With Al and P Contaminants

The specimen containing both contaminants shows even an increased complexity. However, even under this condition, the existence of both contaminants are detectable, as can be seen in Figure 6.

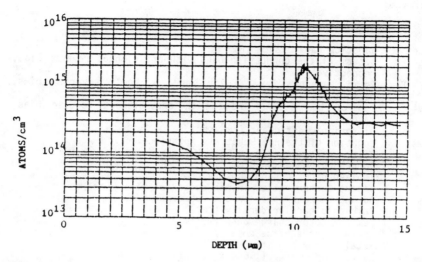

Figure 6.   Specimen deliberately contaminated with aluminum and phosphorus.

Any attempt to obtain quantitative data on each of the contaminants, would be ill advised because of the diffusion of the aluminum into the epitaxial film.

SUMMARY

It has been shown that electrically active contaminants, when permitted to come in contact with the surface of a polished, single crystal semiconductor, can be detected by standard CV technique after an epitaxial layer, matching the type and resistivity of the substrate, has been deposited. It is sufficient to use a Schottky barrier diode to establish the necessary criteria to perform a dopant profile test across the region of interest.

This test is economical, and fast. And, though it presently lacks precision in providing quantitative data, it can be used as a dependable monitor to control the quality of wafer surfaces.

ACKNOWLEDGMENTS: The authors wish to thank K. Mitani, and M. Boydston for the preparation of the EPI samples.

SYMBOLS:

C_{sc}	Junction capacitance (F)
E_c^1, E_c	Bottom of the conduction band with and without reverse bias, respectively.
E_F^1, E_F	Fermi energy level with and without reverse bias, respectively.
E_v^1, E_v	Top of the valance band with and without reverse bias, respectively.
D	Diffusion Coefficient (cm^2/sec)
I_{es}	Location of the EPI/Substrate interface.
k	Boltzmann's constant (8.62×10^{-5} eV/°)
N	Donor doping density (cm^{-3})
N^+	Ionized donor doping density (cm^{-3})
N	Dopant Concentration in the epitaxial film ($/cm^3$)
N_s	Dopant Concentration in the substrate ($/cm^3$)
n_i	Intrinsic carrier density (cm^{-3})
Q_{sc}	Semiconductor charge density (cm^{-3})
Q	Contaminant surface dose ($/cm^2$)
Q^-	Metal charge density (cm^{-3})
q	Electronic charge (1.602×10^{-19}c)
T	Temperature (°k)
V	External bias potential (V)
V_i	Built-in polential (V)
x	Linear displacement (cm)
ε_0	Permittivity constant (8.854×10^{-14} F/cm)
ε_{Si}	Relative permittivity of Silicon (11.9)
λ_n	Extrinsic Debye screening length (cm)
ω	Depletion length under reverse bias (cm)
ω_0, ω_0^1	Minimum depletion-layer width into the substrate and the EPI layer, respectively.
$\phi(x)$	Electrostatic potential as a function of displacement (V)
ρ	Net charge density (c/cm^3)

REFERENCES

[1]   Ziegler, K., Klausmann, E., and Dar, S.,"Determination of the Semiconductor Doping Profile Right Up to its Surface using the MIS Capacitor", Solid State Electronics, Vol 18, 1975, p 189.
[2]   Wang, F.F.Y., "Impurity Doping Processes in Silicon", North-Holland, New York, 1981
[3]   Gelder, V. W. and Nicollian, E. H., "Silicon Impurity Distribution as Revealed by Pulsed MOS C-V Measurements", Journal of Electrochemical Society, Vol. 118, 1971, p.138.
[4]   Hilibrand, J. and Gold, R. D., "Determination of Impurity Distribution in Junction Diodes from Capacitance - Voltage Measurements", RCA Review, Vol. 21, 1960, p 245.
[5]   Kennedy, D. P., Murley, P. C., and Kleinfelder, W., IBM Journal Research and Development, Vol. 12, 1968, p 399.

[6]   Brews, J. R., "Correcting Interface-State Errors in MOS Doping Profile Determinations", Journal of Applied Physics, Vol. 44, 1973, p 3228.

[7]   Sze, S. M., "Physics of Semiconductors", Wiley-Interscience New York

[8]   Johnson, W. C. and Panovsis, P. T., "The Influence of Debye Length on the C-V Measurement of Doping Profile", I.E.E.E. Transactions on Electron Devices, Vol. ED-18, 1971, p 965.

[9]   Kern, W., "New Process Technologies for Microelectronics", RCA Review, Vol. 31, No. 2, June, 1970, pg. 185

[10] Kawado, S., Tanigaki, T., Maruyama, T., Yamazaki, M., Nishima, O., and Oka, Y., "SIMS Analysis of Aluminmum Contaminants on Silicon Surfaces", Semiconductor Silicon 1986, H.R. Huff, T. Abe, B. Kolbesen, Eds., The Electrochemical Society, Vol. 86-4, 1986, p989.

[11] Abe, T., SEH Japan, 1985, Unpublished

[12] Mollenkopf, H., SEH America, 1987, Unpublished

[13] Nipoti, R., Garrido, J. and Guerri, S., "Samarium as a Schottky Barrier on P-Type Silicon", Solid State Electronics, Vol. 29, No. 12, 1986, p 1267.

[14] Katsuhiko, M. and Naosato, Y., "Determination of Impurity Distribution in P-Type Si Epitaxial Layers by C-V Analysis of Sm on P-Type Si Schottky Diodes", Japanese Journal of Applied Physics, Vol.23, No. 5, 1984, p L336.

[15] Grove, A. S., Roder, A. and Sah, C. T., "Impurity Distribution in Epitaxial Growth", Journal of Applied Physics, Vol. 36, No. 3, 1965, p 802.

[16] Wylie, C.R., Barret, L.C., "Advanced Engineering Mathematics", fifth edition, McGraw Hill pg. 265

Gabriella Borionetti, Marcello Domenici, Giancarlo
Ferrero

OPTIMUM POLYSILICON DEPOSITION ON WAFER BACKS FOR GETTERING PURPOSES

REFERENCE: Borionetti, G.,Domenici, M., Ferrero,
G., "Optimum Polysilicon Deposition on Wafer
Backs for Gettering Purposes," Semiconductor Fabrication: Technology and Metrology, ASTM STP
990, Dinesh C.Gupta, editor, American Society
for Testing and Materials, 1989.

ABSTRACT: Polysilicon deposition process parameters have been addressed for the preparation of
poly layers having characteristics that increase
extrinsic gettering behaviour, irrespective of
oxygen enhanced precipitation, thus making them
particularly suitable for relatively high device
processing temperatures.
Morphological parameters that correlate with extrinsic gettering efficiency have been found to
be grain sizes and their preferred orientation,
so care was given to produce and consistently
reproduce such characteristics by a suitable
choice of the deposition process parameters.

KEYWORDS: gettering, polysilicon layer, CVD,
Oxygen precipitation, polysilicon
structure.

INTRODUCTION

In the present VLSI Era attention is ·more and more
devoted to reducing unwanted impurities in silicon wafer
device area which adversely affect the performance of
microdevices.

This result can be obtained by avoiding impurities introduced in silicon wafers (that is by improving "clean"
processes) or/and by building up in silicon wafers defective regions far from the active device zones where
the impurities can migrate and be captured during thermal device processing.

The authors work in Research and Development Department of DNS Electronic Materials, Viale Gherzi 31,
28100 Novara (ITALY).

400

This second approach is called impurity "gettering".
Historically it has been accomplished by extrinsic gettering in which the wafer back side is subjected to a
process that creates a disordered region (1-3) (mechanical damage, laser induced damage, ion implantation damage).
More recently intrinsic gettering (4-6), due to oxygen
precipitates grown after particular thermal cycles, 20-
30 μ beneath the front surface, has been developed.

This paper is concerned with a particular extrinsic gettering scheme developed recently (7-9) consisting of a
polycristalline silicon layer deposited on the backside
of the silicon wafer.

The purpose of this work has been to explore the correlation between the main structural characteristics of
the polysilicon layer deposited by Low Pressure Chemical
Vapour Deposition (LPCVD) technique and gettering efficiency.

Particularly this study has focused on the relationships
among the following set of parameters:

(a)   PROCESS PARAMETERS
- temperature
- gaseous species, gas flow
- pressure
- geometrical configuration in the reactor chamber

(b)   STRUCTURAL PARAMETERS
- grain size
- preferred orientation

(c)   PERFORMANCE
- gettering efficiency
- mechanical behaviour (warpage)

It has been found that various sets of process parameters may yield films with similar structural characteristics (transition from conditions (a) to (b)). Figures
(1a, b) and (2a, b) show our results in which poly grain
size and preferred orientation change not only with temperature but for instance with SiH_4 partial pressure at
constant T; i.e. by playing with different combinations
of process parameters, similar poly structure can be obtained. The detailed conditions of these measurements
will be discussed in the next section.

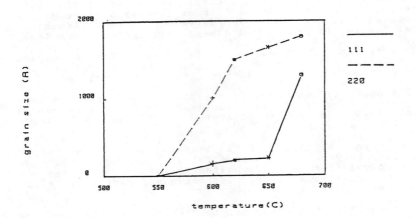

FIG.1a -- Poly grain size versus deposition temperature. SiH₄ partial pressure = 300 mT
See next table 2 for definition of symbols (+,■,* □)

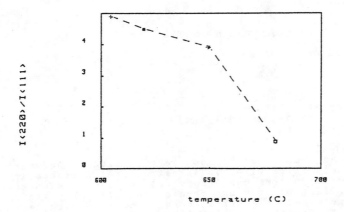

FIG.1b -- Poly preferred orientation versus deposition temperature. SiH₄ partial pressure = 300 mT
See next table 2 for definition of symbols (+,■,*,□)

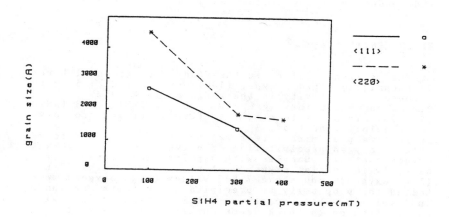

FIG.2a -- Poly grain size versus SiH4 partial pressure.
Deposition temperature = 680°C

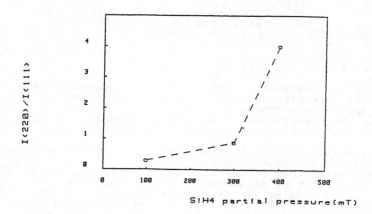

FIG.2b -- Poly preferred orientation versus SiH4
partial pressure. Deposition temperature = 680°C .

This work intends to show the correlation between conditions (b) and (c): gettering and mechanical performance seems to be determined by polysilicon morphology, almost independently of the process used to reach it.

EXPERIMENTAL

The silicon wafers in the study were grown with the Cz technique, doped P type, (100) orientation, 125 mm in diameter, resistivity in the range of 25-45 Ωcm.
Oxygen concentrations were always below $7 \cdot E17$ cm-3 (ASTM F121-83). This was to minimize effects arising from oxygen precipitation (10).
In fact, a preliminary test was performed in order to evaluate oxygen precipitation of polyback samples versus oxygen content. Samples with a polysilicon layer on the back, with initial oxygen content values below $7 \cdot E17$ (low oxygen) and above $7 \cdot E17$ values (high oxygen) were tested for propensity to precipitate. Results are shown in table 1, which suggests that low oxygen wafers with polysilicon on the back show negligible precipitation within the range studied here.
Polysilicon deposition was performed in LPCVD reactor on the chemical etched surfaces of both sides of the wafers; a subsequent polishing step removes the film on the front side. The polysilicon thickness on all the samples was about 1.3μ measured by an automatic interferometer system on previously oxidized monitor wafers processed in the same run. Tab.2 shows the deposition conditions of the samples and the structural results obtained by X.ray diffraction (powder method).
Preferred orientation is expressed as I (220)/I (111), the ratio of peak intensities for the (220) and (111) reflections. (The ASTM ratio for randomly oriented polysilicon is 0.6). Grain sizes were determined from the peak width using a suitable algorithm (11). The structural results are already shown in the previous figures (1a, 1b).
Wafer warpage induced by polysilicon layer deposition on the backside has been determined as the difference between warpage before deposition and after polishing. Measurements have been done by a capacitive instrument and the sign (+ or -) has been determined by a laser optical system.
Gettering efficiency has been evaluated by the Palladium Test and the Drift test.
In the Palladium test procedure (12) the wafer is contaminated by scratching the backside in a point with Palladium and diffusing it at high temperature (1100°C). The diameter of the circular haze area after decoration etching of poly deposited samples and undeposited reference samples are measured so that a quantitative evaluation of Palladium atoms trapped by the poly can be deduced using the Palladium diffusion curve.

TABLE 1 -- Oxygen precipitation on poly back sample [a]

Samples	[Oi] initial (10E17 at/cc)		[Oi] final (10E17 at/cc)		Δ_{oi} (10E17 at/cc)
	$\bar{X}$	S(n-1)	$\bar{X}$	S(n-1)	
Low oxygen	5.45	0.12	5.32	0.19	0.13
High oxygen	7.34	0.35	2.87	1	4.47

a) Precipitation cycle is at T = 1000°C   t = 15 h, nucleation cycle is substituted by poly-silicon deposition cycle.
No. of samples each group: 10
Ambient gas: N_2

TABLE 2 -- Process conditions and strucutral results

Samples Label	Deposition Temperature (°C)	SiH4 partial pressure (mT)	Deposition rate (A/min)	$\frac{I(220)}{I(111)}$	Average <111>	Grain Size (A) <220>
	550	300	22	amorphous	structure	
◄	580	300	40	0.2	800	800
+	600	300	55	4.9	150	1000
■	620	300	100	4.9	200	1500
*	650	300	180	3.9	220	1650
□	680	300	250	0.9	1300	1800

According to the drift test procedure wafers are subjected to a similar thermal cycle without any intentional
contamination and the content of the electrically active
impurities coming from not "clean" processes diffused in
silicon wafers is determined by a change in resistivity
(13).

RESULTS AND DISCUSSION

A decrease in warp is seen to correlate with an increase in grain size and with a reduction in preferred
orientation along the (220) direction as shown in fig.
(4a, b).

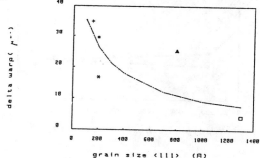

FIG.4a -- Delta warp versus poly grain size
          See table 2 for definition of symbols
          (+,■,*, □)

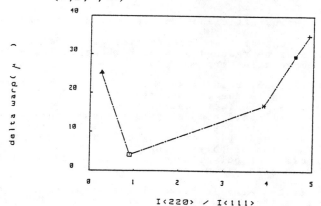

FIG.4b -- Delta warp versus poly preferred orientation
          See table 2 for definition of symbols
          (+,■,*, □)

Polysilicon stress changes from tensile to compressive on passing from 580°C to 600°C deposition temperature. Experimental data labelled with full triangle are related to polysilicon with tensile stress.

Fig. 5 illustrates the observed improvement of gettering efficiency measured by Palladium and drift test with decreasing grain size.

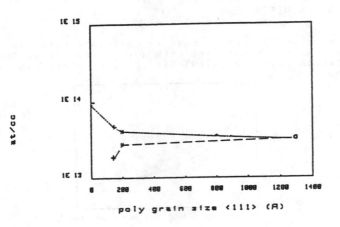

Donor impurities concentration measured by drift test.

Pd atoms trapped in poly layer (Palladium test)

FIG.5 -- Gettering efficiency versus poly grain size

These results suggest that for practical applications a compromise must be reached between high gettering efficiency and acceptable warp.

Gettering efficiency results seem to indicate that polysilicon gettering is due to impurity segregation at the grain boundaries. In fact smaller grain size with minimum preferred orientation develops a maximum intergrain surface area. To support this hypothesis two different tests were performed: (1) gettering efficiency was measured as a function of polysilicon thickness; and, (2) the depth profile of polysilicon samples intentionally contamined with gold was measured by SIMS.

Fig.6 illustrates the increase of gettering efficiency (expressed in gettered Pd atoms) with film thickness: saturation seems to take place at about 1.5μ thickness. Polysilicon deposited at 680°C was chosen for this gettering evaluation because of its low contribution to warpage.

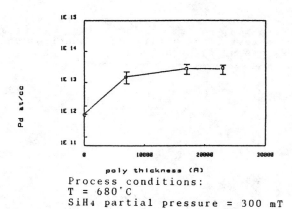

Process conditions:
T = 680°C
SiH₄ partial pressure = 300 mT

FIG.6 -- Gettered Pd atoms concentration versus poly
        thickness.

To see exactly where the impurities are trapped a wafer
with polysilicon on the back deposited at 680°C was intentionally contamined with gold evaporated on the backside and submitted to a Au diffusion heat treatment (T
= 1150°C, t = 4h).

SIMS analysis suggests that upon heat treatment the gold
atoms migrated and got trapped within the poly film as
shown in fig.7.   Also here a starting saturation seems
to appears at the left hand side of Au curve.

CONCLUSIONS

     It has been shown that the relevant parameters that
enable one to maximize the gettering efficiency by polysilicon layer deposition are structural parameters that
can be obtained in more than a single CVD process recipe.   It has also been shown that increasing the poly
layer thickness beyond a certain saturation value is u-
seless and, instead, care has to be taken to reduce the
grain size to develop a higher intergrain surface area
responsible for the impurity trapping phenomenon.
Finally it has been made evident how impurity trapping
takes place throughout the poly layer thickness starting
from the poly/single crystal interface with a tendency
to diminish only at the "saturation" thickness.

Work will be continued by using the described techniques
in order to follow the gettering phenomenon in simulated
and actual thermal process steps for manufacturing typical devices: it is expected that those steps will influence both morphological parameters and gettering ac-
tions.

Note added in proof :.   a work on the effect of
Silane pressure on polysilicon structure was recently
published by Joubert et at. (14) which confirms our results and comments of figures 1-2.

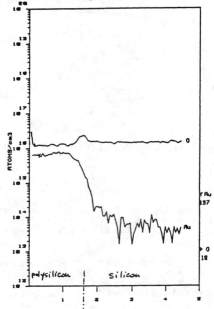

FIG.7 -- Au depth profile in polysilicon on the back
sample

ACKNOWLEDGMENTS

    The authors are indebt to Dr. Sukanta Biswas of Sur-
face Analysis Technology Plc for SIMS analysis. This
work was performed under the partial financial support
of Italian CNR

REFERENCES

[1] Goetzberger, A. and Shockley, W., "Metal precipita-
    tes in Silicon p-n- Junctions," <u>Journal of Applied
    Physics</u>, Vol.<u>31</u>, No.10, Oct.1960, pp.1821-1824.

[2]   Cerofolini, G.F. and Polignano, M.L., "A Comparison
      of Gettering Techniques for Very Large Scale Inte-
      gration," Journal of Applied Physics, Vol.55, No.2,
      Jan.1984, pp.579-585

[3]   Wolf, S. and Tamber, R.N., "Silicon Processing for
      the VLSI Era Vol. 1- Process Technology," Lattice
      Press, 1986

[4]   Livingston, F.M., et al "An infrared and neutron
      scattering analysis of the precipitation of oxygen
      in dislocation free Silicon," Solid State Physics,
      Vol.17, pp.6253-6276, 1984.

[5]   Inoue, N., Wada, K. and Osaka, J., "Oxygen Precipi-
      tation in Cz Silicon - Mechanism and Application,"
      Semiconductor Silicon 1981, pp.282-293

[6]   Patrick, W.J., Hu, S.M. and Westdorp, W.A., "The
      effect of SiO$_2$ precipitation in Si on generation
      currents in MOS capacitors," Journal of Applied
      Physics, Vol.50, Mar. 1979, pp.1399-1402.

[7]   Stacy, W.T., Arst, M.C., Ritz, K.N., de Groot, J.C.
      and Noicott, M.H., "The Microstructure of Polysili-
      con Back surface Gettering," Semiconductor Silicon
      1983, pp.423-432

[8]   Arst, M.C. and de Groot, J.G., "Increased Oxygen
      Precipitation in Cz Silicon Wafers covered by Poly-
      silicon" Journal of Electronic Material, Vol. 13,
      No.5, 1984, pp.736,778.

[9]   Hu, S.M., "Method of gettering using backside poly-
      cristalline silicon" U.S.Patent   Oct.11,   1977,
      N°4053335

[10] Herng Der Chian, "Oxygen precipitation behaviour
      and Control in Silicon Crystals," Solid State Te-
      chnology, Mar. 1987, pp-77,81.

[11] Cullity, B., "Elements of X-ray diffraction," Addi-
      son Wesley, 1978

[12] Graff, K., Hefner, A. and Pieper, H., "Palladium
      test: A tool to evaluate gettering efficiency," Ma-
      terial Research Society Symposium   Proceedings,
      Vol.36, 1985, pp.20-24.

[13] Domenici, M., Malinverni, P. and Pedrotti, M., "Pu-
      rification and Impurity Detection in Silicon for
      Microelectronics," Journal of Crystal Growth, Vol.
      75, 1986, pp.80-87.

[14] Joubert, P., Loisel, B., Chouan, Y. and Haji, L.,
      "The effect of Low Pressure on the Structure of
      LPCVD Polycristalline Silicon Films", Journal of E-
      lectrochemical Society, Vol. 134, Oct.1987,
      pp.2541-2545.

Control Charts, Standards, and Specifications

David J. Friedman

MODIFICATION OF CONTROL CHARTS FOR USE IN AN INTEGRATED CIRCUIT
FABRICATION ENVIRONMENT

REFERENCE: Friedman, D. J., "Modification of Control Charts for Use
in an Integrated Circuit Fabrication Environment," Semiconductor
Fabrication: Technology and Metrology, ASTM STP 990, Dinesh C. Gupta,
editor, American Society for Testing and Materials, 1989.

ABSTRACT: For on-line statistical process control to be effective, it is necessary to
correctly specify the distribution of the process generating the defects. Manufacturing and
assembly operations have traditionally assumed measurement data to follow the normal
distribution and defect data to follow the Poisson distribution. This paper will discuss the
Integrated Circuit manufacturing industry, where the Poisson distribution assumption is
known to be false. Suggestions will be made on how to modify existing control charts to
allow for the clustering effects known to occur in IC manufacturing. By modifying
control charts which assume the Poisson distribution, the same procedures and
interpretations may be used in many cases: only the sample size or control limits would
change. With other control charts however, significant clustering precludes their use.

KEYWORDS: Quality control, clustered defects

When defects are quantified on a control chart, the Poisson distribution is
generally assumed. This is a particularly appealing assumption in integrated circuit
manufacture, since wafers are already partitioned into discretized units, each of which will
either pass or fail functional tests. A situation thus appears to exist in which an inspector
is summing a series of independent binomial trials. If the trials are independent and if the
probability of failure is small, for a sufficiently large sample of chips the Poisson
assumption is valid. Unfortunately, it is well known ([1] and [2]) that defects in integrated
circuit fabrication tend to cluster. The clustering implies a lack of independence among
chips thus invalidating the use of the Poisson distribution. As an alternative to the Poisson
distribution, use of the Neyman Type-A distribution has been suggested.

THE NEYMAN DISTRIBUTION

The Neyman Type-A distribution [3] as a distribution in the class generally called
'contagious' distributions. These distributions all assume clustering; the Neyman

David J. Friedman is a Member of Technical Staff at AT&T Bell Labs, 600 Mountain Ave.,
Murray Hill, NJ 07974

distribution assumes the number of clusters is distributed as a Poisson random variable, with the number of defects within each cluster also following the Poisson distribution. The distribution is defined by:

$$P_k(\lambda,\phi)=Pr\,[X=k]=\sum_{j=1}^{\infty}e^{-\lambda}\frac{\lambda^j}{j!}e^{-j\phi}\frac{(j\phi)^k}{k!} \qquad (k>0)$$

and

$$P_0(\lambda,\phi)=Pr\,[X=0]=e^{-\lambda(1-e^{-\phi})}$$

where X is a discrete and unbounded random variable. The relation between the Neyman distribution and IC manufacturing can best be seen by visualizing a wafer as having imperfections of various types on the wafer surface. These imperfections (scratches, particles, problems with the reticle, etc.) may cause either single chips to fail (as is often the case with particulate problems) or cause groups of adjacent chips to fail (as is the case with scratches). If it is assumed that there are a Poisson number of defect sources, with mean λ, and each source contains a Poisson number of bad chips, with mean ϕ, the Neyman distribution is appropriate.

The Neyman distribution has a mean of $\lambda\phi$ and a variance of $\lambda\phi(1+\phi)$. Notice that the variance exceeds the mean by a factor of $(1+\phi)$. Since for the Poisson distribution, the variance equals the mean, it can be said that ϕ is a measure of the extent of clustering in the system (called the 'index of clumping' [4]). As a percentage the inflation of the variance due to clustering is $100\phi\%$, and as the parameter ϕ goes to zero (and the mean is held constant), the Neyman distribution collapses to the Poisson distribution.

Parameter Estimation

The maximum likelihood estimate of the Neyman Type-A distribution is found by solving the following two formulas:

$$n^{-1}\sum_{i=1}^{n}x_i=\hat{\lambda}\hat{\phi}$$

$$\sum_{i=1}^{n}(x_i+1)\frac{P_{x_{i+1}}(\hat{\lambda},\hat{\phi})}{P_{x_i}(\hat{\lambda},\hat{\phi})}=n\hat{\lambda}\hat{\phi}.$$

In practice, the method of moments estimates tend to be used due to their closed form format and easy computation. They are:

$$\hat{\lambda}=\frac{\sum_{i=1}^{n}x_i}{n\hat{\phi}}$$

$$\hat{\phi}=\frac{s^2-\bar{X}}{\bar{X}}$$

For information on these and other estimates see [5].

Example 1:
    The following data was collected during electronic tests run on wafers containing 200 chips per wafer, after photolithography. Each chip was tested and the total number of chips on the wafer failing the test was recorded. The histogram recording the results of 700 wafers is shown, with the fitted Neyman distribution and Poisson distribution superimposed, in Figure 1. As can be seen, the Neyman distribution appears to do a significantly better job of describing the data. A Chi Square Goodness of Fit test confirms this observation: the null hypothesis that the sampled distribution is Poisson is rejected, while the assumption of the Neyman distribution is not. Looking at it as a process control problem: assume a 3 sigma limit was established based on a Poisson distribution assumption. It is expected (if the generating distribution were truly Poisson) that an observation would fall outside the 3 sigma limit with probability 0.00213 (or 2130 parts per million). In fact, the proportion of observations outside this limit is 0.197, or close to 200,000 parts per million.

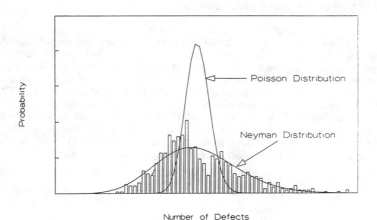

Number of Defects

Figure 1 -- Histogram of IC Defect Data

    Clearly the Poisson distribution is an inappropriate modeling tool in the above example. How to measure the 'appropriateness' of a control chart will be discussed in the following section.

THE USE OF THE AVERAGE RUN LENGTH

    When assessing the effectiveness of a control chart in monitoring an ongoing process, average run length (ARL) is an often used metric. The ARL represents the average number of in-control readings that will be recorded before an out-of-control signal is generated. In a well designed control chart the ARL of any system running under control should be large, but shorten considerably when the system goes out-of-control. This is clearly analogous to establishing limits for Type I and Type II errors. Just as the experimenter would want Type I and Type II errors to both equal zero, the control chart designer would want an in-control system to run forever and an out-of-control system to stop immediately. As with Type I and Type II errors however, there is usually a trade-off based on time and cost considerations between letting a bad system run and stopping a good system. The ARL's in this paper were calculated using the method of [6].

THE USES OF ATTRIBUTE CONTROL CHARTS FOR PROCESS CONTROL

Attribute Control Charts have been effectively used in industry since their introduction more than 40 years ago. They are based on establishing 3 standard deviation limits around the expected performance level of the process. Any observation outside these limits is assumed to be caused by a change in the underlying nature of the process and to have an assignable cause. This will result in an out-of-control signal being generated and the process being stopped.

Use of Attribute Control Chart for Samples of Size 1

The simplest control chart to be discussed is the attribute control chart for samples of size 1 (since the sample size is constant, this is a C-Chart). In this chart, one wafer per lot is inspected and charted. If the total number of defects exceeds the upper control limit (or UCL: the 3 standard deviation limit placed on the process), the process is halted. Since the C-Chart is a memoryless system, the ARL is just the inverse of the Type I error of the system. With reference to example 1, this implies that the expected ARL was 469 (since expected Type I error was 0.00213), but the actual ARL was 5 (since the observed Type I error was 0.197). The implications of this are clear: if an operator is stopping a working system 90 times as often as expected, the control chart will very quickly be ignored. The C-Chart generated for example 1 is shown in Figure 2.

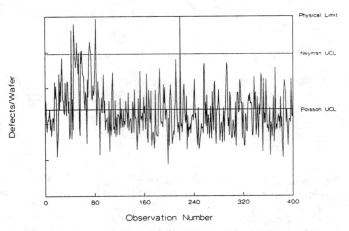

Figure 2 -- Control Chart For 400 Sampled Wafers

As an alternative to using Poisson limits, using Neyman limits to generate the UCL is also shown in Figure 2. Notice with the appropriate distribution specified, the Type I error of 0.0086 and ARL of 117 is much closer to what three sigma control limits would be expected to produce.

Example 2:

Wafers are sent through ion implant in batches of 20 wafers. The first wafer (the control wafer) is then inspected for defects. Batches are run every 10 minutes. If a wafer of 100 chips contains 50 defective chips or fewer it is considered an acceptable yield, any more than 60 defects per wafer however is unacceptable and the system should be stopped and examined for assignable causes. From this information a design for a control chart can be constructed. If the designer wanted an in-control ARL of 500 and an out-of-control ARL of 15 this implies the operator would mistakenly stop the machine every 80-85 hours, while if a true out-of-control situation develops it will be detected in 2-3 hours. Table 1 shows this case. Under the assumption of a Poisson distribution with mean of 50 defects/unit, if the true mean is 50 (i.e. the system is under control) the ARL is 497.51, and if the true mean is 60 defects/wafer (the level of the specified out-of-control shift) the 13.91 value is even better than the desired value of 15. If there are complaints that the system is being unnecessarily stopped too often, the 3 sigma limits could be increased (for example, if 3.5 sigma limits were used, the in-control ARL would rise to about 1000). If there were complaints that it took too long to detect an out-of-control system, the limits could be cut to 2.5 sigma to sensitize the system. If you wished to make the system respond more quickly to an out-of-control system without decreasing the in-control ARL however, no amount of fiddling with the control limits will accomplish this. The only solution would be to designate multiple control wafers in each batch. This alternative will be discussed in the following section.

Table 1 Average Run Length Poisson Control Limits (3σ) In-control mean = 50				
		True Process Mean		
Dist'n	50	55	60	65
Poisson	497.51	62.65	13.91	4.81
Neyman $\phi=1$	46.71	15.66	6.78	3.68
Neyman $\phi=10$	5.68	4.19	3.26	2.65

This sampling plan is implemented: inspect the control wafer in every batch and if more than $50+3\sqrt{50}=71.2$ defects are found, stop the process. The system now stops on average once every hour (i.e. an ARL of 6, since there are samples every 10 minutes). This causes much confusion as the operators become frustrated as process engineers claim there is nothing wrong with the system, consumers downstream in the process are annoyed that production schedules are not met, and quality engineers are baffled. Examination of row 3 of Table 1 identifies the true source of the problem: for the Neyman distribution with $\phi = 10$ (i.e. an average of 10 defects per cluster) the in-control ARL is 5.68. So by incorrectly specifying the defect generating distribution, a misleading design has been implemented.

There are two possible solutions: the first and obvious solution is to re-specify the UCL in accordance with the true sigma value. As can be seen in Table 2, this helps considerably: the new control limit would be: $50+3\sqrt{50*11}=120.4$ and the system would have an in-control ARL of 195.5 and an out-of-control ARL of 56.8. The primary advantage of this is the existing plan can be re-interpreted to give more realistic goals. Unfortunately, note that the in-control ARL is shorter and the out-of-control ARL is shorter. It is entirely possible that an out-of-control ARL of 56.8 (i.e. almost 10 hours) is far to long to let the machine run. In that case, the second alternative of re-designing the inspection plan is the only alternative.

	Table 2 Average Run Length Neyman Control Limits (3σ) In-control mean = 50			
			True Process Mean	
Dist'n	50	55	60	65
Poisson	497.51	62.65	13.91	4.81
Neyman $\phi=1$	367.02	86.52	27.26	10.95
Neyman $\phi=10$	195.49	100.99	56.84	34.40

Use of C-Charts for Samples of Size n

Often the in-control or out-of-control ARL values are unacceptable using a sample size of 1. To compensate for the increased variation due to clustering, a multiplier of $(1+\phi)$ is suggested. Under the assumption that increasing the sample size will not alter the density of the clusters (generally a valid assumption unless the size of the cluster exceeds the size of the field of view (FOV)) this leads to a distribution with the sample mean equal to the sample variance. Although (obviously) this does not make the mean of a Neyman distribution of size $(1+\phi)$ equivalent to a Poisson distribution of size 1, it gives an easy rule-of-thumb approximation for how large a compensation factor is necessary. Thought of another way, this could be considered the inspection size necessary for the Central Limit Theorem to take effect. The result of this increased sample size may be seen in Table 3. The values were found by calculating the ARL's of a standard C-Chart for the samples indicated. As can be seen, the results are quite close to the ARL values generated by the Poisson distribution and a sample of 1. To extend this, a factor of $(1+\phi)$ may be used to convert any C-Chart to account for clustering. If ϕ were approximated to be 7 then, a sample of 2 wafers per batch would be converted to a sample of 16.

Table 3 Average Run Length Neyman Control Limits (3σ) In-control mean = 50		True Process Mean			
Dist'n	Sample Size	50	55	60	65
Poisson	1	497.51	62.65	13.91	4.81
Neyman ϕ=1	2	404.86	55.83	13.00	4.63
Neyman ϕ=10	11	442.24	52.12	13.01	4.60

Summary

Any attribute control chart may be modified to account for clustering by employing one of two methods. The first method, that of using Neyman control limits, has the advantage of using the same sample size as the Poisson assumption (insuring that the cost of sampling will not rise) but the disadvantage of not being as accurate as the Poisson plan it is replacing (i.e. the 'good' processes will stop more often and 'bad' processes will run longer). Increasing the sample size by a factor of $(1+\phi)$ has the advantage of providing an accuracy almost as good as the Poisson plan it is replacing, but the disadvantage of escalating the sampling costs. In Example 2 for instance, to compensate for a ϕ of 10, a sample of 11 wafers per batch would have to be inspected. This is 55% of the batch itself: clearly increasing the cost of sampling tremendously and, if the inspection is time consuming, decreasing the product velocity. There is no reason the two methods cannot be combined, of course. Increasing the sample as much as is economically viable, then expanding the UCL to account for the rest of the cluster induced variation is an alternative often worth considering.

CUMULATIVE SUM CONTROL CHARTS

Advances in technology in the field of integrated circuit fabrication have given the modern factory a well controlled system to adjust machinery automatically. Steppers, for example, can be adjusted automatically from batch to batch to compensate for previous problems. In areas such as these, it often becomes necessary to anticipate potential problems by detecting persistent, but small, deviations from desired accuracy. This is a difficult problem for C-Charts to detect, since in their basic form they are designed to detect large, sudden changes in the process, and are in fact a memoryless system. Although modifications have been suggested to search for patterns ([7] and [8] for example), a more sensitive method, designed specifically to detect small shifts in parameter settings would be advantageous.

The Cumulative Sum (CUSUM) Control Chart, first proposed by [9], is an appropriate method for dealing with this situation. By accumulating defects over a series of observations, the system is afforded a memory which will monitor long term conformance to expected performance. This is of particular importance in the field of IC manufacturing: wafer yield is true metric of economic performance, and any shift must be detected quickly. As pointed out [10],the CUSUM Charts offers the advantage of increased sensitivity but the disadvantage of eliminating slack in processes where some slack is permissible. For a more complete discussion of the properties of the CUSUM chart, the reader is referred to [11], [12], [13].

An issue discussed in [10] is one to be considered before any control chart scheme is adapted. For many processes within the fabrication process, the in-control number of defects is simply too high (since the variance would increase with the mean for both the Poisson distribution and the Neyman distribution, a high mean number of defects would imply high variance). In high variance systems it would not be reasonable to even look for small defect shifts. The investigation into the use of the CUSUM Chart will therefore be limited to low defect rate samples.

A CUSUM Chart accumulates the difference between an observed value Y_i and a reference value k, which may be viewed as the largest value the manufacturer is willing to endure. The reference value is generally compute as a function of the in-control defect rate μ_a and the out-of-control defect rate μ_d . The CUSUM value is computed as:

$$S_i = MAX(0, Y_i - k + S_{i-1})$$

If S_i ever exceeds H, the process is declared out-of-control. Published tables for the ARL's expected for various values of k (between 0.25 and 10) and H (between 1 and 20) have appeared in [14]. Thus, for low defect rates and a Poisson distribution assumption an appropriate control chart can be found by using the charts. The investigation in this paper will involve the effect of clustering on these ARL's and the resulting designs.

To calculate an appropriate value for k, Lucas suggests:

$$k = (\mu_d - \mu_a) / (ln(\mu_d) - ln(\mu_a))$$

Example 3:

A total of 5 field of view (FOV) observations are made on an unpatterned wafer, to look for ink splatters. If a single imperfection is noted, this is not considered serious, but if 3 of more imperfections are noted (over the 5 FOV's) the CUSUM Chart should detect this quickly. Calculating k:

$$k = (3-1)/(ln(3)-ln(1)) = 1.82$$

Rounding off to 2, the sampling plan chosen is H=7 and k=2. According to the Lucas tables this design would stop the process every 23600 trials if the process mean were 1, but once every 7 trials if the process mean were 3. As an alternative, consider the approach of simply using the value k=1 (since 1 is the acceptable defect rate). In this case a design of H=10 and k=1 would stop the process every 117 trials if the defect mean is 1 and every 5.6 trials if the defect mean equals 3. If k is set equal to 3, at best an H=2 stops the process every 158 trials with defect rate equal to 1 and every 4.7 trials with a rate of 3. It would appear H=7 and k=2 gives the best sensitivity.

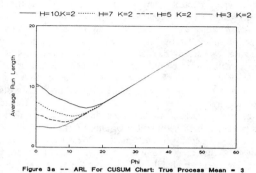

Figure 3a -- ARL For CUSUM Chart: True Process Mean = 3

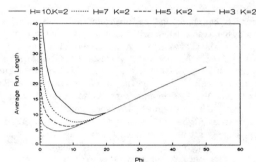

Figure 3b -- ARL For CUSUM Chart: True Process Mean = 2

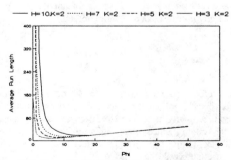

Figure 3c -- ARL For CUSUM Chart: True Process Mean = 1

While this is a valid control chart design for Poisson distributed defects, clustering of defects will change the projected ARL's (pointed out in [15]). Figures 3a-c demonstrate how increasing ϕ will alter the ARL, in some cases dramatically. When the system is running at a rate of $\mu_d =3$ (Graph 3a), the ARL decreases (as it generally will for small ϕ values) then increases at a steady rate for all $\phi > 10$. There are a number of points of interest in this. First, as will always be the case for unacceptable defect rates, the ARL is relatively insensitive to small values of ϕ. Second, as the clusters become denser (i.e., increases) the ARL asymptotically approaches the C-Chart ARL previously discussed. As the cluster density becomes large relative to the CUSUM limit H, it becomes more and more likely that whenever any defect at all is found, the cluster will be so dense that it will send an out-of-control signal. The expected number of clusters (previously defined as λ) is the process mean divided by the density of each cluster. With $\phi=30$ for example, $\lambda=0.1$, implying an average of 0.1 clusters per sample are expected. Since any cluster will generate an out-of-control signal, the probability of stopping the system at any step is

$$1-P[X=0 \mid X\tilde{}Poisson(0.1)]=1-0.90484=0.09516.$$

From this, the ARL can be found by inverting this probability, since this is essentially a memoryless system (any defect will be in a cluster large enough to put the system out-of-control, so S_{i-1} is always zero for an in-control system). The ARL is therefore calculated to be 10.51 which is the exact value of the ARL for H=3, H=5, H=7, and H=10. This observation leads to an important result: for significant clustering, the CUSUM Control Chart will reduce to a corresponding C-Chart. Looking at Figure 3b, the same patterns emerge, only now the ARL is more sensitive to the small values of ϕ. This becomes becomes a real problem if in example 3, ϕ were equal to 10. This would mean that for a process mean of 2 an ARL of 34 is expected but an ARL of 7.5 is realized. Since the out-of-control ARL is set at 7, significant problems would arise. Notice, as before, for $\phi >20$ the same asymptotic approach to the C-Chart ARL is encountered. Finally, in Figure 3c, the acceptable defect rate of 1 is examined. There is tremendous sensitivity here to even small values of ϕ, as for our design of H=7 and k=2, the ARL of 23600 for the Poisson distribution virtually drops to 28 for a $\phi=5$. This sensitivity makes this and any other CUSUM design virtually useless if clustering occurs.

In summary, if clustering is known to exist, using a CUSUM Control Chart would not appear to be a viable alternative, unless significant design changes are made (such as defining a defect as any cluster of one or more defects).

EXTENSIONS

It is known that defects do not occur randomly on a wafer (sections on the periphery of the wafer often have significantly higher defect rates). It has been suggested [16]) that using separate control charts in different areas of the wafers surface would give more accurate control of the system. Since what might constitute a random pattern on the periphery of the wafer could be an unacceptably high defect rate in the center of the wafer, this is the only way such variations could be detected.

An investigation could also be made to see if CUSUM Charts could be adapted to clustered defect environments. Some possibilities include basing the CUSUM Control

Chart on the number of clusters of defects, rather than the number of defects. Algorithms already exist which will group defects into clusters; if they could be used in conjunction with CUSUM control charts with standard Poisson limits (since the number of clusters is assumed to be Poisson), control could be established (assuming, as before, the density of the clusters is constant).

SUMMARY

The question of using control charts in an integrated circuit manufacturing environment (or any environment producing clustered defects) has been studied. It has been concluded that C-Charts may be adapted to a clustered defect environment by first running a process capability study to get estimates of the Neyman parameters λ and ϕ, then either modifying the control chart UCL or the size of the inspection sample. If the UCL is modified, the revised limit should be calculated by using the standard deviation of the Neyman distribution. If the inspection sample size is modified, it should be increased by a factor of $(1+\phi)$. This would allow the Poisson UCL to be used, and Poisson ARL values to approximate the true ARL of the system. It has also been concluded that CUSUM Control Charts, as they are presently structured, would be of little value for process control in integrated circuit fabrication. For any significant clustering, the in-control ARL drops so rapidly that any reasonable analysis is not possible. For dense clustering, the behavior of the CUSUM Control Chart is identical to the simpler C-Chart.

ACKNOWLEDGEMENTS

The author wishes to acknowledge the generous contributions of the referees, whose suggestions added great clarity to the material.

REFERENCES

[1] Stapper, C.H. [1985] "The Effect of Wafer to Wafer Density Variations on Integrated Circuit Defect and Fault Distributions," IBM J. Res. Devop., V. 29, 87-97.

[2] Stapper, C.H. [1986] "On Yield, Fault Distributions, and Clustering of Particles," IBM J. Res. Devop., V. 30, N. 3, 326-338.

[3] Neyman, J. [1939] "On a New Class of 'Contagious' Distributions, Applicable in Entomology and Bacteriology," Ann. Math. Stat. 10, 35-57.

[4] David, F.N. and P.C. Moore [1954] "Notes on Contagious Distributions in Plant Populations," Annals of Botany (New Series), 53, 47-53.

[5] Johnson, N.L. and S. Kotz [1969] Discrete Distributions, Houghton-Mifflin Co.

[6] Brook, D. and D.A. Evans [1972] "An Approach to the Probability Distribution of CUSUM Run Lengths," Biometrica, 59, 539-549.

[7] Western Electric [1956] Statistical Quality Control Handbook, Western Electric Co., Indianapolis, IN.

[8]   Duncan, A.J. [1974] <u>Quality Control and Industrial Statistics</u>, Fourth Edition, Irwin.

[9]   Page, E.S. [1954] "Continuous Inspection Schemes," <u>Biometrics</u> V. 41.

[10] Gibra, I.N. [1975] "Recent Developments in Control Chart Techniques," <u>Journal of Quality Technology</u>" V. 7, N. 4, 183-192.

[11] Johnson, N.L. and F.C. Leone [1962a] "Cumulative Sum Control Charts: Mathematical Principles Applied to Construction and Use, Part I," <u>Industrial Quality Control</u>, V. 18, N. 12, 15-21.

[12] Johnson, N.L. and F.C. Leone [1962b] "Cumulative Sum Control Charts: Mathematical Principles Applied to Construction and Use, Part II," <u>Industrial Quality Control,</u> V. 19, N. 1, 29-36.

[13] Johnson, N.L. and F.C. Leone [1962c] "Cumulative Sum Control Charts: Mathematical Principles Applied to Construction and Use, Part III," <u>Industrial Quality Control,</u> V. 19, N. 2, 22-28.

[14] Lucas, J.M. [1985] "Counted Data CUSUMs," <u>Technometrics</u> V. 27, N. 2, 129-144.

[15] Gardiner, J., D.J. Friedman and D.C. Montgomery [1987] "A Note on Cumulative Sum Control Charts for Defect Data," <u>Journal of Quality and Reliability International</u>

[16] Friedman, D.J. [1987] "Statistical Quality Control in an IC Fabrication Line," <u>IEEE International Electronic Manufacturing Technology Symposium Proceedings</u>

Gerald A. Keller, Whitson G. Waldo, and Richard F. Babasick

PERKIN-ELMER 544 OVERLAY EVALUATION USING STATISTICAL TECHNIQUES

REFERENCE: Keller, G. A., Waldo, W. G., and Babasick, R. F., "Perkin-Elmer 544 Overlay Evaluation Using Statistical Techniques," Semiconductor Fabrication: Technology and Metrology, ASTM STP 990, Dinesh C. Gupta, editor, American Society for Testing and Materials, 1989.

ABSTRACT: A recently developed optical overlay measurement system is used to perform factorial design statistical experiments on the Perkin-Elmer 544 Micralign. The overlay measurement system (Perkin-Elmer's OMS-1) is used to check out the operation of computer offsets and microstage scale corrections in the Micralign 544 with a half fractional factorial test for five factors. This is a resolution five experiment. OMS-1 compares a resist image to a previously etched substrate. This offers fast turnaround time and contactless measurement of product wafers. We have found that with a minimum of equipment utilization, a Perkin-Elmer scanner can be checked out for operation on many different programmable settings. Experimental data is reported in real time since the development step is the only process required before wafers are measured. Information will also be presented on the functionality of the OMS-1 with respect to reproducibility and repeatability. The Perkin-Elmer scanner is tested for stability over time using the OMS. Also, we demonstrate efficiency of the OMS in overlay measurement processing and a method to evaluate the alignment distribution offsets needed to achieve optimal registration.

KEYWORDS: overlay, registration, factorial, gauge, capability

Gerald A. Keller is a process development engineer specializing in optical photolithography for Motorola's Bipolar Technology Center. **Whitson G. Waldo** is a stepper process development engineer for 0.5 micron optical lithography for Motorola's Bipolar Technology Center. **Richard F. Babasick** is an applications engineer for Perkin-Elmer's Semiconductor Equipment Division.

427

Competitive semiconductor integrated circuit manufacturing requires a high process capability for registration. A goal was established to optimize the equipment capability of the Perkin-Elmer 544 model scanner. This paper presents that work. Additional work done to optimize the process is not treated here, except that gauge capability of the overlay measurement is discussed.

Optimization of the scanner's performance results when the equipment is performing at its design limits. Without reviewing the design criteria, several things are known. The overlay errors are controlled through software entries. Software entries to correct overlay errors should be linear in their response between inputs and outputs. Software entries are made in ppm units, which is a convenient response unit, so the slope of the linear correlation should be unity. It must be statistically determined that there are no interactions between individual software factors. Finally, repetition of runs should indicate that factors can be changed reproducibly and without hysteresis.

Demanding device overlay tolerances require real time adjustment capability as lithographic layers are processed on different aligning tools. A real time overlay gauge in lithography might be defined to have the characteristic of being capable of measuring a developed resist target registered to a previous layer prior to etch processing. [1] In order to evaluate the gauge (Perkin-Elmer's OMS-1) used to estimate the layer to layer registration error incurred, and also to evaluate the functionality of programmable offsets on the Perkin-Elmer 544, statistical design experiments may be employed. [2] This is done by randomization of experimental runs and repetition of the runs at programmable overlay offsets. Gauge capability testing can be used to establish more confidence in the overlay measurement system, in much the same fashion that repetitive techniques were used in the factorial system. [3] When this is complete, the statements about stability and distribution of overlay error data on the Perkin-Elmer 544 that follow are statistically significant, as are results of adjustment techniques.

EXPERIMENTAL METHOD

The Factorial Experiment

The particular experimental design employed was a two level fractional factorial, or more specifically, a two to the five minus one, resolution five design. This design allows one to examine main effects and two way interactions of factors (in our case, programmable offsets for overlay). Interactions between three or more experimental factors are confounded.

The estimated linear model for the effects used in the computer analysis is:

$$y = \beta_0 + \beta_1 x_1 + \beta_2 x_2 + \beta_3 x_3 + \beta_4 x_4 + \beta_5 x_5 + \beta_{12} x_1 x_2 + \beta_{13} x_1 x_3 + \qquad (1)$$
$$\beta_{14} x_1 x_4 + \beta_{15} x_1 x_5 + \beta_{23} x_2 x_3 + \beta_{24} x_2 x_4 + \beta_{25} x_2 x_5 + \beta_{34} x_3 x_4 + \beta_{35} x_3 x_5$$
$$+ \beta_{45} x_4 x_5$$

where,
Y = The overlay response to software inputs.
β_0 = The average of estimates for factor setting.
$B_{i=}$ 1-5 = Slope of measured vector error response from the + and
− settings on the X factors.

$X_{i=1\,through\,5}$ are values of programmable offset factors, 2304x, 2304y1, 2304yr, 245, 250, respectively, and

$\beta_{i=1\,through\,4}$ are estimates of the X factors' coefficients.

The pooled variance for the factorial experimentation is calculated from the factorial cells as:

$$s_p{}^2 = \frac{(n_1-1)s_1{}^2 + (n_2-1)s_2{}^2 + \dots + (n_i-1)s_i{}^2}{(n_1-1) + (n_2-1) + \dots + (n_i-1)} \qquad (2)$$

where,

S_p = Pooled standard deviation

S_i = Sigma, standard deviation of cell i

n_i = Sample size of cell i

The standard error, or experimental "noise" calculations can be made as shown:

$$S.E. = (t_{\infty/2}, .05)(s_p) \qquad (3)$$

where $t_{\infty/2}$, $.05$ = 95% confidence t table value.

The experimental noise calculations can be made because of repetitions of runs in each cell. The number of repetitions is selected based on considerations for the time needed to run the experiment, the anticipated process variation, and the desired confidence level. Each run represents a four inch wafer measured with the OMS-1 on seventeen site locations. The randomized run order for the cell runs is shown in Table 1 below. Once the experiment is run, values for the registration error (in our case, vectors taken at seventeen sites per wafer) are measured and entered in Yate's order to a computer program for calculation of the responses of the Model 544 to the programmed offsets. The analysis of variance computer program adds the plus level overlay responses and then subtracts the minus level responses on each experimental run for each factor and then displays the effect of each factor or adjustment.

Table 1 - Randomized Run Order and Programmable Offsets

Run	Yate's	1	2	3	4	5
1	9	−	−	−	+	−
2	15	−	+	+	+	−
3	5	−	−	+	−	−
4	6	+	−	+	−	+
5	32	+	+	+	−	+
6	8	+	+	+	−	−
7	27	−	+	−	+	+
8	7	−	+	+	−	+
9	12	+	+	−	+	−
10	16	+	+	+	+	+
11	14	+	−	+	+	−
12	1	−	−	−	−	+
13	28	+	−	−	+	−
14	2	−	+	+	+	−
15	18	+	−	−	−	−
16	10	+	−	−	+	+
17	4	+	+	−	−	+
18	26	+	−	−	+	+
19	11	−	+	−	+	+
20	13	−	−	+	+	+
21	21	−	−	+	−	−
22	29	−	−	+	+	+
23	31	−	+	+	+	−
24	3	−	+	−	−	−
25	30	+	−	+	+	−
26	23	−	+	+	−	+
27	25	−	−	−	−	+
28	17	−	−	−	+	+
29	24	+	+	+	−	−
30	20	+	+	−	−	+
31	19	−	+	−	−	−
32	22	+	−	+	−	+

Table 1 - Randomized Run Order and Programmable Offsets

FACTOR	+	−	FACTOR#
2304x	.19	.49	(1)
2304Yl	.30	.60	(2)
2304Yr	.33	.63	(3)
245	−2.93	−4	(4)
250	−3.92	−6.92	(5)
255	Leave at 2.54		
5117	Leave at .13		

Gauge Capability

Gauge capability is calculated after loading, measuring, and unloading wafers from the "gauge," in this case the OMS-1. Repeatability is defined by the difference in measurements due to one operators' variability in measurement. Reproducibility is defined as the error between two operator's measurements. Ten randomized wafers were measured twice by two operators for the test. The gauge capability of the OMS was defined as the sum of the variances of repeatability and reproducibility. Gauge capability results are shown in Table 2.

where:

1. R_k= Average of differences between 1st and 2nd wafer readings.

2. X_k= Average of the ten different readings.

3. RT= Average of the RK calculations.

4. R_x= Reproducibility or high minus low of operator averages.

5. $1/d^2T$= Variance coefficient from Luftig. (3)

6. (Sigma) e= S value for repeatability of experiment.

7. 6.[8] /TT= 6 divided by the total tol. value .12um or greater is acceptable.

GAGE CAPABILITY CALCULATION

REPEATABILITY AND REPRODUCIBILITY ANALYSIS FORM   **PROCESS POTENTIAL STUDY**

GAGE: OMS-1   DATE: 7/13/87
PART NAME: OVERLAY WAFER TEST SET 089   PART #: MOD 300 TARGETS
CHARACTERISTIC: TOOL 1 TO TOOL 3   TOTAL TOLERANCE: +/-.25
PLANT: MESA   AREA: BTC   EVALUATOR: G. KELLER

INSPECTOR: #1:   #2:

TRIALS PART	FIRST MEASURE	SECOND MEASURE	Difference (D)	FIRST MEASURE	SECOND MEASURE	Difference (D)
1	0.279	0.288	0.009	.274	.283	0.009
2	0.206	0.193	0.013	.202	.204	0.002
3	0.294	0.301	0.007	.307	.310	0.003
4	0.351	0.319	0.032	.349	.341	0.008
5	0.404	0.377	0.027	.395	.384	0.011
6	0.290	0.253	0.037	.282	.289	0.007
7	0.262	0.266	0.004	.261	.269	0.008
8	0.260	0.272	0.012	.284	.273	0.011
9	0.300	0.291	0.009	.310	.314	0.004
10	0.302	0.274	0.028	.272	.282	0.010
Rk:	XXXXX	XXXXX	0.018	XXXXX	XXXXX	0.007
Xk:	0.295	0.283	0.289	0.294	0.295	0.294

X11 = 0.295   X12 = 0.283   X1 = 0.289   X21 = 0.294   X22 = 0.295   X2 = 0.294

0.5   <<TT

[4] $Rt = (R1+R2)/2 =$ .013

[6] $[(1/d2)T * Rt]^2 =$ .0001
$(1/d2)T =$ 0.862

[8] $SQRT \{ [6] + [7] \} =$ 0.011   << (Sigma)e
<1 station x 10 parts = 10 for A,B = 2

[5] $Rx = Xh - Xl =$ .005

[7] $[(1/d2)D * Rx]^2 - ([6]/(n*r)) =$ .0000
$(1/d2)D =$ 0.885   <A=1, B=2

[9] $6*[8]/TT =$ .138   << P/T Ratio

Table 2 - OMS Gauge Capability Calculations

Perkin-Elmer Adjustment and Overlay Distribution

Overlay on the Perkin-Elmer 544 is best thought of as the interaction of alignment with distortion. Process engineering responsibilities include attempting to adjust the complex set of operator offsets and optical components to achieve overlay goals. Normally, a contact printed set of wafers is utilized to adjust micrometers and software values for programmable offset, skew, and magnification components of distortion. Although this technique is well documented, additional error for overlay (which includes alignment) may be considerable, and requires adjustment capabilities of a suitable gauge if an automatic fine alignment program is to achieve aggressive goals. [4]

Once adjustments are made, then it is feasible to study the nature of the overlay distribution and the stability of the distribution over time (e.g., three months). It should be mentioned here that all overlay error reporting is in vector, not scalar form, and that a quarter micron error in x and y direction would be equivilent to a .35 micron vector error. The overlay may be studied with the use of a statistical package for such deviations from normal as skewed or bimodal distributions. [5] The particular program used in data analysis distributes data in a way similar to a normal probability plot, with a percentage value of the data values on the dependent axis. A straight line implies that the data conforms to a gaussian error distribution. We also study the nature of overlay data pooled from three aligning tools. It is important to be able to describe the data distribution, even when the data is skewed, or non-normal relative to the interval. The statistical program used in this paper's analysis assumes a normal distribution.

RESULTS

Factorial Experiment

Figure 1 illustrates an example of the response of two Model 544's to the factorial design experiment for average cell data. Consistency of results for this experiment can be seen, as well as a response on the first factor, 2304x. Responses on all but one of the rest of the factor main effects were seen through the use of data extraction of equations that fit the factor being tested. These equations were:

$$DX = Tx - (y \cdot oy) + (x \cdot magx)$$
$$(3)$$
$$Dy = Ty + (x \cdot ox) + (y \cdot magy),$$

where,

Tx, Ty, o, magx, and magy are distortion terms, and x and y are site location coordinates. Table 3 is a summary of 1/2B, or significant response of main effects.

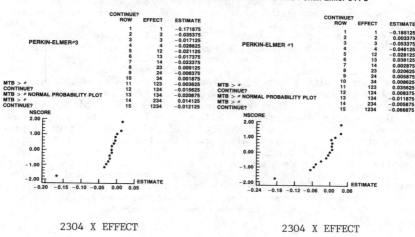

Figure 1 - Programmable Offset Factor Estimates on Effects-Two Perkin Elmer 544's

2304 X EFFECT

2304 X EFFECT

TABLE 3, ESTIMATES (IN MICRONS)

	Factor 1	Factor 2	Factor 3	Factor 4	Factor 5
Raw Data	-.1718	★	★	★	★
Tx,Ty	★	-.1796	-.1326	★	★
Magx,Magy Experiment	★	★	★	★	.0063
Noise,SE	.0721	.0670	.0960	.0470	.0034

RESULTANT RESPONSES AFTER DATA MODELING

Adjustment and 544 Overlay Distribution

Figure 2 illustrates how the OMS-1 was used to adjust alignment and distortion components of overlay error on seven programmable offsets to achieve a very small distribution of error (around an average of less than a tenth of a micron). These results were generated by first printing a set of wafers with a distortion adjusted alignment tool. Once the Perkin-Elmer was adjusted with this technique, the drift in average was found to be .04 micron in one month, with a one sigma distribution less than .05 micron. We used a computer program for analysis of variance to look at the way overlay error is distributed on the Perkin-Elmer 544 in Figure 3. This was on a maintenance adjusted tool, and the average was .07 micron with a 3 sigma distribution of .12 micron. It was found that each of the seventeen sites positioned around the wafer were at variance with another at the 99.9% F table confidence level. Visually this can be seen as a slight dip in the total vector overlay error distribution, Figure 4. The computer normal probability plot test for gaussian distribution with data entered for the month (i.e., five wafers, seventeen sites) demonstrates a fairly normal distribution in Figure 5, for this sample data population.

Figure 2 - Adjustment Series Using Seven Programmable Adjustments from OMS-1

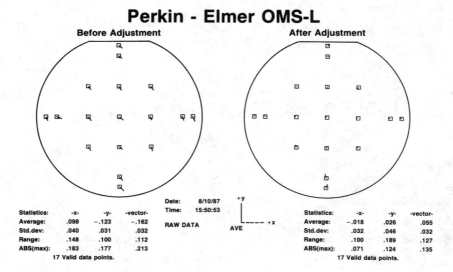

Figure 3 - Analysis of Variance on Seventeen Location Sites per Wafer

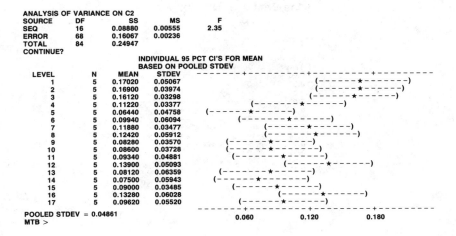

WHERE c^2 = VECTOR REGISTRATION ERRORS IN MICRONS

The same test may be applied to three months of data represented by Figure 6, which shows a skewed distribution with 99.2% of data between 0 and .4 microns. The reasons for handling the data in this fashion are presented later. Tool to tool matching results have been shown that report a vector average of between a tenth and two-tenths of a micron and a .05 micron one sigma distribution, as seen in Figure 7. Figures 8 and 9 are representative of pooled data from three alignment tools matched to the same mask and wafer set, again measured seventeen sites per wafer. Figure 8 shows the histogram and statistical treatment of the data, along with an N-score test on the skewed distribution. Figure 9 shows the analysis of variance treatment for tool to tool, wafer to wafer, and site to site. These treatments indicate that the pooled averages for effects of the different factors show that they are at variance with each other. In this case it is best to describe the data in terms of a percentage that relates to 3 sigma, or 99.7% of the data population. If we throw out the high and low values of the distribution for Figure 8, we find the remaining population, or 99.2% of the remaining data, to fall between 0 and .35 microns or ± .175 microns. For the skewed distribution, a sigma description would have implied a distribution that went into a negative area for which there is no data represented.

Figure 4 - Histogram Representing Non-Gaussian Dip
at the Center of Distribution

MICRONS

MIDDLE OF INTERVAL	NUMBER OF OBSERVATIONS	
0.00	1	★
0.02	3	★ ★ ★
0.04	7	★ ★ ★ ★ ★ ★ ★
0.06	12	★ ★ ★ ★ ★ ★ ★ ★ ★ ★ ★ ★
0.08	10	★ ★ ★ ★ ★ ★ ★ ★ ★ ★
0.10	9	★ ★ ★ ★ ★ ★ ★ ★ ★
0.12	10	★ ★ ★ ★ ★ ★ ★ ★ ★ ★
0.14	12	★ ★ ★ ★ ★ ★ ★ ★ ★ ★ ★ ★
0.16	9	★ ★ ★ ★ ★ ★ ★ ★ ★
0.18	2	★ ★
0.20	7	★ ★ ★ ★ ★ ★ ★
0.22	2	★ ★
0.24	1	★

Figure 5 - Gaussian Test Using "Minitab" Nscore Program

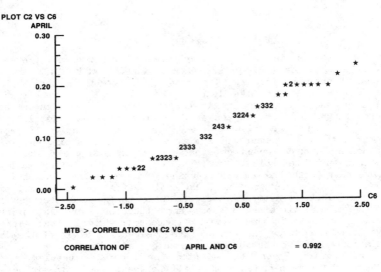

MTB > CORRELATION ON C2 VS C6

CORRELATION OF   APRIL AND C6   = 0.992

WHERE c^2 = CALCULATED PERCENTILE OF THE RANK

WHERE c^6 = MICRONS OF ERROR

Figure 6 - Three Months Pooled Data

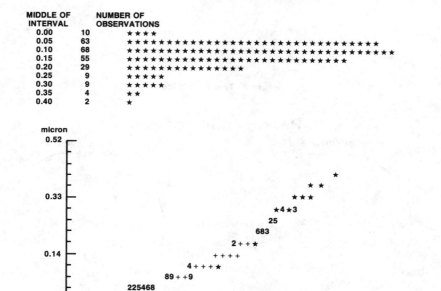

MIDDLE OF INTERVAL	NUMBER OF OBSERVATIONS	
0.00	10	★ ★ ★ ★
0.05	63	★ ★
0.10	68	★ ★
0.15	55	★ ★
0.20	29	★ ★ ★ ★ ★ ★ ★ ★ ★ ★ ★ ★ ★ ★
0.25	9	★ ★ ★ ★ ★
0.30	9	★ ★ ★ ★ ★
0.35	4	★ ★
0.40	2	★

6 MISSING OBSERVATIONS

CORRELATION OF   micron AND C7   = 0.969

	C6
N	249
MEAN	0.1244
MEDIAN	0.1160
TMEAN	0.1194
STDEV	0.0769
SEMEAN	0.0049
MAX	0.4080
MIN	−0.0040
Q3	0.1615
Q1	0.0680

Figure 7 - Tool To Tool Matching

Perkin - Elmer OMS-L

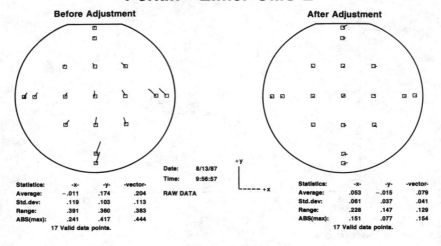

Before Adjustment				After Adjustment			

Date: 8/13/87
Time: 9:56:57
RAW DATA

+y
+x

Statistics:	-x-	-y-	-vector-
Average:	−.011	.174	.204
Std.dev:	.119	.103	.113
Range:	.391	.360	.383
ABS(max):	.241	.417	.444
	17 Valid data points.		

Statistics:	-x-	-y-	-vector-
Average:	.053	−.015	.079
Std.dev:	.061	.037	.041
Range:	.228	.147	.129
ABS(max):	.151	.077	.154
	17 Valid data points.		

Figure 8 - Pooled Matching Data, Three Align Tools, One Mask and Wafer Set

MICRON
  EACH ★ REPRESENTS 2 OBSERVATIONS

MIDDLE OF INTERVAL	NUMBER OF OBSERVATIONS	
0.00	7	★★★★
0.05	64	★★★★★★★★★★★★★★★★★★★★★★★★★★★★★★★★
0.10	96	★★
0.15	47	★★★★★★★★★★★★★★★★★★★★★★★★
0.20	23	★★★★★★★★★★★★
0.25	10	★★★★★
0.30	5	★★★
0.35	2	★
0.40	0	
0.45	0	
0.50	1	★

MTB > DESCRIBE C4

	MICRON
N	255
MEAN	0.1162
MEDIAN	0.1030
TMEAN	0.1106
STDEV	0.0692
SEMEAN	0.0043
MAX	0.5220
MIN	0.0040
Q3	0.1450
Q1	0.0700

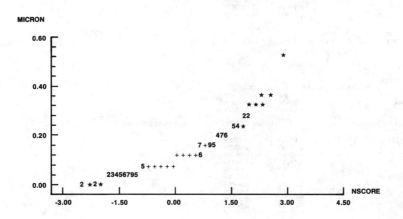

MTB > CORRELATION ON C4 VS C5

CORRELATION OF MICRON AND NSCORE = 0.943

Figure 9 - Analysis of Variance - Wafer to Wafer, Site to Site and Tool to Tool

```
MTB > ONEWAY ON C4 LEVELS C1 - TOOL TO TOOL

ANALYSIS OF VARIANCE ON MICRON
SOURCE        DF        SS          MS              F
TOOL           2     0.03570     0.01785         3.81
ERROR        252     1.17946     0.00468
TOTAL        254     1.21516
                                             INDIVIDUAL 95 PCT CI'S FOR MEAN
                                             BASED ON POOLED STDEV
   LEVEL     N      MEAN      STDEV    ---+---------+---------+---------+--
     1       85    0.1051    0.0765    (--------*--------)
     2       85    0.1326    0.0707                 (---------*---------)
     3       85    0.1108    0.0565       (---------*---------)
                                         ---+---------+---------+---------+--
POOLED STDEV = 0.0684                     0.096      0.112     0.128     0.144
MTB > ONEWAY ON C4 LEVELS C2


CONTINUE?
ANALYSIS OF VARIANCE ON MICRON  WAFER TO WAFER
SOURCE        DF        SS          MS              F
WAFER         14     0.21794     0.01557         3.75
ERROR        240     0.99722     0.00416
TOTAL        254     1.21516
CONTINUE?                                    INDIVIDUAL 95 PCT CI'S FOR MEAN
                                             BASED ON POOLED STDEV
   LEVEL     N      MEAN      STDEV   ----------+---------+---------+------
     1       17   0.09394   0.06944      (-----*-----)
     2       17   0.08441   0.04648   (-----*-----)
     3       17   0.11118   0.05211         (-----*-----)
     4       17   0.10482   0.07726      (-----*-----)
     5       17   0.13118   0.11705            (-----*-----)
     6       17   0.12318   0.03401          (-----*-----)
     7       17   0.19141   0.03487                        (-----*-----)
     8       17   0.15465   0.08953                   (-----*-----)
     9       17   0.10424   0.07042       (-----*-----)
    10       17   0.08935   0.06116   (-----*-----)
    11       17   0.08435   0.04398   (-----*-----)
    12       17   0.09288   0.03385    (-----*-----)
    13       17   0.15182   0.05922                  (-----*-----)
    14       17   0.10841   0.05621       (-----*-----)
    15       17   0.11653   0.06422        (-----*-----)
                                     ----------+---------+---------+------
POOLED STDEV = 0.06446                        0.100     0.150     0.200
MTB > ONEWAY ON C4 LEVELS C3


CONTINUE?
ANALYSIS OF VARIANCE ON MICRON - SITE TO SITE
SOURCE        DF        SS          MS              F
SITE          16     0.28436     0.01777         4.54
ERROR        238     0.93080     0.00391
TOTAL        254     1.21516
CONTINUE?                                    INDIVIDUAL 95 PCT CI'S FOR MEAN
                                             BASED ON POOLED STDEV
   LEVEL     N      MEAN      STDEV   --+---------+---------+---------+----
     1       15   0.14933   0.08004                (----*----)
     2       15   0.12087   0.05381            (----*----)
     3       15   0.09667   0.04710   (----*----)
     4       15   0.09540   0.04965   (----*----)
     5       15   0.08287   0.04337  (----*----)
     6       15   0.08847   0.04894  (-----*----)
     7       15   0.08387   0.04708  (----*----)
     8       15   0.09300   0.04204  (----*----)
     9       15   0.09213   0.03394  (----*----)
    10       15   0.21700   0.09732                          (----*----)
    11       15   0.14600   0.11032               (----*-----)
    12       15   0.09347   0.06508  (----*----)
    13       15   0.11240   0.05796       (----*----)
    14       15   0.11680   0.06434       (----*----)
    15       15   0.14047   0.05389             (----*----)
    16       15   0.14193   0.05296             (----*----)
    17       15   0.10400   0.06327   (----*----)
                                     --+---------+---------+---------+----
POOLED STDEV = 0.06254                0.060      0.120     0.180     0.240
MTB >
```

Summary

A statistical design experimental approach was employed to test the OMS measurement gauge and Perkin-Elmer 544 alignment tool capability, by examining factor main effects. OMS gauge capability testing studied repeatability and reproducibility. The OMS gauge was used to adjust the alignment tool and measure stability instead of verniers. The vector overlay error population was further analyzed to reveal a slight non-gaussian dip in the overlay error distribution for the month of April. A normal distribution for all three months, including April was proven by use of a computer program that makes a correlation on a normal probability plot. An analysis of wafer to wafer, site to site, and align tool to align tool for three Perkin-Elmers is given to determine what might be the greater error contributor, by use of the F number from analysis of variance. Data from an abnormal overlay error population is discussed. A total error in aligner matching of ± .175 microns for 99.2% with a mean at .1 micron is achieved.

ACKNOWLEDGMENTS

Skip Weed and Mike Holkenbrink for their useful discussions. Donna Allen and Sue Allen gave invaluable technical assistance.

REFERENCES

(1) Cote, Daniel R., Clayton, Robert R., Lazo-Wasem, Jeanne E., "Advanced Optical Overlay Measurement System," SPIE, March 1987.
(2) Box, George E. P., Hunter, William G., Hunter, J. Stuart, "Fractional Factorial Designs at Two Levels," Statistics for Experimenters, John Wiley and Sons, Inc., New York, 1978, pp. 374-417.
(3) Luftig, Jeffrey T., "Guidelines for a Practical Approach to Gage Capability Analysis," East Michigan University Technical Services Center, October, 1984.
(4) Keller, Gerald A., "Practical Process Applications of a Commercially Available Electrical Overlay and Linewidth Measuring System," SPIE, March, 1985.
(5) Ryan, Thomas A. Jr., Joiner, Brian L., Ryan, Barbara F., Minitab Reference Manual, Duxbury Press, Boston, MA., 1982.

Robert K. Lowry

REVOLUTIONIZING SEMICONDUCTOR MATERIAL SPECIFICATIONS

REFERENCE: Lowry, R. K., "Revolutionizing Semiconductor
Material Specifications", Semiconductor Fabrication:
Technology and Metrology, ASTM STP 990, Dinesh C. Gupta,
editor, American Society for Testing and Materials, 1989.

ABSTRACT: Statistical process control is being widely
adopted to improve yields and profitability in semiconductor
manufacturing. Controlling and reducing key process
parameter variability is essential for yield improvement and
cost control. Accordingly, statistically-controlled
processes must be supplied with raw materials which are
similarly statistically controlled. This need has been
inadequately recognized by vendors and standards-writing
groups. This paper discusses the importance of controlling
materials variability. Examples from IC manufacturing are
given. It is shown that raw material specifications cannot
be based solely on engineering limits, but must include
centered means, statistical control limits, and the requirement that vendors deliver their products from their own
in-control manufacturing processes.

KEYWORDS: specifications, statistical process control,
semiconductor materials, standards

If you sell materials to the IC industry to be used in manufacturing integrated circuits, you need to be aware of major phil-
osophical changes now beginning to occur in specifying the quality of
tnese materials.

The microelectronics business has been undergoing significant
transformations. Soft markets, overcapacity, and foreign competition
have combined to make microelectronics a perilous business. The reliability requirements for microcircuits are increasing, adding another
facet to the problem of building affordable products. And in particular, technological innovations do not drive the business the way they
used to; it is producibility and manufacturability which are emerging
as the most significant factors in profitability for IC makers.

Mr. Lowry is Manager of the Analytical Service Laboratories, Harris
Semiconductor, P. O. Box 883, M.S. 62-07, Melbourne, FL 32901.

One of the tools IC manufacturers can use to improve profitability, indeed perhaps even to survive, is statistical process control (SPC). SPC principles are based on the work of Deming, Shewhart, et al [1, 2]. Their primary aim is to define, control, and reduce the variability which is inherent in all processes and all materials.

To begin to appreciate the need to control variability, we must understand that materials and processes are not 0-1, off-on entities. They vary. An understanding of their variability is essential to making reliable products, and making them affordably.

Accordingly, many IC manufacturers are at some stage of adopting SPC in their manufacturing operations. SPC will help them achieve manufacturing consistency by establishing control of process variability [3, 4]. It is the identification, control and reduction of variability which holds the key to continuous improvement of quality. Bringing variability under control is essential in order to:

- cut scrap
- reduce rework
- improve product consistency
- bring about more favorable manufacturing logistics.

All these things are required to improve the control of manufactured product cost.

With this as a background, it is the purpose of this paper to describe necessary changes which must occur in vendor/customer relationships [5] and in the writing of standards which will facilitate and extend the use of statistical control in manufacturing of microelectronic devices.

STATISTICAL APPLICATIONS

Materials for IC Manufacturing

The raw materials used for building IC's may be divided into five categories:

1. silicon and other substrates
2. chemicals: acids, solvents, photolithographic materials
3. gases
4. metallization sources
5. packages and associated assembly materials.

This categorization is not entirely arbitrary. It is dictated to a certain extent by unique traits of how the materials are made and the implementation of statistics to control their manufacture. For example, silicon wafer lots are composed of large collections of individual units. Chemical and gas lots are generally large batches (one unit) characterized by assay and/or impurity levels. Metallization sources are individual unit items made in sequence by physical/chemical processing and are characterized both by chemical and dimensional attributes. Packaging material lots are composed of high populations of individual pieces with strong quality dependence on consistency of physical/dimensional attributes. These distinctions are made because the classical Shewhart charting methods can work well for categories 1, 4, and 5, but applying them to large-batch (sub-group of one) processes of categories 2 and 3 presents special challenges [6]. It is not the purpose here to discuss details of implementing SPC in the manufacture of these items, but it is necessary to understand that different manufacturing processes will require different SPC approaches.

Examples

Oxygen content of silicon wafers: The effective control of O_2 in silicon wafers is a subject receiving increased attention. Means for measuring O_2 in silicon [7] and detailed discussions of the importance for its control [8] have been widely documented. In particular, too low an O_2 content may lead to insufficient precipitation and wafer warpage, while too high an O_2 content can give rise to thermal donors and warpage; the optimum O_2 content of wafers has been quoted as 26-28 $\pm$ 2-3 ppma [9].

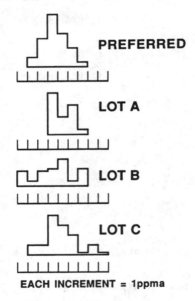

PREFERRED

LOT A

LOT B

LOT C

EACH INCREMENT = 1ppma

Figure 1 -- A preferred distribution and the observed distributions of the oxygen content of three product wafer lots.

Actual histograms of three non-statistically specified wafer lots' O_2 content are shown in Figure 1. None of the lots contain a normal distribution of O_2 content. They do not have centered means, the apparent mean for each lot shifts, and the lots cover a 9 ppma range of distribution. Based on reference [9], it would be preferred that the lots have a centered means with an approximate normal distribution not exceeding a 6 ppma range.

A wafer manufacturing process characterized in this way, and using control charts as shown in the following example to establish process capability, comprise the "database" for a statistical process control quality program for silicon wafer oxygen content.

Sodium content of hydrofluoric acid: This is an excellent example of the need for statistical data. Sodium is a pernicious contaminant ion responsible for multitudes of device electrical problems. Hydrofluoric acid is used in intimate contact with devices at multiple places in the fabrication process. The usual "Certificate of Analysis" received with each lot shipment of hydrofluoric acid states the analyzed sodium content of that lot. This is useful but very limited information. It is so much better that a control chart like that of Figure 2 be the C of A for the lot being received.

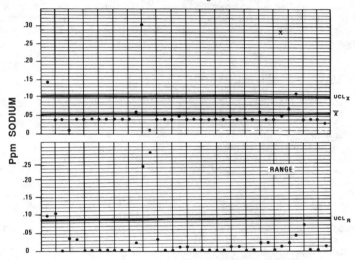

xR CHART OF SODIUM CONTENT
Figure 2 -- OF SUCCESSIVELY MANUFACTURED LOTS
OF HYDROFLUORIC ACID

Figure 2 is an x, R control chart for sodium content of 39 successively manufactured lots of HF. Individual part per million readings for sodium in each lot are plotted on the vertical axis of the x chart, while the associated rolling range values are plotted on the vertical axis of the R chart. The charts show that this manufacturing process is delivering HF with a mean sodium content near 0.05 ppm, with a 3-sigma upper control limit (calculated from the R value) of 0.10 ppm.

The control chart is the fundamental SPC implement. It tells how the newly received lot compares with previous manufactured lots, giving at a glance the track record of the product with regard to its sodium content. We might be able to relate a troubled process to lots of HF elevated in sodium, or superior process yields to especially clean lots of HF.

Such data are important not only to the user of the HF but also to its manufacturer. Fig. 2 (real data) suggests that the natural tolerance of the process for controlling sodium in HF, i.e. the process capability, has a three sigma upper statistical control limit of 0.10 ppm Na. This is 10 times better than published industry standards for this quality parameter [10]. Note also that the mean value most of the lots contain is 0.05 ppm, 20 times better than published standards. If this manufacturer could find assignable causes for the out-of-control points and eliminate them, he would achieve an immediate and substantial product improvement relative to the engineering specification. More importantly, the consistency of the product is defined for his customer.

Calculation of the natural tolerance of a particular parameter from control chart data might determine a manufacturing process to be highly capable of meeting engineering spec limits. The same calculation of another parameter may reveal that the process is not at all capable of meeting engineering spec limits.

Revolutionizing Specifications

Judging material quality with a control chart like that of Figure 2 brings sweeping changes to specmanship. An assessment of quality by variability control via a control chart essentially obviates the original engineering specification to which the material is made. Once a manufacturing process is started up, the essence of quality as defined by statistical principles is not whether the product "meets the spec", because meeting the spec is not the measure of goodness of the product.

As previously mentioned, product goodness is not 0-1, good when in spec and bad when out of spec. Product goodness, as experienced by a process using the product, is the historical mean value seen by the process and the extent to which the process is perturbed by the patterns and magnitudes of variances from the mean in the raw material.

Think about this in light of the example in Figure 2. In this case, HF-containing etchant solutions for IC processing have historically had a sodium x value of 0.05 ppm, with a three sigma upper control limit of 0.10 ppm. Suppose that a lot of HF is supplied to the process whose sodium content is ten sigma higher than the mean, i.e., containing 0.22 ppm sodium. All other factors being equal, this is a perturbation to the process not only of statistical significance (above the upper control limit), but also of practical significance. This means that an acceptable yield being obtained when the usual HF sodium mean is 0.05 ppm might well degrade to unacceptable levels if the HF lot containing 0.22 ppm is used. Therefore, the information that this lot contains 0.22 ppm is not fully adequate to describe the quality of the HF.

These facts give rise to important new considerations in quality

control protocols. The IC industry will evolve new acceptance criteria
for raw materials, based on the need to supply SPC-controlled processes
with materials from similarly controlled processes. As Figure 3 shows,
a product which is out of spec but in statistical control may be
acceptable, while a product that is in spec but out of statistical
control may not be acceptable. Product goodness is a variable, getting
worse the farther away its quality parameters get from historical mean
values. Acceptance criteria based on the track-record capability of
the process by which a product is made may be needed.

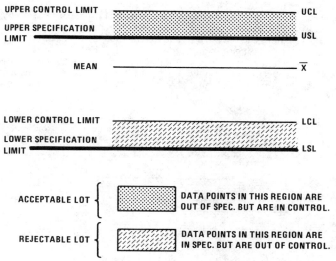

Figure 3 -- Revolutionary Specification Criteria

Advantages

The advantages to be realized in specifying quality with SPC charts
as in Figure 2, supplemented by the notions of Figure 3, are important
to the concepts of cost containment in IC manufacturing. Processes
operated according to SPC can be supplied with raw material which
itself was manufactured by a controlled process. Wherever comprehen-
sive process characterization is done, the portion of process variability contributed by raw material can be estimated. Supplying from
controlled processes enables true just-in-time material logistics,
because goods can be shipped to stock without incoming inspection.

Even the venerable military specification system is beginning to
recognize the importance and pervasiveness of SPC, as recent amendments
to specification documents governing IC manufacturers' quality posture
allow the discontinuing of incoming material inspection when materials
are procured from processes under SPC control [11].

The SPC approach to specifying quality also provides the time
format for process and product improvement, and the statistical

approach provides a definition for product improvement. It is not enough anymore to just be "in spec". The priority must be on continuous improvement, with ever decreasing variability, about a stable mean.

Measurements

Process control is interwoven with measurement. To construct a control chart something must be measured. Any measurement itself contains some error, i.e., it also has variability. So, it must be understood that total process or product variability expressed by a control chart is the actual process variability plus the measurement variability. To know the actual process variability we must know the variability of the measurement procedures used. Measurements, therefore, must be characterized. There are cases where measurement variability is the major component of total variability. Measurements themselves must be in control and their variabilty quantified for SPC to be effective.

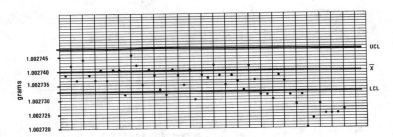

Figure 4 -- x Chart of Repetitive Weighings
of 1g Mass by Laboratory Balance
(Limits From Associated Range Chart)

Figure 4 is an example of controlling measurement variability. It is a control chart of repetitive daily weighings of a 1.000 gram standard mass on a laboratory balance. For a long time the balance weighed the weight consistently. But then a disturbing trend developed, with the balance yielding an ever smaller value for the constant standard weight. The control chart signaled the problem, which turned out to be degradation of the knife edge mechanisms in the balance. If SPC monitoring was not used, the problem could have continued indefinitely. The undiscovered problem would have affected the monitoring of the variabilities in product or process being measured, and consequently would have affected the outgoing product quality.

CONCLUSIONS

This paper has discussed the impact on production and material quality programs brought about by the use of SPC in microelectronics manufacturing. It has emphasized that SPC is a prerequisite for cost effective manufacture of quality IC's. Therefore, SPC controlled processes must be supplied with materials from SPC controlled processes. It has pointed out that engineering specifications for materials from established manufacturing processes are meaningless; the actual track-record capability of the processes by which materials are made must be known.

Finally, it is emphasized that among the acceptance criteria of tomorrow's electronic materials procurement specifications must be centered means, statistical control limits, and manufacturing processes governed by statistical control with efforts toward continuous improvement.

ACKNOWLEDGMENT

The assistance of Dottie Bush in preparing the manuscript is greatly appreciated.

REFERENCES

[1]   Deming, W. E., "Out of the Crisis" (MIT Press, 1986).
[2]   Shewhart, W. A. (edited by W. E. Deming), "Statistical Method from the Viewpoint of Quality Control" (Washington, D.C.: The Graduate School, Department of Agriculture, 1939), p.49.
[3]   Peters, J. D., and Parr, W. C., "Managing the Process: Introducing SPC", Survey of Business, 21(3), 1986, pp. 19-23.
[4]   Hahn, G. J., and Boardman, T. J., "Statistical Approaches to Quality Improvement", Chemtech, July, 1987, pp. 412-417.
[5]   Electronics, January 27, 1986, pp. 19-20.
[6]   Hahn, F. J., and Cockrum, M. B., Appl. Stat., 1987, 14(1), 33-50.
[7]   Baghdadi, A., "Measurement of the Oxygen and Carbon Content of Silicon Wafers by Fourier Transform IR Spectrophotometry", in Microelectronics Processing: Inorganic Materials Characterization, ACS Symposium Series 295, L. A. Casper, ed., 1986, pp. 208-229.
[8]   Herng-Der Chiou, "Oxygen Precipitation Behavior and Control in Silicon Crystals", Solid State Technology, March, 1987, pp. 77-81.
[9]   Meieran, E. S., Flinn, P. A., and Carruthers, J. R., "Analysis Technology for VLSI Fabrication", Proceedings of the IEEE, 75(7), July, 1987, pp. 908-955.
[10] Book of SEMI Standards, C1 STD. 8-82, 1987.
[11] MIL-STD-976B Draft, Paragraph 5.1.2.7.

Gregory C. Tassey, Robert I. Scace, and Judson C. French

ECONOMIC IMPACT OF STANDARDS ON PRODUCTIVITY IN THE SEMICONDUCTOR
INDUSTRY

REFERENCE: Tassey, G.C., Scace, R.I., and French, J.C.,
"Economic Impact of Standards on Productivity in the Semicon-
ductor Industry", Semiconductor Fabrication: Technology and
Metrology. ASTM STP 990, Dinesh C. Gupta, editor, American
Society for Testing and Materials, 1989.

ABSTRACT: The generic role of standards in the development
and diffusion of technology is reviewed. Examples of the
economic value to the semiconductor industry of standards and
the metrological research that underlies them are given to
show the substantial return on investment that usually is
obtained. Current metrological issues are raised to show that
the present level of effort in standards development in this
field is not sufficient and is cause for serious concern.

KEYWORDS: automation, economic value of standards, linewidth,
metrology, National Bureau of Standards, productivity,
resistivity of silicon, semiconductor industry, standards,
technological diffusion, test structures, wire bonding

Productivity growth contributes fundamentally to the economic well-
being of nations. Productivity growth rates began to decline in most
industrialized nations in the mid 1960's. This trend accelerated after
the oil embargo in 1973, and in some countries, including the United
States, productivity growth rates actually became negative for short
periods of time. This contributed to loss of competitiveness in world
markets and reduced rates of economic growth.

Manufacturing productivity growth rates have revived in the 1980's
due in part to changes in corporate tactics. Changes with the greatest
short-term impact often involve squeezing higher levels of performance
out of existing plant. But in the long run, new technologies must be

---

* J.C. French and R.I. Scace are Director and Deputy Director, respec-
tively, of the Center for Electronics and Electrical Engineering, and
G.C. Tassey is Senior Economist in the Program Office, at the National
Bureau of Standards, Gaithersburg, MD 20899. Contribution of the
National Bureau of Standards. Not subject to copyright.

developed and put to use more effectively. Effective use implies both improved productivity and improved quality. These have been viewed as conflicting corporate objectives in the past, but more recent experience has shown that often the new technology that lowers cost can also improve productivity [1]. Appropriate standards are essential tools for improvement and maintenance of both productivity and quality.

STANDARDS AND THE DEVELOPMENT AND DIFFUSION OF NEW TECHNOLOGIES

Industrial standards constructively affect nearly every stage of technological development, beginning with basic research, continuing through the evolution of generic technology, and most of all in the development and use of proprietary products and processes. Standards can also stimulate the use of new technology at each of these stages of development. By definition, technology-driven productivity growth can only occur when new technology is used. Any activity that promotes technological diffusion and use deserves increased attention.

The role of standards in diffusing technology and stimulating productivity is not generally appreciated. In this paper, we present information on the impact of standards on the semiconductor industry extracted from studies by the National Bureau of Standards on the effects of standards on technology-based competition [2].

The Economic Role of Standards

Standards provide one or more of the following:

(1) Information: verified data, terminology, test and measurement methods for evaluating product attributes;

(2) Compatibility: properties that a product should have to be compatible with a complementary product or with other components within a "system";

(3) Variety reduction: limitations on the range or number of allowable levels of product characteristics, such as physical dimensions; and

(4) Quality: specification of levels of product performance including stability, reliability, and durability.

Information: The transfer of technological information requires adequately defined terminology. The production of technical information requires standard test and measurement methods, both to provide accurate research results and to convince users of their validity. Standard product acceptance test methods provide data acceptable to both buyer and seller and reduce the incidence of performance-related disputes.

Efficient conduct of R&D and effective control of production processes require standard scientific and engineering data bases with known levels of accuracy, associated predictive models, standard methods

for validating these data bases, and standard formats and terminology
for data dissemination. Without suitable information standards and
data, firms attempt to create their own, which are typically incomplete,
less accurate, and frequently in conflict with those of other firms.

Compatibility: Standards define the physical or functional interface between pieces of equipment which must work together, for example,
as part of an automated production process. Without this compatibility,
equipment users must either purchase all components of a system from a
single vendor or modify the components themselves to achieve compatibility. In either case, the user is likely to pay a higher price, which
slows market penetration of a new technology. An interface standard
allows users to integrate equipment from different vendors into one
system. The result is increased competition among vendors, and increased confidence on the part of users. The economic impact is faster
diffusion of the technology and hence faster productivity growth.

Variety Reduction: Standards may limit the variety of products*.
Variety reduction of some physical attribute, such as the size of the
product, can bring about economies of scale in production. Limits on
the number of sizes of a product can lead to innovations in equipment
interfacing with the product, enabling further economies to be realized.

Quality: Standards can specify performance levels for one or more
product attributes. This may more clearly define market segments and
discourage the production of products unsuited to an application. Thus,
specification of quality levels can also effect variety reduction [1].

Standards and Systems

Efficient systems for automated manufacturing require competitive-
ly-produced system components with a high performance-price ratio, and
the option of replacing obsolete components easily and cheaply. The
standards which affect these situations are "interface" standards,
because they define the functional or physical interfaces among the
components of a system. Competition based on the proprietary technology
embodied in the components is unaffected by the nature of the interface.
In this sense, an interface standard is in theory competitively neutral,
but only if the standard is established before the products it affects
have been designed. Otherwise, an existing design may form the basis
for the standard and other firms have to bear the cost of changes.

THE IMPACT OF STANDARDS ON THE SEMICONDUCTOR INDUSTRY

All of the above considerations apply in the use of standards by
the semiconductor industry. For example, standards have had significant
economic impact in the automation of manufacturing processes. Some of

* This is the only role ascribed to standards in most economics texts.

the standards contributing to automation and the economic functions
they performed were

* wafer dimensions (variety reduction)

* wafer carriers (compatibility)

* equipment communication (compatibility)

* wafer marking (information)

These standards were developed by Semiconductor Equipment and Materials
International (SEMI) in the order in which they are listed. Each of the
later ones depends logically on those that precede it. These SEMI
standards are specifications which define the allowable attributes of
wafers, carriers, and the like.

The numerical values in these specifications are measured by standard
test methods, most of which are the product of the American Society for
Testing and Materials (ASTM) Committee F-1 on Electronics. This committee has produced nearly 200 standards, mostly test methods, for the
semiconductor and allied industries. In cooperation with ASTM, the
generic metrological research which underlies many of these standards
was done by the National Bureau of Standards (NBS). This has given NBS
an opportunity to determine the effect of some of these standards on the
productivity of the semiconductor industry. The linkages among the
functions performed by these standards, the industry segment(s) that
benefited from them, and their impacts on productivity are summarized in
Table 1.

CONTRIBUTIONS OF MEASUREMENT STANDARDS TO PRODUCTIVITY

    Economic analyses in 1981 examined the impact of NBS measurement
research in the 1970s on silicon resistivity, thermal properties of
devices, and on process controls associated with wire bonding. To a
lesser extent, the impact of linewidth measurement research was also
examined. All of these research topics were undertaken as a result of
requests from the industry. In each case, the measurement methods have
become industry standards.

    One way by which economists measure the impact of a technology is
to calculate a rate of return. A number of studies have estimated the
rates of return for innovations developed by industry in general [3, 4].
The 1981 NBS study included extensive surveys of U.S. semiconductor
firms to gather data on the impact of the above measurement topics [5].
Rates of return were calculated and compared with those found for
private-sector innovations. These comparisons are shown in Table 2.

    For analytical purposes, data from the surveys were compared with
information in NBS industry-contact files. The average rate of return
based on data from the contact files was 98 percent, which is quite
close to the result from the survey data (the more accurate of the two).
The contact file data were processed through an econometric model to

TABLE 1

FUNCTIONS OF STANDARDS AND IMPACTS ON PRODUCTIVITY

STANDARDS	Wafer Dimension			Wafer Carrier	Wafer Measurements	Equipment Communication	Wafer Marking
FUNCTIONS	Variety reduction	Quality	Compatibility	Compatibility	Information	Compatibility	Information
INDUSTRY SEGMENT	Wafer	Equipment	Device	Device, Equipment	Wafer, Device, Equipment	Device, Equipment	Device
IMPACTS ON PRODUCTIVITY	economies of scale, better inventory management	better handling and fixturing	accelerated automation	accelerated automation, reduced handling costs	more suitable wafer specifications, tighter process control, reduced market transaction costs	accelerated automation	improved process and inventory control

TABLE 2
COMPARISONS OF RATES OF RETURN FOR
PRIVATE AND STANDARDS-RELATED TECHNOLOGY

Study	Technical Area	Average Internal Rate of Return
Mansfield et al.	Miscellaneous (18 industrial innovations)	77
Tewksbury et al.	Miscellaneous (20 industrial innovations)	108
NBS	Semiconductors (thermal conductivity, resistivity, wire bonding)	128

obtain an estimate of the productivity impact. The analysis found that NBS research (and the subsequent standards) increased the semiconductor industry's productivity level by one percentage point over the period 1973-77; the saving due to this productivity increase was $187 million during the period. The semiconductor industry averaged 4.7 percent productivity growth per year over the same period, for a total growth of 26 percent in five years (Fig. 1). The NBS contribution was thus about 4 percent of the total productivity growth.

The causes for the dramatic improvement in productivity growth beginning in the mid-1970's, shown in Fig. 1, can only be speculated upon. Standards and related improvements in metrology were appearing in good volume beginning at that time. Standard wafer dimensions and wafer cassettes allowed the first major steps to automation to be taken. The change from in-house constructed to purchased manufacturing equipment was essentially completed. Offshore assembly was developing rapidly, but the value of offshore work and the associated labor have been specifically excluded from Fig. 1.

NBS research on measurement of silicon resistivity and the resulting standards were estimated by the industry to have saved over $30 million (over 100 times the cost of the work) in marketplace transactions, and perhaps ten times that amount in manufacturing economies over the ten years from 1967-1976.

Work at about the same time on the causes of wire bond failures and standard test methods based on that research led to increases in production yield of high-reliability devices by factors of 2 to 35 in various companies and to dramatic improvements in the reliability of military and space systems.

By improving linewidth measurements, NBS research and the standard reference material and calibration procedures which resulted have provided estimated savings in 1987 alone of over $30 million on a worldwide merchant market volume of $375 million in photomasks. The unknown captive production of masks probably enjoyed a commensurate benefit. The NBS research program cost less than $5 million.

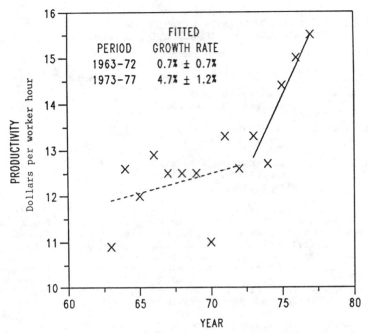

Fig. 1.   U.S. semiconductor factory productivity, 1972 dollars.

[Sources: Data from Semiconductor Industry Association, American Electronics Association, Electronics Industry Association, Dataquest, and Department of Commerce.   Unpublished analysis by R.I. Scace, 1979.]

Although quantitative estimates of economic impact are important, qualitative analyses are useful in understanding which activities are affected by standards and the nature of the impacts.   The NBS study included questions concerning the benefits realized by the semiconductor industry from NBS standards-related research. The percentage of responses indicating given qualitative benefits is tabulated in Table 3.

An example of such qualitative benefits stems from NBS work on thermal properties.   Early work on theory and metrology led to improved standards and reliability.   A recent result on second breakdown in power transistors was the development of non-destructive methods for defining the safe operating area of power transistors [6], which previously required destruction of large numbers of devices and much engineering time.   The non-destructive methods are much quicker, give more reliable results, and use many fewer devices.

TABLE 3
QUALITATIVE BENEFITS REALIZED FROM STANDARDS-RELATED RESEARCH
AS A PERCENTAGE OF REPLIES IN FOUR NBS RESEARCH AREAS

Nature of Benefit	Silicon Resistivity	Wire Bonding	Thermal Properties	Linewidth Measurements	Weighted Average
Improved product features	31	31	37	38	33
Cost reduction	29	28	11	19	25
Improved product reliability	34	82	63	42	53
Increased production yields	50	52	15	39	44
Improved ability to meet customer specifications	43	23	30	53	40
New directions for company research	25	14	15	24	20
Number of respondents	113	65	27	85	320

Source: Charles River Associates [5]

CURRENT METROLOGICAL ISSUES

The trend toward submicrometer feature sizes on integrated circuits has generated a pressing need in the semiconductor industry for new measurement tools and associated standards. Both optical and electron microscope systems are currently being used by the industry, and both are under study at NBS [7, 8]. At the present time, the needed levels of accuracy or traceability to NBS are not available for critical dimension measurements on wafers at any scale, nor for photomasks for features smaller than 1 μm.

Existing standard reference materials for thin-layer (photomask) measurements cannot be used for accurate calibration of critical dimension measurements on wafers. Until improved techniques are developed for measuring integrated-circuit features, no linewidth standard reference materials for silicon wafers will be available. Nor will the industry have acceptable accuracy in linewidth measurements on these wafers. For the present, semiconductor device manufacturers must use in-house standards for instrument set-up and day-to-day process control. The best that can be done is a reproducible measurement whose accuracy is not known. But even in today's practice, the uncertainties in measurement accuracy and reproducibility are of nearly the same mag-

nitude as the feature sizes being measured. This results in the acceptance of large numbers of out-of-tolerance parts and the rejection of
too many good ones [7], with a clear negative effect on productivity.

Test structures of many kinds have long been used to assess how
well integrated circuit manufacturing processes have been executed.
Some early test structures were not well designed, and inadvertently
measured more than one variable at a time. These problems have been
significantly reduced by NBS work, but effective use of test structures
is still limited by the sheer volume of data with which the process
engineer must cope. It is difficult even to find the specific data
which point to deviations of a given process or tool adjustment from the
norm. A joint NBS-industry program is applying expert systems to this
problem with encouraging initial results [9].

The lag of measurement technology and subsequent standards behind
the needs of the industry may be rationalized by citing the rapid pace
of product and process technological advances, which have been faster
than corresponding developments in metrology. However, given the
important economic roles of standards described above and given the
substantial benefits to the semiconductor industry from measurement
technology provided by NBS in the past, these lags can have a disastrous
effect on productivity and competitiveness. Neither NBS nor the volun-
teers now on standards committees can solve this problem without much
more collaborative help from the chief beneficiary of their work, the
semiconductor industry.

CONCLUSIONS

The economic effects of standards have been recognized to a limited
degree for some time. However, when the full range of effects is
presented, as is done here, the importance of standards to corporate
success is seen to be considerably greater than is commonly believed.
When new technology begins to penetrate a market, the nations whose
industries can offer products with assured performance and compatibility
with other products will gain market share, all other things being the
same. Further, intense international competition increases the importance of the timing of the implementation of standards.

Timely establishment of standards requires cooperation between
industry and government to provide the technical foundation for the
standards and the means for conducting the standardization process both
domestically and internationally.

Standards developed by private-sector organizations and the metrological research by NBS that supports the development of standards have
been shown to provide important economic benefits to the semiconductor
device industry and to the equipment and materials industries that
supply it. Historical examples show a consistent payback far larger
than the cost of providing this support.

Integrated circuits are becoming smaller and denser. Process
tolerances are shrinking. At the same time, the problems of measuring

physical and chemical properties and how processes and equipment perform are becoming more difficult. Yet the level of effort given to providing standards is not increasing nearly enough to meet these needs. Without a solution to this problem, the semiconductor industry will soon have serious difficulty in meeting the needs of its customers and the challenges of its competitors.

REFERENCES

[1]   Tassey, G.C., "Strategies for Improving Industrial Quality", to be published.

[2]   Link, A.N. and Tassey, G.C., "The Impact of Standards on Technology-Based Industries: The Case of Numerically Controlled Machine Tools in Automated Batch Manufacturing", in Product Standardization and Competitive Strategy, H. Landis Gabel, Ed., North-Holland Press, New York, 1987, pp. 217-237.

[3]   Mansfield, E., et al, "Social and Private Rates of Return from Industrial Innovations", Quarterly Journal of Economics, vol. 91, no. 2, May 1977, pp. 221-240; ibid., The Production and Application of New Industrial Technology, W.S. Norton and Co., New York, 1977.

[4]   Tewksbury, J.G., et al, "Measuring the Societal Benefits of Innovation", Science, vol. 209, No. 8, August 1980, pp. 658-662.

[5]   Charles River Associates, Productivity Impacts of NBS R&D: A Case Study of the NBS Semiconductor Technology Program, National Bureau of Standards, Gaithersburg, MD, 1981; summarized in Tassey, G.C., "Infratechnologies and the Role of Government", Technology Forecasting and Social Change, vol. 21, July 1982, pp. 163-180, and Tassey, G.C., "The Role of the National Bureau of Standards in Supporting Industrial Innovation", IEEE Transactions on Engineering Management, vol. 33, no. 3, August 1986, pp. 162-171.

[6]   Blackburn, D.L., "Turn-off Failure of Power MOSFETs, IEEE Transactions on Power Electronics, vol. PE-2, no. 2, April 1987, pp. 136-142; Hower, P.L., Blackburn, D.L., Oettinger, F.F., and Rubin, S., "Stable Hot Spots and Second Breakdown in Power Transistors", in Power Transistors: Device Design and Applications, B.J. Baliga and D.Y. Chen, eds., IEEE Press, New York, 1984.

[7]   Nyyssonen, D. and Larrabee, R.D., "Submicrometer Linewidth Metrology in the Optical Microscope", Journal of Research of the National Bureau of Standards, vol. 92, no. 3, May-June 1987, pp. 187-204.

[8]   Postek, M.T. and Joy, D.C., "Submicrometer Microelectronics Dimensional Metrology: Scanning Electron Microscopy", Journal of Research of the National Bureau of Standards, vol. 92, no. 3, May-June 1987, pp. 205-228.

[9]   Linholm, L.W., Khera, D., Reeve, C.P., and Cresswell, M.W., "A Developmental Expert System for Test Structure Data Evaluation", to be published in Proceedings of the 1988 IEEE International Conference on Microelectronic Test Structures, February 1988.

Appendix

APPENDIX

WORKSHOP AND PANEL DISCUSSIONS

The material presented in this appendix has been written by W. Murray Bullis for Gettering and by Dave Rogers for Gallium Arsenide. It is based on their best recollections. The material did not go through the review process and is presented for information only.

1. WORKSHOP ON GETTERING TECHNIQUES AND CHARACTERIZATION

Chairmen: W. Murray Bullis, Siltec Silicon, and

Robert B. Swaroop, Electric Power Research Institute.

The workshop on Gettering Techniques and Characterization included the interactions between extrinsic and intrinsic gettering mechanisms, consistent and reliable methods of producing gettering, and characterization of gettering related parameters. Of particular interest was the issue of what, if any, of the characterization methods should be standardized.

Extrinsic gettering mechanisms include those based on mechanical damage (such as abrasion, ion implantation, laser-induced damage, and wet or dry bead impingement), metallurgical deformation (such as polysilicon back surface films, interfacial germanium-rich films, and back surface nitride films), or adjustment of the electrochemical by phosphorus diffusions or phosphorus-rich oxides. Intrinsic gettering is most commonly associated with the presence of oxide precipitates but recently papers have appeared which suggest that oxygen is not required for intrinsic gettering.

Characterization issues include determination of gettering efficiency (by methods such as measurement of generation lifetime by MOS C-t techniques, scratch and

463

etch techniques, observation of S-pits, direct observation of impurity trapping, and device yields), precipitate characteristics (such as precipitation rates by oxygen reduction measurement, precipitate density by sectioning and preferential etching, and precipitate morphology by direct observation by TEM), and denuded zone width (by methods such as sectioning and preferential etching, infrared tomography, spreading resistance profiling to establish thermal donor distribution, x-ray topography, surface photovoltage, and thermal wave analysis). In addition, the issue of how to relate the effects of bulk defects to surface properties must be considered.

Bob Swaroop (then at Fairchild Semiconductor) opened the discussion by introducing a problem encountered in bipolar processing. The substrate was a medium doped p-type wafer with (111)-orientation and oxygen concentration of either 28-29 ppma or 32-33 ppma (old ASTM specification). Back surface gettering techniques used included mechanical abrasion, wet honing (bead impingement), and polysilicon film. After high temperature processing he observed stacking fault defects in both the bulk and epi layer (if present) for the higher oxygen cases except with polysilicon back surface gettering; such defects were not observed after low temperature processing, or after high temperature processing in low oxygen wafers or in the wafers with polysilicon back surface gettering. Despite considerable discussion of the possibilities, a model to explain these results did not evolve.

Murray Bullis described some results on the influence of a polysilicon back surface film on oxygen precipitation. The key result was that the presence of the polysilicon film enhanced the oxygen precipitation more than a simple heat treatment at the same temperature and time. This suggests that the film properties themselves are influencing the process in addtion to the formation of oxide precipitate nuclei which occurs during the deposition process. The increase in precipitation is thought to result because the polysilicon acts as a sink for silicon interstitials, reducing the interstitial concentration in the bulk and thus favoring the precipitation process in which excess silicon interstitials are generated.

Shin Takasu (Toshiba Ceramics) described the use of infrared tomography to view the oxygen precipitates in silicon. The work was a collaborative effort with K. Kashima (Toshiba Ceramics) and K. Moriya (Mitsui Mining and Smelting). One motivation in developing this technique was the possibility of eliminating the need to use chrome-bearing defect etches to reveal the defects. In this technique, an infrared beam is directed on the polished surface of a wafer cleaved along a {110} plane and the scattered light is observed through the cleaved surface. In the equipment described, the light is obtained from a YAG laser with a collimating lens and the cleaved surface is viewed by an infrared sensitive TV camera through a microscope objective. The spot examined may be scanned in three mutually perpendicular directions. Precipitates larger than 40 nm, dislocations and stacking faults serve as scattering centers. In a series of measurements on seven wafers with oxide precipitates and well-formed denuded zone widths than were indicated by the preferential etching method. Estimates of precipitate size and density could also be made. The measurement is rapid compared with other means for observing oxide precipitates and denuded zones and is sensitive to smaller precipitates than can be observed by defect etching or by x-ray topography.

George Rozgonyi (North Carolina State University) presented a report of the work of a student, D. M. Lee, on the use of structures with misfit dislocations for studying extrinsic gettering phenomena in epi wafers. These structures provide an ideal vehicle for such studies since they allow for the controlled introduction of the contaminating impurity (gold, nickel, iron, and copper were studied), a defect-free controlled thickness region (the epi layer or the wafer bulk) for diffusion, and a sink with known properties in a known location (the line of misfit dislocations near the epi-substrate interface). Patterned regions on the front or back surface were used to control the areas where the impurities were introduced. All four impurities studied have very high diffusivity; the controlling parameter is the solubility of the impurity. Solubilities of these four impurities vary over about three orders of magnitude, thus accounting for observed differences in their behavior. TEM examination of the cross section of the structure after various heat treatments clearly revealed trapping of the impurities along the line of misfit dislocations.

Although several interesting points were discussed and some novel approaches for characterizing precipitates and gettering mechanisms were described, no clear preference for one or another technique could be established and no mandate for standardization of methods for evaluating gettering efficiencies or gettering-related phenomena emeged. Perhaps it is too early for such concerns to be sufficiently widespread to support development of standard methods.

2. WORKSHOP ON GALLIUM ARSENIDE

Chairman: Dave Rogers, Cominco Ltd.

The discussions in this workshop addressed the connections between GaAs wafer properties, and the properties of the devices made on them. The panelists included Robert Adams, Epitronics, Jerry Galt, Harris Microwave Semiconductor, Paul Golden, Monsanto Electronic Materials, W.N. "Bud" Jones, AT&T Bell Laboratories and Les Palkuti, ARACOR.

Paul Golden and Bud Jones both addressed the challenge of qualifying, and improving, the ion implant performance of GaAs wafers. Paul pointed out that these days wafer vendors are giving their boules a long anneal cycle. This smooths out the electrical inhomogeneities that occur during boule growth, thus removing the main cause of ion implant variation across each wafer and from the seed end to the tail end of the boule. He showed the data which indicated that the largest remaining souce of ion implant variation is residual trace impurities in the boule. Romoving these impurities is the major challenge for wafer producers today. Bud Jones supported these comments, and described the standard ion implant test which SEMI is designing for GaAs wafers.

Jerry Galt reviewed the work on rapid versus slow cooling of GaAs wafers to control their resistivity. Wafers cooled from 850 C to room temperature in less than an hour remain semi-insulating, while those cooled over several hours become conductive. Both phenomena are reversible.

Les Palkuti reported on newer methods for characterizing GaAs wafer surfaces: photon backscatter, damage delineation etch, sensitive stylus profiling, and scanning tunneling microscopy. Today's state-of-the-art GaAs wafers have a surface microroughness with a typical peak-to-valley height of 10 angtroms height over a wavelength of $\sim$ 1 micrometer, plus a longer wavelength texture of 20 angstroms height over wavelengths of 40-100 micrometers. With the polishing technique during the past few months, there is no longer any sub-surface lattice damage on commercial wafers.

Bob Adams presented many examples to underscore the immediate need for standards in GaAs materials and device technology.

Indexes

Author Index

471

Subject Index

473